D1020076

Epoxy Resins

Epoxy Resins

A symposium sponsored by
the Division of Organic
Coatings and Plastics
Chemistry at the 155th
Meeting of the American
Chemical Society, San
Francisco, Calif.,
April 3-4, 1968.

Henry Lee,
Symposium Chairman

ADVANCES IN CHEMISTRY SERIES **92**

AMERICAN CHEMICAL SOCIETY

WASHINGTON, D. C. 1970

Coden: ADCSHA

Library of Congress Catalog Card 70-113408

PRINTED IN THE UNITED STATES OF AMERICA

Advances in Chemistry Series

Robert F. Gould, *Editor*

AMERICAN CHEMICAL SOCIETY PUBLICATIONS

FOREWORD

ADVANCES IN CHEMISTRY SERIES was founded in 1949 by the American Chemical Society as an outlet for symposia and collections of data in special areas of topical interest that could not be accommodated in the Society's journals. It provides a medium for symposia that would otherwise be fragmented, their papers distributed among several journals or not published at all. Papers are refereed critically according to ACS editorial standards and receive the careful attention and processing characteristic of ACS publications. Papers published in ADVANCES IN CHEMISTRY SERIES are original contributions not published elsewhere in whole or major part and include reports of research as well as reviews since symposia may embrace both types of presentation.

CONTENTS

PREFACE

Since the invention and discovery of epoxy resins in the late 1930's by Pierre Castan in Switzerland and Sylvan Greenlee in the United States of America, production of epoxy resins and their literature have grown steadily. Undoubtedly the biggest spurt in production and literature occurred in the decade between 1955 and 1965.

However, much research continues, and numerous papers continue to be published. Many of these fill in side issues or bridge gaps which were by-passed by early pioneering investigators.

Many of these newer papers provide the essential information needed to tie various phenomena together and thus to increase our depth of understanding of the formulation and performance of these versatile resins.

It is this further unification and advancement of knowledge that these papers bring which prompts us to publish this symposium hard on the heels of the definitive treatises which have recently appeared on epoxy resins, mechanical dynamics, etc.

The Epoxylite Corp.
South El Monte, Calif.
September 1969

HENRY LEE

1

Novel Thermosetting Epoxy Resins Based on Pentaerythritol

J. M. JORDAN, FRANCIS W. MICHELOTTI, E. M. PEARCE, and M. ZIEF

J. T. Baker Chemical Co., Phillipsburg, N. J. 08865

A novel polyglycidyl ether of pentaerythritol has been synthesized which exhibits a number of new and interesting features. It is water-soluble, low in chlorine content (< 0.5%) and viscosity (400-1500 c.p.s., depending on synthetic reaction conditions), and is completely aliphatic in nature. Under typical curing condition, it exhibits high reactivity, and yields castings with high heat distortion temperatures with most epoxy curing agents studied. Details of the physical properties of uncured epoxy resin as well as mechanical, electrical, and chemical resistance properties of the resultant thermosets cured with many typical anhydride and amine curing agents, respectively, are given.

There is considerable patent literature which alleges the preparation of glycidyl ethers of pentaerythritol. Zech (*3, 4*), for example, describes the preparation of a polyepoxide from the condensation of a mixture of pentaerythritol and trimethylolpropane with epichlorohydrin by BF_3 catalysis followed by dehydrochlorination with sodium aluminate to give a product with 2.7 epoxide groups per molecule, a molecular weight of 427 and containing 7.6% chlorine. No data on resin performance are given. A comparable product is described by Price *et al.* (*2*)—*i.e.*, a polyglycidyl ether of a mixture of pentaerythritol, glycerin, and trimethylolpropane with chlorine contents varying from 7.7–11.6%. Again, no data on the performance of the cured resins are given. Zuppinger *et al.* (*5*) described the synthesis of a polyepoxide from pentaerythritol in an aqueous/epichlorohydrin medium under basic conditions and obtained a product with approximately 8.65% oxirane oxygen (equiv. wt., *ca.* 185), 12.9% hydroxyl groups (hydroxyl equiv. wt., *ca.* 132) and 3.7% total chlorine. Again, no data on resin performance are cited.

This paper describes the properties of a polyglycidyl ether of pentaerythritol (which shall henceforth be referred to as DP X100) which is low in chlorine content, low in viscosity and high in oxirane oxygen functionality and presents extensive data of the cured resin with a variety of curing agents. The physical properties of the resin are listed in Table I.

Table I. Physical Properties of DP X100

Epoxide equivalent wt.	110-119
Hydroxyl equivalent wt.	124-150
Viscosity, c.p.s., 25°C.	1000-1500
Total chlorine content, %	0.3-0.5
Solubility	most solvents, including water; insoluble in saturated aliphatic hydrocarbons
Color, Gardner scale	9-11
Density	1.20 grams/cc.
Surface tension	51 dynes/cm.
Shelf stability	well in excess of three months
Flash Point (Cleveland Open Cup)	*ca.* 240°C.

Chemistry

The details of the synthesis and structure of DP X100 resin will be the subject of a separate paper in the near future. However, the following simplified reaction scheme will indicate the major constituents believed to be present in the resin.

$$C(CH_2OH)_4 \xrightarrow[\text{excess}]{CH_2\text{—}CH\text{—}CH_2Cl \ (\text{epoxide, O})} (HOH_2C)_2C(CH_2O\text{—}CH_2\text{—}CH\text{—}CH_2)_2 \ (\text{epoxide, O})$$

Experimental

Preparation of Samples for Testing. One-eighth inch-thick sheets and 1/2 inch x 1/2 inch x 5 inches heat distortion temperature bars were cast from resin and various hardeners in the following manner. The desired amounts of resin and curing agent were weighed into a beaker. With aliphatic amine curing agents, the resins and amines were precooled to 0°–10°C. to prevent excessively short pot life—less than 10 minutes after mixing at room temperature. *p,p'*-Methylenedianiline (MDA) and hexahydrophthalic anhydride (HHPA) curing agents were premelted, maintained 0°–10°C. above their melting points, and then mixed into resin preheated to about 60°C. The components were mixed with a laboratory electric stirrer and subsequently degassed for several minutes in a vacuum desiccator (until no more bubbles occurred at 1–5 mm. Hg).

All amines were used at 100%, and all anhydrides were used at 90% of theoretical stoichiometry based on epoxide functionality. With DP X100, anhydride cures were accomplished either with or without benzyldimethylamine accelerator. With the diglycidyl ether of bisphenol A, benzyldimethylamine was used with all anhydride cures. The resin-hardener solutions were poured into Teflon sprayed or coated aluminum molds to produce 8 inches × 8 inches × 1/8 inch sheets or 5 inches × 1/2 inch × 1/2 inch bars.

Initial cure was accomplished at room temperature or lower with the aliphatic amine hardeners, and at 80°C. for MDA, NMA (Nadic Methyl Anhydride), and HHPA. Post-cures at higher temperatures (such as 150°C.) were generally used to improve the properties of the castings prior to testing.

Test Methods

Test	*ASTM No.*
Ult. Tensile Strength & Ult. Elongation	D-638-61T
Dielectric Constant & Dissipation Factor	D150-59T
Volume Resistivity	D257-61
Gel Time	Tecam Gelation Timer
Coefficient of Linear Thermal Expansion	D696-44
Heat Deflection Temperature (HDT)	D648-56
Compressive Strength	D695-61T

Discussion and Results. Results obtained in curing DP X100 with amine curing agents are summarized in Table II, while those obtained with some typical anhydrides are shown in Table III. For comparative purposes, data obtained under comparable conditions with a diglycidyl ether of bisphenol A (DGEBA, epoxide equivalent weight of 190) is shown in parenthesis. The unexpectedly high HDT's obtained with DP

Table II. DP X100 Cured with Amines

Curing Agent	*Cure Schedule*	*HDT, °C.*	*Tensile, p.s.i.g.*	*Elongation, %*
TETA[a]	7 days RT	57 (54)	10,450 (8,890)	3.9 (5.0)
	Above + 4 hrs. 100°C.	148 (119)		
MDA	2 hr. 80°C. + 4 hr. 150°C.	206 (150)	10,250 (8,900)	3.4 (5.2)
	Above + 16 hr. 175°C.	234		

[a] Triethylenetetramine.

X100 as compared with conventional epoxy resins may arise from the relative compactness and spiro-like character of the molecule. As is typical with most anhydride-cured epoxy systems, maxima in HDT's were obtained at approximately 90% of theoretical stoichiometry.

Table III. DP X100 Cured with Anhydrides

Curing Agent	*Cure Schedule*	*HDT, °C.*	*Tensile, p.s.i.g.*	*Elongation*
NMA	4 hrs. 80°C. + 22 hrs. 150°C.	187 (147)	6,200 (11,125)	1.4
	Above + 16 hrs. at 200°C.	233 (173)	7,620	2.6
HHPA	2 hrs. 80°C. + 4 hrs. 150°C.	144 (125)	8,000	3.0

It should be noted that reactions of DP X100 epoxy resin are extremely rapid with all types of aliphatic amines or polyamides at room temperature. This marked reactivity may be caused by the accelerating characteristic of hydroxyl functionality (*1*). With anhydride cures there is no need for tertiary amine catalysis as is customary with conventional epoxy resins although the use of such catalysis in DP X100 systems markedly enhances reactivity (Table IV). Depending on curing agent, DP X100 is approximately from two to eight times as reactive as DGEBA (data in parenthesis).

Table IV. Exotherm and Gel Time Data for DP X100 Cured with Two Hardeners

Curing Agent	*NMA*	*NMA*	*MDA*
BDMA accelerator, phr.	--	1.0 (1.0)	-- (–)
Mass of sample, grams	250	250 (250)	250 (500)
Bath temp., °C.	80	80 (80)	80 (70)
Time to initial exotherm, min.	~200	40-50 (110)	~5 (40)
Time to peak exotherm, min.	350	57 (137)	~10 (57)
Tecam gel time, min.	>240	46 (122)	~5 (–)
Temp. at peak exotherm, °C.	<108	132 (120)	-- (270)

Table V. Solvent Resistance[a] of DP X100 Cured with NMA and MDA

Solvent	*NMA*[b]	*MDA*[c]
Acetone	0.3 (2.6)	−0.1 (1.3)
Toluene	0.2 (0.2)	--
Water	1.0 (0.4)	1.0 (0.5)

[a] % weight change after 1 week immersion.
[b] Cured 4 hrs. @ 80°C., 22 hrs. @ 150°C.
[c] 2 hrs. @ 80°C., 4 hrs. @ 150°C.

Solvent Resistance. Table V shows solvent resistance of DP X100 cured with NMA and MDA. For comparison, results obtained with DGEBA under identical conditions are shown in parenthesis.

With NMA cure, DP X100 is markedly more resistant to acetone than DGEBA, comparable in toluene and somewhat poorer in water. With MDA cures, DP X100 is somewhat superior to DGEBA in acetone, but poorer in water.

Coefficient of Linear Thermal Expansion (CLTE). DP X100 exhibits CLTE which is quite comparable with those obtained with DGEBA (Table VI). These results are somewhat surprising in that a compact small reactive molecule might have been expected to display larger CLTE's.

Table VI. Coefficient of Linear Thermal Expansion/°C.

Curing Agent	*CLTE (DP X100)*	*CLTE (DGEBA)*
MDA	4.2×10^{-5}	4.8×10^{-5} [a]
NMA	5.5×10^{-5}	5.6×10^{-5}

[a] Literature value.

Compressive Strength. Ultimate compressive strength of DP X100 with various curing agents is considerably greater than that of DGEBA (Table VII). Yield strengths also tend to be fractionally higher as are % compressive strain values.

Table VII. Compressive Strength of DP X100 and DGEBA Cured with Various Hardeners

Resin	DP X100	DGEBA	DP X100
Curing Agent	NMA	NMA	MDA
Cure Schedule	4 hrs. @ 80°C. + 22 hrs. @ 150°C.	4 hrs. @ 80°C. + 22 hrs. @ 150°C.	1 hr. @ 80°C. + 4 hrs. @ 150°C.
Compressive Strength, p.s.i.g.			
Ultimate	>40,000	18,100	>40,000
Yield	19,560	19,120	22,250
% Compressive Strain			
Ultimate	>33.7	33.7	>30.4
Yield	9.0	9.0	12.7

Electrical Properties of DP X100. Table VIII shows the data for dissipation factors for DP X100 cured with NMA and BDMA under normal conditions and after heat-aging for four weeks at 155°C. Figures in parenthesis represent data for corresponding DGEBA system. The data indicate DP X100 provides dissipation factors very close to those for DGEBA up to 200°C.

Table IX shows the preliminary data for the dielectric constants and volume resistivities of DP X100 cured with NMA. The figures in parentheses are again for DGEBA cured and tested under identical conditions.

The results indicate that cured DP X1000 is comparable with cured DGEBA in dielectric constant and is slightly inferior in volume resistivity at 200°C.

DP X100/DGEBA Blends. When used in blends with DGEBA, DP X100 acts as a highly reactive diluent providing reduced viscosity, higher allowable filler loadings and accelerated cure rates. The viscosity-DP X100/DGEBA ratio relationship is shown in Table X.

Table VIII. Dissipation Factors for DP X100 Cured with NMA + BDMA

	Cure Schedule	*c.p.s.*	*RT*	*155°C.*	*200°C.*
A)	4 hrs. @ 100°C.	10^2	0.006 (0.002)	0.006	0.063 (0.070)
	+ 22 hrs. @ 150°C.	10^3	0.008 (0.005)	0.004	0.020 (0.056)
		10^5	0.017 (0.017)	0.008	0.013 (0.010)
B)	4 hrs. @ 100°C.	10^2	0.004	0.002 (0.002)	0.042 (0.046)
	+ 22 hrs. @ 150°C.	10^3	0.013	0.003 (0.004)	0.022 (0.043)
	+ 4 wks. @ 155°C. heat aging	10^5	0.031	0.009 (0.002)	0.012 (0.050)

Table IX. Dielectric Constants and Volume Resistivity of Heat-aged[a] DP X100 Cured with NMA

	RT	*200°C.*
Dielectric Constants, 10^3 c.p.s.	3.76 (3.22)	3.7 (4.24)
Volume Resistivity, Ohm-cm.	$>10^{14}$	$0.9\ (1.5) \times 10^{11}$

[a] Cured 4 hrs @ 100°C. + 22 hrs. @ 150°C.; heat aged 4 weeks @ 155°C.

Table X. Viscosity of DP X100/DGEBA Blends

Wt. % DP X100	0	10	20	30
Wt. % DGEBA	100	90	80	70
Viscosity, c.p.s. (25°C.)	16,000	12,000	7,400	4,500

Table XI. Exotherm and Gel Time Data for DP X100 Blended with DGEBA and Cured with Methylenedianiline

Wt. % DP X100	100	30	0
Wt. % DGEBA	0	70	100
Mass of sample, grams	125	125	125
Bath temp., °C.	60	60	60
Time to peak exotherm, min.	22	87	137
Tecam gel time, min.	22	87	137
Temp., peak exotherm, °C.	250	128	119

Table XI indicates the reactivity of several of these blends cured with methylenedianiline. Cured resin properties of the blends show moderate HDT advantages as well as marked improvements in ketone resistance. Water resistance is reduced only fractionally with 20% DP X100 in DGEBA (Table XII).

Table XII. Properties of DP X100/DGEBA Blends Cured with NMA (Cured 4 hrs. @ 80°C. plus 22 hrs. @ 150°C.)

% DP X100	0	20	100
% DGEBA	100	80	0
Curing agent	NMA	NMA	NMA
Accelerator	BDMA (1 phr.)	BDMA (1 phr.)	BDMA (1 phr.)
HDT	147	161	185
Tensile str., p.s.i.g.	11,125	10,050	6,200
Tensile elongation, %	3.3	2.9	1.4
Acetone resistance [a]	2.6	1.3	0.3
Toluene resistance [a]	0.2	0.2	0.2
Water resistance [a]	0.4	0.5	1.0

[a] 1 week immersion at room temperature.

Applications of DP X100. Data obtained to date indicate that DP X100 may be used in many applications in which conventional bisphenol A, novolac, and cycloaliphatic epoxies are presently employed. As a blending agent for such resins, DP X100 may permit the attainment of difficultly achievable specific handling characteristics for given end-use applications before curing. It has been shown that little or no sacrifice in many basic properties of the cured resins results from employing DP X100 as a reactive diluent.

One of the unique features of DP X100 is its water solubility in the uncured state as well as acceptable water resistance following cure. These facts allow the consideration of DP X100 for all types of water-based systems. For example, preliminary data in our laboratory indicate that DP X100 will form thermosetting systems with water-soluble acrylics and melamines to yield hard, tough, flexible coatings.

Literature Cited

(1) Lee, H., Neville, K., "Encyclopedia of Polymer Science and Technology," Volume 6, p. 226, Interscience Publisher, Div. of J. Wiley & Sons, New York, 1967.
(2) Price, H. P., Belanger, W. J., *U. S. Patent* **3,033,803** (1962).
(3) Zech, J. D., *U. S. Patent* **2,538,072** (1951).
(4) Zech, J. D., *U. S. Patent* **2,581,464** (1952).
(5) Zuppinger, P., Hofmann, W., Fish, W., *U. S. Patent* **2,898,349** (1959).

RECEIVED June 10, 1968.

2

Fluorine-Containing Epoxy Components and Plastics

JAMES R. GRIFFITH and JAMES E. QUICK

Naval Research Laboratory, Washington, D. C.

*Tetrafluoro-*m*-phenylenediamine reacts with epoxy resins more slowly than* m*-phenylenediamine to produce plastics with comparable properties. In combination with 1,4-cyclohexane diepoxide, it produces an exceptionally rigid plastic with improved water resistance. Glycidyl ethers can be prepared from 4,4′-dihydroxyoctafluorobiphenyl and tetrafluororesorcinol which react to produce plastics with the fluorinated diamine. Partial esters of trimesic acid or trimellitic anhydride and aliphatic fluoroalcohols cure epoxy resins to produce hydrophobic plastics.*

Recent advances in the chemistry of heavily fluorinated compounds have made possible the syntheses of some epoxy plastics which contain appreciable amounts of fluorine. There is little information in the literature concerning multifunctional components which are suitable as epoxy intermediates of high fluorine content. The effects of the halogen upon the reactivities of components and the properties of plastics is essentially unknown for the case of densely crosslinked systems of the usual epoxy type. It may be possible to produce materials with the convenient use properties of epoxies which "cure" to yield plastics with such fluorocarbon properties as non-wetting by water, low suface friction, and high thermal stability. This report is concerned primarily with some fluorinated components suitable for making epoxy plastics and with some effects of water upon these plastics.

Epoxy reactions of the coupling type in which an active hydrogen atom adds across the epoxy ring generally produce stronger plastics than catalytic reactions which produce polyethers. A widely used reaction is the addition of an amino hydrogen across the epoxy ring:

$$-\overset{|}{N}-H + \underset{\diagdown O \diagup}{CH_2-CH}- \rightarrow -\overset{|}{N}-CH_2-\underset{\underset{OH}{|}}{CH}-$$

Since the co-reactant, or "curing agent," becomes as integral a part of the plastic molecular network as the epoxy component, it is necessary for both to be fluorinated if the plastic is to have the highest possible content of fluorine. Plastics of high strength are commonly produced from aromatic diamines, and three such materials are now available commercially upon which the hydrogen atoms of the aromatic ring have been replaced by fluorine. These are tetrafluoro-*m*-phenylenediamine (FMPDA), the para isomer, and 4,4′-diaminooctafluorobiphenyl. Of the three, FMPDA is the best curing agent for epoxies because it is the lowest melting, most soluble in resins, and most reactive.

The fluorinated aromatic diamines react more slowly with typical epoxy resins than the unfluorinated analogs. This probably results from the electron-attracting property of fluorine which is transmitted to the amino groups and makes them less nucleophilic. The normal *m*-phenylenediamine (MPDA) reacts to "B" stage (a semi-cured, brittle state) with epoxies of the diglycidyl ether type at 25°C. within 24 hours, but FMPDA reacts only with the most aggressive resins at this temperature. A cure temperature of 160°C. for 16 hours or more is usually required for the fluorinated diamine to effect a thorough cure. The plastics so produced from the diglycidyl ether of bisphenol A with the fluorinated and unfluorinated MPDA have heat distortion temperatures (ASTM D648-56) of 146°C. and 150°C., respectively, which indicates that they are of comparable rigidity and crosslink density.

The FMPDA has been studied as a curing agent for 1,4-cyclohexane diepoxide. This small-molecule epoxy resin is cured by aromatic diamines to produce some of the most rigid plastics known with mechanical moduli of about 1,000,000 p.s.i.g. It is an unusually reactive resin and is converted to "B" stage by FMPDA at room temperature in about six weeks.

A major disadvantage of the plastics produced from 1,4-cyclohexane diepoxide is that they contain high concentrations of hydrophilic hydroxyl and amino groups which render them sensitive to damage by water. Some improvement in this defect can be realized by substituting FMPDA for the more water-soluble MPDA as the curing agent, as illustrated in Figure 1. The fluorine-containing plastic does not spall as readily upon being removed from boiling water as the normal material, but it is also exceptionally water-absorptive (Figure 4).

Some of the mechanical properties of the plastic produced from 1,4-cyclohexane diepoxide and FMPDA in stoichiometric amounts are as follows: Heat distortion temperature (ASTM D648-56), 208°C. Compressive yield (ASTM D695-63T) 42,000 p.s.i.g. at 15% deflection. Compressive ultimate, 72,000 p.s.i.g. at 46% deflection. Tensile ultimate (ASTM D638-64T) 14,000 p.s.i.g. at 2% elongation. Tensile modulus, 900,000 p.s.i.g. Compared with a common MPDA-cured diglycidyl ether

Figure 1. The effect of short-term exposure to boiling water upon 1,4-cyclohexane diepoxide cured with fluorinated and unfluorinated m-*phenylenediamine*

Right: FMPDA
Left: MPDA

of bisphenol A, the heat distortion temperature of this plastic is some 60°C. higher, its compressive strength properties are double, and its elongation is about one-third.

Fluorine on the aromatic rings of the curing agent appears to have small effect upon the thermal stability of plastics produced from bisphenol-A diglycidyl ether or 1,4-cyclohexane diepoxide. Table I shows that major decompositions occur in air between 240° and 280°C.

Table I. Weight Losses in Air of 1.5-Gram Solid Plastics Cured with FMPDA during 5 Hours' Exposure at Each Temperature

	Bisphenol A Diglycidyl Ether		*Cyclohexane Diepoxide*	
Temperature, °C.	*Progressive*	*Single Exposure*	*Progressive*	*Single Exposure*
200	0.26%	0.26%	0.30%	0.30%
220	0.47	0.31	0.45	0.34
240	0.67	0.55	0.49	0.51
260	6.2	2.1	25	28
280	22	21	33	29
300	32	32	34	59

Because of the availability of the fluorinated aromatic diamines, the syntheses of some similar diglycidyl ethers with fluorine in place of hydrogen on the aromatic rings was undertaken. Two suitable phenolic intermediates are 4,4′-dihydroxyoctafluorobiphenyl and tetrafluororesorcinol (*1*). The biphenyl derivative reacts with excess epichlorohydrin in the presence of alkali to produce a diglycidyl ether in good yield (*2, 4*).

$$\underset{\diagdown O \diagup}{CH_2—CH}—CH_2—O—C_6F_4—C_6F_4—O—CH_2\underset{\diagdown O \diagup}{CH—CH_2}$$

This material was purified by recrystallization from methanol. It is a white, crystalline solid with a melting point of 75°–77°C. The theoretical epoxy equivalent weight is 221, and a value of 242 was determined by the pyridinium hydrochloride in pyridine method.

Anal. Calcd. for $C_{18}H_{10}F_8O_4$: C, 48.88; H, 2.28; F, 34.36
Found: C, 49.15; H, 2.50; F, 34.43

The infrared spectrum of this material (Figure 2) was determined on the solid in a compressed potassium bromide window. Prominant features of the spectrum include the C—F bands between 9.0 and 10.5 microns and the epoxy band at 11.1 microns.

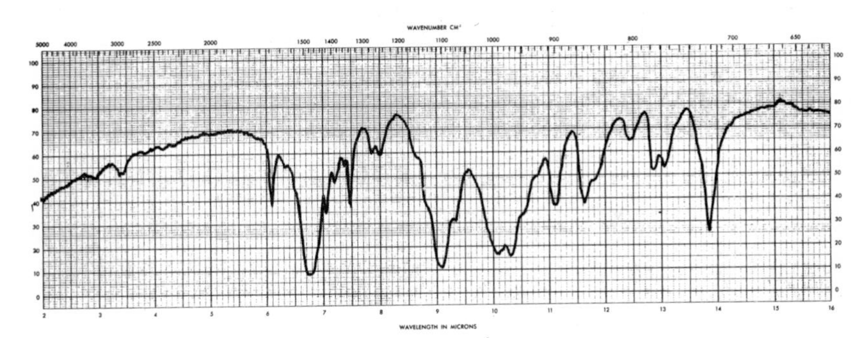

Figure 2. Infrared spectrum of 4,4′-diglycidyl ether of octafluorobiphenyl

Tetrafluororesorcinol reacted readily with epichlorohydrin before any alkali was added. Most of the product in this case was a chocolate-brown resinous solid. This was extracted with benzene after most of the epichlorohydrin was removed by vacuum evaporation. Benzene was then removed by vacuum evaporation, and the liquid residue was vacuum distilled at 170°–175°C. (1 mm.) in a Hickman still. A clear, liquid product was obtained in low yield which contained glycidyl groups and 22.69% fluorine. A pure product was not isolated, but the epoxy equivalent weight of 250 indicates that the material may be principally the dimer (Theoretical E.E.W. = 256).

$$\underset{\diagdown O \diagup}{CH_2\text{—}CHCH_2}\text{—O—}C_6F_4\text{—O—}CH_2\underset{OH}{CH}CH_2\text{—O—}C_6F_4\text{—O—}CH_2\underset{\diagdown O \diagup}{CH\text{—}CH_2}$$

FMPDA cures these fluorinated resins at 165°C. during 24 hours to produce plastics. The maximum fluorine-to-carbon ratio by number of atoms on a disubstituted aromatic ring is 2-to-3. Although these plastics carry fluorine on all available ring positions, they are not markedly hydrophobic nor of low surface friction. In Figure 4, it can be seen that the water absorption of the plastic produced from the diglycidyl ether of octafluorobiphenyl and FMPDA is only slightly less than that of a common epoxy plastic. The presence of perfluorinated aliphatic units within the molecular network of the plastic is apparently necessary if properties similar to those of fluorocarbon polymers are to be realized in epoxy systems. The polar hydroxyl and amino groups within the network detract from hydrophobic properties, and the glycidyl region appears to be unaffected by aromatic fluorocarbon within the structure.

The strength properties of epoxy plastics depend upon the development of a tightly crosslinked, three dimensional molecular network during the cure reactions. The inclusion of perfluorinated aliphatic units into such a network should be accomplished ideally in such a manner that the compact, functional nature of the components is not impaired. Numerous $—CF_3$ groups on aromatic resins and curing agents would constitute a favorable means of including aliphatic fluorocarbon. However, the chemistry of fluorine compounds has not advanced to the point that many di- or tetrafunctional intermediates heavily laden with trifluoromethyl groups are known.

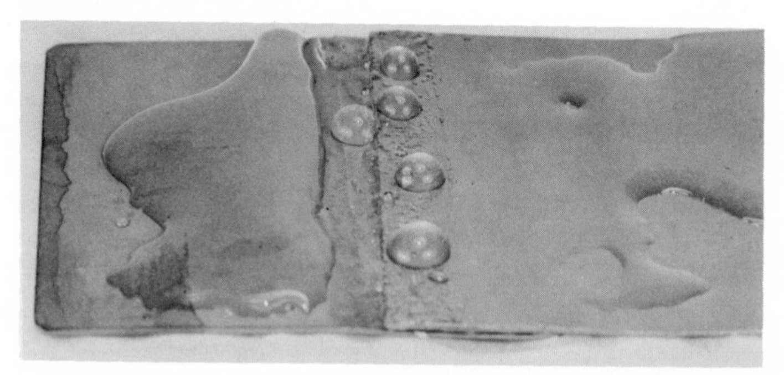

Figure 3. Water retracts from a bonded joint adhered with an epoxy containing perfluoroaliphatic chains

In order to obtain an indication of the effects of perfluorinated aliphatic groups upon the behavior toward water of epoxy plastics, some polyfunctional fluoroester curing agents for epoxy resins were synthesized. Esters of 1H, 1H-fluoroalcohols have been reported to be exceptionally stable to hydrolysis and pyrolysis (*3*), and the synthesis from acid chlorides and alcohols occurs readily. For example, the ester-anhydride of trimellitic acid was prepared as follows:

$$ClC(=O)\text{-}C_6H_3(CO)_2O + CF_3(CF_2)_nCH_2OH \rightarrow CF_3(CF_2)_nCH_2O\text{—}C(=O)\text{—}C_6H_3(CO)_2O$$

The acid chloride function is sufficiently more reactive with these fluoroalcohols than the anhydride function that the selective esterification can be accomplished, leaving the anhydride for subsequent use in curing epoxy resins.

A similar reaction with trimesoyl chloride, followed by hydrolysis of the excess acid chloride, was used to prepare partial esters with acid functions for use in curing epoxies.

$$C_6H_3(C(=O)Cl)_3 + CF_3(CF_2)_nCH_2OH \xrightarrow[(2)\ H_2O]{(1)\ \text{reflux}} (HOOC)_2C_6H_3\text{—}C(=O)\text{—}O\text{—}CH_2(CF_2)_nCF_3$$

Partial esters of 1H,1H-heptafluorobutanol and 1H,1H-pentadecafluorooctanol were prepared from the trimellitic anhydride and trimesic acid in this manner. The products were difficult to obtain in high purity because of unusual solubility characteristics and the similar nature of the contaminants, such as the diester of trimesic acid. However, partial esters of sufficient purity to function as epoxy curing agents were obtained.

The ester anhydrides of trimellitic acid are lower melting and more soluble in epoxy resins than are the partial esters of trimesic acid. During the cure reactions, the long pendant fluorocarbon chains apparently concentrate in the resin surface and render the cured plastic hydrophobic. Figure 3 shows a lap bond between two steel panels adhered with a composition of the diglycidyl ether of bisphenol A and the 1H-1H-pentadecafluorooctyl ester of trimellitic anhydride. Water applied to the bonded region retracts from the adhesive on to the steel, or stands in beads with high contact angles as illustrated.

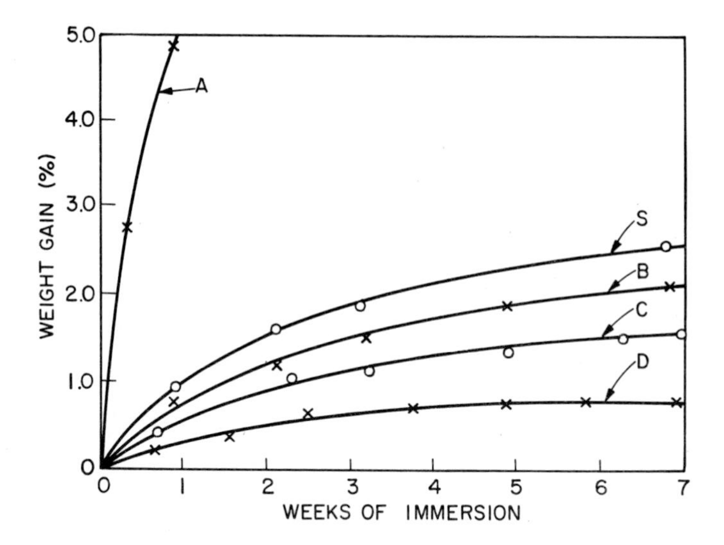

Figure 4. Water absorption at 25°C. of the following plastics: (A) 1,4-cyclohexane diepoxide and tetrafluoro-m-phenylenediamine; (B) diglycidyl ether of 4,4'-dihydroxyoctafluorobiphenyl and tetrafluoro-m-phenylenediamine; (C) diglycidyl ether of bisphenol A and mono-pentadecafluorooctyl trimesic acid; (D) diglycidyl ether of bisphenol A and pentadecafluorooctyl trimellitic anhydride; and (S) diglycidyl ether of bisphenol A and aromatic diamine

Fluoroaliphatic chains within an epoxy plastic apparently render it resistant to the internal penetration of water also. Curves C and D in Figure 4 show the relatively low water absorptions of bisphenol A resin cured with the trimesic and trimellitic fluoroesters respectively. The amount of weight increase of these plastics during six weeks' immersion in distilled water at room temperature is about half that of the standard amine-cured material. These data were determined on discs of plastic approximately the diameter and thickness of a nickel coin.

The inclusion of large amounts of fluorocarbon into epoxy resins in an optimum manner is dependent upon further developments in the chemistry of heavily fluorinated, polyfunctional intermediates. If the ratio of polar groups to fluoroaliphatic units can be reduced in the cured plastics, and the fluorocarbon can be located close to and distributed along the molecular network units, then epoxy plastics with outstanding resistance to the effects of water should be obtained.

Acknowledgment

The authors wish to acknowledge the assistance of Arthur G. Sands in preparing and testing plastic samples.

Literature Cited

(1) Air Force Materials Laboratory, *Tech. Rept.* **AFML-TR-65-13, Part III** (April 1967).
(2) Erich, W., Bodnar, M. J., *J. Appl. Polymer Sci.* **3,** No. 9, 296 (1960).
(3) Faurote, P. D., O'Rear, J. G., *Ind. and Eng. Chem.* **49,** No. 2, 189 (1957).
(4) Kelly, P. B., Landua, A. J., Marshall, C. D., *J. Appl. Polymer Sci.* **6,** No. 22, 425 (1962).

RECEIVED June 10, 1968.

3

A Novel Process for Preparing Glycidyl Ester Copolymers

DARRELL D. HICKS

Polymer Research Laboratory, Celanese Coatings Co., Louisville, Ky. 40299

A process for preparing copolymers of ethylenically unsaturated carboxylic acid glycidyl esters obviates the need for isolating the glycidyl ester monomer. The process involves forming a copolymer of the appropriate unsaturated carboxylic acid in an epichlorohydrin-rich medium, converting the carboxyl groups to the chlorohydrin ester derivative, and subsequently dehydrohalogenating with alkali in the epichlorohydrin-rich medium to form the glycidyl ester. The excess epichlorohydrin is distilled from the system, and the copolymer product is recovered in a suitable solvent. Copolymer compositions described include those containing glycidyl acrylate, glycidyl methacrylate, and glycidyl crotonate at weight levels up to 72% in combination with various other vinyl monomers. Dehydrohalogenation efficiencies (ratio of actual to theoretical epoxy content) of up to 85–91% are readily obtained by such a process.

Glycidyl esters of certain ethylenically unsaturated carboxylic acids corresponding to the structure:

$$\mathrm{R{-}CH{=}\overset{\displaystyle R^1}{\overset{|}{C}}{-}\overset{\displaystyle O}{\overset{\|}{C}}{-}O{-}CH_2{-}\overset{\;\;O}{CH{-}CH_2}}$$

$$\mathrm{R,R^1 = H \text{ or } CH_3}$$

are well known compounds whose preparation (*1*) and utility (*3*) have been reported in the literature. The acrylate and methacrylate ester monomers possess copolymerization parameters that make possible the preparation of a wide variety of useful copolymer compositions. Such copolymers, accordingly, contain pendant reactive 1,2-epoxy groups which may be utilized to form thermosetting film and plastic compositions *via* reaction with other polyfunctional materials such as acids, acid anhydrides, and amines.

While copolymers of unsaturated glycidyl esters are obtainable by the conventional route of copolymerizing the proper monomers, such a route does entail at least two serious disadvantages. First, the toxicity of the lower unsaturated glycidyl esters is such that very special handling techniques must be used—these materials have been known to cause severe cases of dermatitis. Secondly, the glycidyl ester monomers are relatively expensive to produce.

An alternate method for forming solution type glycidyl ester copolymers which eliminated the need for preparing and isolating the glycidyl ester monomer has been successfully employed. The process consisted essentially of the following steps:

1. Form the precursor unsaturated acid copolymer in an epichlorohydrin or epichlorohydrin-rich medium.
2. Form chlorohydrin ester derivative through reaction of pendant carboxyl groups on copolymer with epichlorohydrin in presence of a carboxy-epoxy catalyst.
3. Dehydrohalogenate chlorohydrin ester groups with alkali in the epichlorohydrin-rich medium.
4. Distill off excess epichlorohydrin, replacing with a desirable solvent.
5. Filter salt from copolymer solution.

Thus, the copolymer products were recovered in an organic solvent and may be used as coating or pre-preg resins.

It is the object of this paper to describe the preparation by such a process of copolymers containing either combined glycidyl acrylate, glycidyl methacrylate, or glycidyl crotonate. Further, certain limits of the process will be discussed and defined. The paper will not deal, therefore, with any utility of the copolymers nor with any detailed characterization. Only the feasibility of the process employed in terms of yield will be covered.

First, the experimental procedures employed will be described followed by a discussion of the results.

Experimental

A variety of comonomers were utilized in forming the acrylate and methacrylate ester copolymers while only vinyl acetate was used in forming the crotonate ester copolymer.

All the copolymers were formed *via* free radical catalysis using organic peroxides as the source of free radicals.

Formation of Precursor Acid Copolymers. The precursor acid copolymers were prepared at monomer/solvent ratios of 25/75 up to 50/50 depending upon both the glycidyl ester level of the product and the mol. wt. desired. The acrylic and methacrylic acid copolymers were formed by slow addition of the monomer-peroxide catalyst solution to the solvent at 115°–121°C. with adequate stirring. The vinyl acetate/crotonic acid copolymers were formed by heating the total charge of monomers, catalyst, and solvent at reflux till conversion was essentially complete.

The polymerization medium employed was epichlorohydrin or a medium containing at least 50 wt. % epichlorohydrin. Surprisingly enough, epi functions quite well as a medium in which to conduct free radical initiated polymerization reactions. Though its chain transfer constant was not determined, viscosity measurements and other data indicate it compares with that of glycol ethers and esters—certainly not nearly as high as that of other halogenated hydrocarbons. It was found, as will be discussed later, that the epichlorohydrin/acid equivalent ratio must be above a certain minimum during the formation of the chlorohydrin ester derivative.

Formation of Chlorohydrin Ester. After the acid copolymer formation was completed, the pendant carboxyl groups were converted to the corresponding chlorohydrin ester by the addition of a suitable carboxy-epoxy catalyst. The reaction involved is shown schematically as follows:

$$\sim\!\!\sim C{-}C(C{=}O)(OH)\!\sim\!\!\sim \; + \; Cl{-}C{-}\overset{O}{\overbrace{C{-}C}} \xrightarrow[\text{110-115°C.}\ \text{1-2 hrs.}]{R_4N^+Cl^-} \sim\!\!\sim C{-}C(C{=}O{-}O{-}C{-}C(OH){-}C{-}Cl)\!\sim\!\!\sim$$

In the presence of certain tertiary amines or quaternary ammonium halides such as, for instance, triethylamine, tetramethylammonium chloride, or benzyltrimethylammonium chloride, the conversion to ester is usually complete after 1–2 hours at 115°C.

Dehydrohalogenation of Chlorohydrin Ester. The pendant chlorohydrin ester groups on the copolymer chain were converted to the 1,2-epoxy derivative according to the reaction shown as follows:

$$\begin{array}{c} \sim\!\sim C{-}C\!\sim\!\sim \\ | \\ C{=}O \\ | \\ O \\ | \\ C \\ | \\ C{-}OH \\ | \\ C{-}Cl \end{array} + NaOH \xrightarrow{25\text{-}90^{\circ}C.} \begin{array}{c} \sim\!\sim C{-}C\!\sim\!\sim \\ | \\ C{=}O \\ | \\ O \\ | \\ C \\ | \\ C \\ O\langle\ \ | \\ C \end{array} + NaCl$$

Sodium hydroxide is added to the system either incrementally or in bulk at 25°–35°C., and the mixture is heated slowly to 90°C. to complete the dehydrohalogenation. One mole sodium hydroxide per equivalent of acid employed in the copolymer gave optimum "dehydrohalogenation efficiency" which is defined as the ratio of theoretical to actual wt./epoxide.

The sodium hydroxide was employed in two forms—as the conventional flake material and as a dispersion in xylene. The dispersed form had a particle size of 5–15 microns and gives roughly a three-fold increase in reaction rate at a lower temperature. A suitable form of dispersed NaOH in xylene was prepared by grinding in a pebble mill for 12–15 hours a mixture comprising a ratio of 40 parts flake NaOH (96% grade), 60 parts xylene, and 0.4 parts dimer acids (Emery Industries Empol 1022).

Distilling off Excess Epichlorohydrin. The excess epichlorohydrin was removed from the reaction mixture by distillation at reduced pressure prior to filtering off the salt. In order to maintain a viscosity which allowed adequate stirring, the desired replacement solvent was added to the mixture as the excess epi distilled over. This, of course, means that some of the replacement solvent is distilled over with the excess epi. When the replacement solvent had a b.p. at least 30°–40°C. higher than epi, efficient removal of the epi was obtained. A satisfactory replacement solvent in this regard was an aromatic hydrocarbon fraction having a boiling range of 157°–180°C. and marketed as Solvesso 100. Copolymers containing more than about 40 wt. % glycidyl ester required some polar solvent (such as a glycol ether) for complete copolymer solution at room temperature. After the distillate was found to be coming over essentially free of epi, the copolymer solution was then filtered to remove the suspended salt.

The epoxide content of the products was determined by dissolving a sample in 25 ml. of 0.2*N* pyridine hydrochloride (16 ml. conc. HCl per liter pyridine), digesting the resulting solution at reflux for 20 minutes, and back titrating excess HCl with 0.1*N* alcoholic KOH using brom thymol blue indicator.

Results and Discussion

Formation of Precursor Acid Copolymers. Listed in Table I are a series of acrylic, methacrylic, and crotonic acid copolymer compositions at various acid levels. Except for the two highest level methacrylic acid systems, the copolymers were formed in an all-epichlorohydrin medium. The two exceptions required a more polar solvent (propylene glycol monomethyl ether) in combination with epi to obtain complete solution.

Table I. Precursor Acid Copolymer Preparation

Copolymer	*GMA-12 (1)*	*GMA-20 (2)*	*GMA-30 (3)*	*GMA-40 (4)*	*GMA-60 (5)*
Charge Ratio (grams)[a]					
VT	38.5		79.5	71.2	52.3
Sty		86.8			
VAc					
MMA	53.5				
BA					
BMA					
MAA	8.0	13.2	20.5	28.8	47.7
AA					
CA					
Bz_2O_2	2.5	2.5	2.5	2.5	2.5
Epi	157.0	124.0	157.0	157.0	143.0
Co-Solvent (PGME)					67.0
Monomer/Solvent	39/61	45/55	39/61	39/61	32/68
Time (Hrs.)/Temp. (°C.)	5/118	4/120	5/120	6/120	5/115
% Conversion	97.5	99.4	99.2	99.4	99.0

Copolymer	*GMA-80 (6)*	*GA-12 (7)*	*GA-20 (8)*	*GA-30 (9)*	*GC-20 (10)*	*GC-40 (11)*
Charge Ratio (grams)[a]						
VT	29.2	93.2		80.4		
Sty			87.7			
VAc					87.0	71.3
MMA						
BA						
BMA						
MAA	70.8					
AA		6.8	12.3	19.6		
CA					13.0	28.7
Bz_2O_2	2.5	2.5	2.5	2.5	3.0	4.0
Epi	143.0	164.0	110.0	207.0	100.0	100.0
Co-Solvent (PGME)	167.0					
Monomer/Solvent	31/69	38/62	48/52	33/67	50/50	50/50
Time (Hrs.)/Temp. (°C.)	5/115	6/115	5/115	5/115	5/80-100	5/88-117
% Conversion	100	99.1	100	99.6	99.0	100

Table I. Continued

Copolymer	*GMA/BA 20/20 (12)*	*GMA/BA 20/30 (13)*	*GMA/BMA 20/30 (14)*	*GMA/BMA 20/40 (15)*	*GA/BMA 30/30 (16)*
Charge Ratio (grams)[a]					
VT	65.1	54.3	54.3	43.4	
Sty					46.0
VAc					
MMA					
BA	21.7	32.5			
BMA			32.5	43.4	34.6
MAA	13.2	13.2	13.2	13.2	
AA					19.4
CA					
Bz_2O_2	2.5	2.5	2.5	2.5	2.5
Epi	108.0	108.0	108.0	108.0	110.0
Co-Solvent (PGME) Monomer/Solvent	48/52	48/52	48/52	48/52	48/52
Time (Hrs.)/Temp. (°C.)	5/115	6/120	6/120	6/120	5/120
% Conversion	100	98.0	99.1	99.2	99.2

[a] VT—vinyl toluene, Sty—styrene, VAc—vinyl acetate, MMA—methyl methacrylate, BA—*n*-butyl acrylate, BMA—*n*-butyl methacrylate, MAA—methacrylic acid, AA—acrylic acid, CA—crotonic acid, Bz_2O_2—benzoyl peroxide, PGME—propylene glycol methyl ether.

Formation of Chlorohydrin Ester. Listed in Table II are the conditions employed and the results obtained in converting the acid copolymers to the respective chlorohydrin ester derivatives.

It was found that during the formation of the chlorohydrin ester derivatives, the epi/acid equivalent ratio should be above a certain minimum when the carboxy/epoxy catalyst is added or the system will cross-link to a gel condition. This minimum ratio varied somewhat depending on the acid level of the copolymer, but generally a ratio of 7–9 moles epi per mole of acid was sufficient to prevent gelation. This tendency towards cross-linking at the lower epi/acid ratios is believed to be caused by the following circumstances which develop once chlorohydrin ester is forming:

The carboxy-epoxy catalyst not only catalyzes the carboxy-epoxy reaction but is also known to catalyze a so-called "disproportionation" reaction (which is nothing more than a dehydrohalogenation reaction) between epi and the formed chlorohydrin ester to generate an epoxy group and 1,3-glycerol dichlorohydrin as follows (2):

$$\sim\!\sim C{-}C\!\sim\!\sim{-}C(=O){-}O{-}C{-}C(OH){-}C{-}Cl \;+\; Cl{-}C{-}\overset{O}{C{-}C} \xrightarrow{R_4N^+Cl^-} \sim\!\sim C{-}C\!\sim\!\sim{-}C(=O){-}O{-}C{-}\overset{O}{C{-}C} \;+\; Cl{-}C{-}C(OH){-}C{-}Cl$$

Table II. Chlorohydrin Ester Preparation

	(1)	*(2)*	*(3)*	*(4)*
Catalyst, grams (BTMACl[a])	0.3	0.3	0.5	0.9
Additional epi, grams	6.5	9.3	263.0	412.0
Excess epi/Acid	17.6	8.7	21.0	18.4
Time (Hrs.)/Temp. (°C.)	2/115	2/115	2/115	2/115
Acid Value (solids)	<1	<1	<1	<1

	(5)	*(6)*	*(7)*	*(8)*
Catalyst, grams (BTMACl[a])	1.4	2.2	0.2	0.3
Additional epi, grams	318.0	467.0	0	64.0
Excess epi/Acid	9.0	8.0	18.7	11.0
Time (Hrs.)/Temp. (°C.)	1/115	2/115	2/115	2/115
Acid Value (solids)	<1	<1	<1	<1

	(9)	*(10)*	*(11)*	*(12)*
Catalyst, grams (BTMACl[a])	0.5	0.3	0.6	0.3
Additional epi, grams	96.0	50.0	239.0	48.0
Excess epi/Acid	12.0	10.7	11.0	11.0
Time (Hrs.)/Temp. (°C.)	2/115	2/115	2/115	2/115
Acid Value (solids)	<1	<1	<1	<1

	(13)	*(14)*	*(15)*	*(16)*
Catalyst, grams (BTMACl[a])	0.3	0.3	0.3	0.5
Additional epi, grams	48.0	48.0	48.0	165.0
Excess epi/Acid	11.0	11.0	11.0	11.0
Time (Hrs.)/Temp. (°C.)	2/115	2/115	2/115	2/115
Acid Value (solids)	<1	<1	<1	<1

[a] BTMACl—benzyltrimethylammonium chloride.

Therefore, when the catalyst is added to the epi-acid copolymer mixture, chlorohydrin ester groups are formed (from the epi-acid reaction) which are then labile to the disproportionation reaction with epi thus to form epoxy groups (as the glycidyl ester derivative) on the copolymer chain as depicted below. Consequently, epoxy groups from two different sources compete for reaction with the remainder of the carboxyl groups on the copolymer chains as shown schematically:

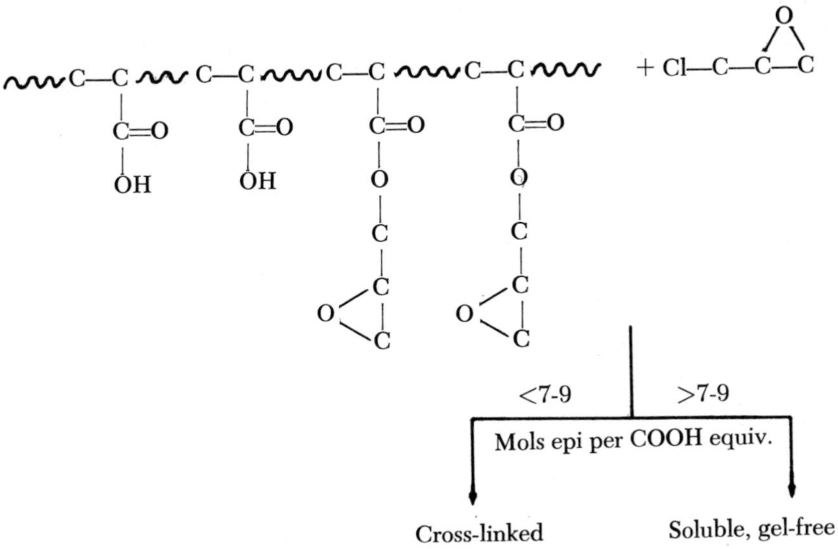

~~C—C~~C—C~~C—C~~C—C~~ + Cl—C—C—C (with O bridging the last two C)

Pendant groups: C=O—OH, C=O—OH, C=O—O—C—C—C (with O bridging the last two C), C=O—O—C—C—C (with O bridging the last two C)

Mols epi per COOH equiv.

<7-9 → Cross-linked

>7-9 → Soluble, gel-free

That is, the epoxy groups on the copolymer chain formed by the disproportionation reaction and the epoxy groups from epichlorohydrin are now competing for the remaining carboxyl groups on the copolymer chain. If many of the epoxy groups on the copolymer chain react, the system will cross-link to a gel. To minimize the glycidyl ester-carboxyl reaction, at least 7–9 moles epichlorohydrin per equivalent of carboxyls appeared to give the epi epoxy groups a statistical advantage over those of the pendant glycidyl ester groups and thus prevent systems from crosslinking.

Dehydrohalogenation of Chlorohydrin Ester. Listed in Table III are the ratios and conditions used for dehydrohalogenating the chlorohydrin ester copolymers. Optimum dehydrohalogenation efficiencies were realized by treatment with NaOH in a medium containing at least a 7–9/1 equivalent ratio of epi/chlorohydrin ester.

Dispersed NaOH was observed in this process to dehydrohalogenate five to 10 times faster at lower temperatures than the flake form. However, the products dehydrohalogenated with flake material filtered faster and had better clarity than those dehydrohalogenated with dispersed

Table III. Dehydrohalogenation of Chlorohydrin Ester Copolymer

	(1)	(2)	(3)	(4)
Excess epi/chlorohydrin	16.6	8.3	20.0	17.4
NaOH, grams (type)[a]	3.7 (d)	6.1 (d)	9.6 (d)	13.4 (d)
Time (mins.)/Temp. (°C.)	60/30-90	60/30-90	60/30-90	60/30-90
	(5)	(6)	(7)	(8)
Excess epi/chlorohydrin	8.0	7.0	17.7	10.0
NaOH, grams (type)[a]	22.2 (d)	32.9 (d)	3.8 (d)	7.5 (f)
Time (mins.)/Temp. (°C.)	60/30-90	80/30-90	60/30-90	360/100
	(9)	(10)	(11)	(12)
Excess epi/chlorohydrin	11.0	9.7	10.0	10.0
NaOH, grams (type)[a]	10.9 (d)	6.0 (d)	15.0 (d)	6.7 (f)
Time (mins.)/Temp. (°C.)	60/30-90	60/30-90	60/30-90	360/100
	(13)	(14)	(15)	(16)
Excess epi/chlorohydrin	10.0	10.0	10.0	10.0
NaOH, grams (type)[a]	6.7 (f)	6.7 (f)	6.7 (f)	11.9 (f)
Time (mins.)/Temp. (°C.)	360/100	360/100	360/100	360/100

[a] (d)—dispersed, (f)—flake.

Table IV. Distilling Excess

	(1)	(2)	(3)
Pot Temp./mm. Hg.	70-4/30	60-74/30	60-70/30
Theo. excess epi, grams	155	120	393
Distillate collected, grams		220	
Epi collected, grams			
Solvent added, grams	450	230	515
Product wt./epox.	1264	798	553
DHH[a] efficiency	89.3	88.9	85.5
	(9)	(10)	(11)
Pot Temp./mm. Hg.	53-62/30	62-77/30	95-100/30
Theo. excess epi, grams	277	136	308
Distillate collected, grams	670	432	835
Epi collected, grams		119	299
Solvent added, grams	550	440	667
Product wt./epox.	507	800	467
DHH[a] efficiency	84.2	89.7	76.0

[a] DHH—dehydrohalogenation.

NaOH. The salt formed using dispersed caustic appeared much more finely divided than that produced with flake caustic.

Distilling off Excess Epichlorohydrin. At this point in the process, the reaction mixture is comprised of the glycidyl ester copolymer dissolved in the excess epi, and the salt (from the dehydrohalogenation reaction) is suspended in the liquid medium. Since epi is, of course, an undesirable solvent in which to recover and use the copolymer product, a solvent interchange was studied.

Listed in Table IV are the conditions employed for distilling the excess epi from each of the systems. The stripping process required pot temperatures up to 70°–100°C. at 20–30 mm. Hg pressure. The amount of distillate required to rid the system essentially free of excess epi depended to some degree on the b.p. of the replacement solvent. When the replacement solvent was a high boiling aromatic hydrocarbon fraction (b.p. = 157°–180°C.) or dipropylene glycol monomethyl ether (b.p. = 190°C.), an amount of distillate (co-distilled epi and replacement solvent) corresponding to about 1.5 times the weight of excess epi to be removed was sufficient to remove essentially all the epi provided the solvent was added at a rate approximately equal to the distillation rate.

Dehydrohalogenation Efficiencies. After stripping the products free of the excess epichlorohydrin and recovering in a suitable solvent, the suspended salt was filtered from the solutions and the products analyzed for epoxy content.

Epi from Copolymer Solution

(4)	*(5)*	*(6)*	*(7)*	*(8)*
60-70/30	60-70	40-50/30	40-50/30	70-2/30
539	407	531	155	158
	1182	1168	377	382
				147
			325	360
394	288	197	1208	725
90.2	82.3	90.2	91.0	88.4

(12)	*(13)*	*(14)*	*(15)*	*(16)*
62-72/30	70-6/30	68-73/30	68-72/30	65-7/30
142	142	142	142	250
383	350	371	371	654
128	125	126	123	239
360	360	360	360	600
817	819	791	801	509
86.9	86.7	89.8	88.6	83.7

Table V lists some physical constants of the copolymer solution products. The per cent glycidyl ester was calculated from the wt./epoxide values and comparisons with theoretical values represent a measure of dehydrohalogenation efficiency which ranged from 76–91% for the compositions in the tables.

Table V. Product Physical Constants

	(1)	*(2)*	*(3)*	*(4)*
% Solids	39.3	36.4	41.6	40.4
Solvent[a]	S. 100	S. 100	S. 100	S. 100
Viscosity, c.p.s. (25°C.)				
Color, Gardner				
Wt./epoxide	1264	798	553	394
% Glycidyl ester, calc.	11.2	17.8	25.7	36.1
	(5)	*(6)*	*(7)*	*(8)*
% Solids	58.7	40.8	48.0	43.8
Solvent[a]	S. 100	S. 100/CA	S. 100	S. 100
Viscosity, c.p.s. (25°C.)				320
Color, Gardner				<1
Wt./epoxide	288	197	1208	725
% Glycidyl ester, calc.	49.3	72.1	10.6	17.7
	(9)	*(10)*	*(11)*	*(12)*
% Solids	35.9	41.4	48.9	47.4
Solvent[a]	S. 100	S. 100/DPGME	DPGME	S. 100
Viscosity, c.p.s. (25°C.)			200	470
Color, Gardner			10	<1
Wt./epoxide	507	800	467	817
% Glycidyl ester, calc.	25.3	17.8	30.5	17.4
	(13)	*(14)*	*(15)*	*(16)*
% Solids	41.9	44.6	45.3	37.3
Solvent[a]	S. 100	S. 100	S. 100	S. 100
Viscosity, c.p.s. (25°C.)	180	470	500	250
Color, Gardner	<1	<1	<1	<1
Wt./epoxide	819	791	801	509
% Glycidyl ester, calc.	17.3	18.0	17.7	25.1

[a] S. 100—Solvesso 100, CA—Cellosolve acetate, DPGME—dipropylene glycol methyl ether.

Apart from the steric factors involved, which may preclude complete dehydrohalogenation, and the possible loss of epoxy groups *via* polymerization during the stripping process, there are at least two competing reactions that could reduce the dehydrohalogenation efficiency. One such possibility is the base hydrolysis of ester linkages by the alkali. The other side reaction, believed less likely to occur, is the formation of inactive chlorine by reaction of epi with a chlorohydrin ester hydroxyl group to produce the following structure:

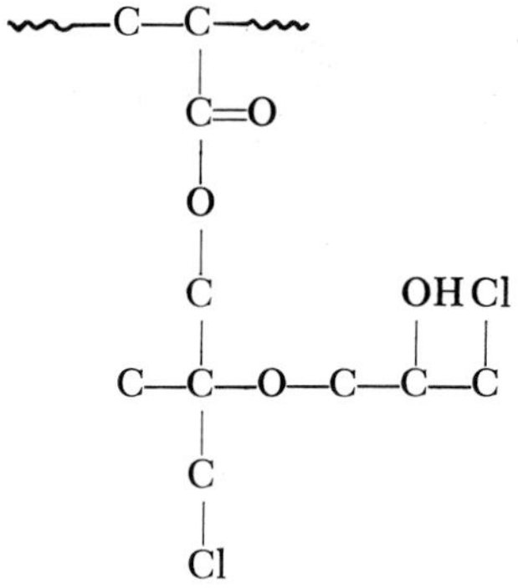

```
~~C—C~~
     |
     C=O
     |
     O
     |
     C          OH Cl
     |          |  |
  C—C—O—C—C—C
     |
     C
     |
     Cl
```

Unfortunately, a suitable method is not available for determining inactive chlorine in the presence of saponifiable ester linkages.

Use of Higher Acrylic Ester Monomers. To determine if higher acrylate or methacrylate comonomers could be utilized in this process without undergoing hydrolysis by the alkaline conditions employed in the dehydrohalogenation step, a series of copolymers was prepared containing up to 40 wt. % butyl ester in the final product.

The copolymer compositions in the last five columns of the tables demonstrate that substantial amounts of "flexibilizing" monomers may be incorporated into the acrylic and methacrylic acid copolymers with no marked effect on dehydrohalogenation efficiency.

Re-use of Distillate. The commercial value of this process would depend to a large degree on whether or not the epi-rich distillate could be re-used. Some study devoted to this indicated that the distillate can be recycled efficiently by forming the precursor acid copolymer in a 65/35 wt. ratio of epi/Solvesso 100 media.

Summary

Glycidyl acrylate, glycidyl methacrylate, and glycidyl crotonate solution copolymers were prepared from their precursor acid copolymers in yields up to 85–91%. Copolymers containing up to 72% by wt. glycidyl methacrylate were demonstrated while yields of glycidyl acrylate and glycidyl acrylate and glycidyl crotonate decreased above levels of about 25 wt. % and 18 wt. % respectively. The feature of the process is that it makes possible the preparation of these copolymers without having to prepare, isolate, or handle the toxic and expensive intermediate glycidyl ester monomers.

Literature Cited

(1) Dorough, D. L., *U. S. Patent* **2,524,432** (Oct. 3, 1950).
(2) Mueller, A. C., *U. S. Patent* **2,772,296** (Nov. 27, 1956).
(3) Simms, J. A., *J. Appl. Polymer Sci.* **5**, No. 13, 58 (1961).

RECEIVED June 19, 1968.

4

A Study of Accelerators for Epoxy-Amine Condensation Reaction

A. M. PARTANSKY

Western Division of the Dow Chemical Co., 2800 Mitchell Drive, Walnut Creek, Calif. 94598

Effects of alcohols, phenols, acids, tertiary amines, sulfur-containing compounds, and other additives on the rate of oxirane group-amine reaction in solvents at 25°C. were studied. Carboxylic acids which contain hydroxyls on the adjacent carbon and, in the case of salicylic acid, also other electronegative-substituent groups, are the best accelerators for aromatic amine-epoxide reaction, while halogenated or nitrated phenols appear to be preferable in systems where the amine is aliphatic in nature.

It would be misleading, as well as incorrect, to speak about reactivity of the oxirane ring without specifying in what type of molecule and in which position in it the oxirane group is located. For instance, reactivity of the oxirane group is different when it is in a long hydrocarbon chain, in a cycloparaffin, or on an aromatic ring compound, to mention a few. It also makes a difference if the oxirane group is attached at one end only or is located in the middle of a molecule, with both ends having an "R" attached to them.

When the oxirane ring is a part of a glycidyl group, the nature of the atom to which the latter is attached, as well as that of the rest of the molecule, also materially affect its reactivity. For instance, the following familiar epoxide types are known to have different epoxide group reactivity.

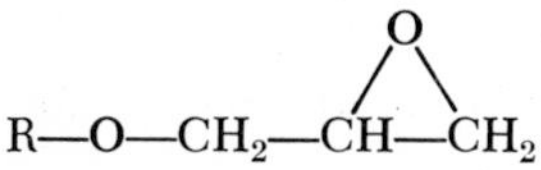

$R—O—CH_2—\overset{O}{CH—CH_2}$ an ether $\qquad$ $R—S—CH_2—\overset{O}{CH—CH_2}$ a sulfide

$R—NH—CH_2—\overset{O}{CH—CH_2}$ a substituted amine

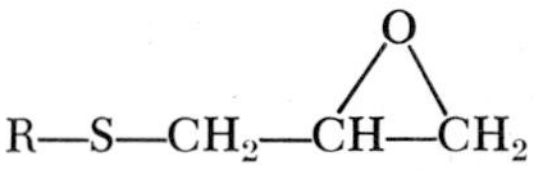

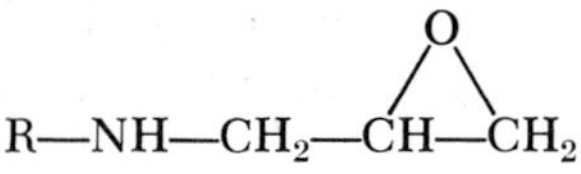

Reactivity of the oxirane groups in the above examples would also vary depending on the nature of the "R" group itself—*e.g.*, whether it is alkyl, cycloparaffin, or aromatic in nature.

The presence of other polar groups in the epoxy molecules may also have a marked effect on the oxirane group reactivity. The classical examples of this are the well-known accelerating effect of alcoholic hydroxyls, present in most commercial bisphenol A-based epoxy resins, and that of halogens in the commercial self-extinguishing types of epoxy resins. In addition to the above mentioned factors, which we may look upon as "internal activators," oxirane rings may also be activated and made more reactive by "external" factors, that is, with the activating entity being located on a different molecule from the oxirane group itself. A preliminary exploration of the nature of these "external" accelerators as well as the relative magnitude of their effect under a standardized set of experimental conditions is the object of this paper.

A generally accepted first step in the condensation reaction involving epoxides is assumed to be the opening of the oxirane ring, and the function of the catalyst is to assist in bringing this about. The opening of the oxirane ring by a hydroxyl compound may proceed according to the following scheme (1):

$$R'R''NH + CH_2\text{—}CH\text{—}R\ (\text{epoxide, O bridging}) + HOX \rightarrow R'R''N(H)\text{---}CH_2\text{—}CH\text{—}R\ (\text{ring O}\cdots HOX)$$

$$R'R''\overset{\oplus}{N}(H)\text{—}CH_2\text{—}C(H)(OH\cdots{}^{\ominus}OX)\text{—}R \rightarrow R'R''N\text{—}CH_2\text{—}C(H)(OH)\text{—}R + HOX$$

However, the actual mechanism by which epoxy-curing agent condensation is catalyzed is probably more complex than the above scheme indicates, and is also dependent on the type of curing agent being used. Thus, it has been observed that different classes of accelerators are more effective in some specific epoxy-curing agent systems and less so, or even not at all, in others. In fact, there are cases when a substance which is an accelerator in one epoxy-curing agent system may have just an opposite effect in a different system.

Selective activation of the oxirane group in respect to different coreacting hardeners by three common catalyst types may be summarized as follows.

	Epoxide Group is:	
Catalyst Type	*Activated in Respect to*	*NOT Activated in Respect to*
Tertiary Amines	Epoxides Anhydrides Phenols	Alcohols Amine H
Lewis Type Acids, (BF_3, etc.)	Epoxides Alcohols	Anhydrides Amine H
Weak Proton Donnors (Phenols, —COOH acids)	Amine H	Anhydrides Alcohols

Thus we see that:

(1) Tertiary amines catalyze reaction of one oxirane group with another, with an acid anhydride group, or with a phenol but are not effective in the epoxide-alcohol reaction or in condensation with primary amines.

(2) Lewis acids, such as BF_3 (in a complex), are useful in catalyzing oxirane-alcohol hydroxyl or oxirane-oxirane reactions but not in the epoxy-anhydride or epoxy-amine reactions.

(3) Weak proton donors are the most effective accelerators in the epoxy-primary (or secondary) amine reaction, and the use of phenols for this purpose is a well established commercial practice.

Chemical reactions involving relatively simple mono- or difunctional molecules, in liquid media, proceed either to completion or to an equilibrium point essentially at a rate controlled by the mass action law. However, in the processes resulting in the formation of three dimensional structures, such as in curing of a thermoset epoxy resin, another factor, which I call the "mobility factor," becomes a very important rate-controlling element.

Formation of a three dimensional structure interferes first of all with a free translational movement of the reacting molecules, and then, as rigidity increases, even with the vibrational movement of the reacting groups themselves, to a point where they are no longer able to get close enough to each other for the reaction to take place. Thus, any further progress of the reaction becomes arrested, as if the system had become "frozen" in place.

In systems of this kind, completeness of the reaction can be improved by increasing, in some way, mobility of the reacting molecules, or at least of the reacting groups. This can be accomplished in a number of ways; among them:

(1) Increasing amplitude of the vibrational movement of the reacting components (both the molecules themselves and/or their functional groups), by increasing their energy—*e.g.*, by raising the temperature of the system.

(2) Providing for a greater freedom of molecular movement by increasing fluidity of the system. This can be done in two ways: by reducing the crosslinking density of the product (by reducing functionality of the reactants) and/or by adding inert solvent-diluents.

With the above considerations in mind, to avoid interference from any unrelated internal and external influences, which I have previously enumerated, it appeared desirable to carry the comparative reaction rate studies in solution and to use whenever possible the simplest model compounds available.

The use of a solvent medium in a study of this kind offers the following important experimental advantages:

(1) Interference from the "mobility factor" is minimized.

(2) Reactive group concentration (per unit volume) can be kept constant regardless of the molecular size of the reactants or incorporation of additives (accelerators) some of which could also be quite bulky.

(3) Reaction temperature is easier to control.

(4) Fast reactions can be slowed down to more reasonable and easier-to-follow rates.

Experimental

Solvent Selection. A good solvent should dissolve all the ingredients, be stable, relatively non-volatile, and have no catalytic effect (either positive or negative) of its own.

Preliminary experiments with 1*M* phenyl glycidyl ether-diethylamine system using a variety of possible solvents showed (*see* Table I) that a solvent can and does have a profound effect on the reaction rate. Thus, the table shows that at 25°C. there was a 37-fold increase in the extent of the reaction in 24 hrs., as the solvent was changed from a neutral hydrocarbon (toluene) to methanol with its 18.8 moles of hydroxyl groups per liter.

MEK was selected in preference to toluene (which is at the top of the list) because of its much better solubility characteristics. There might be some doubt about the advisability of using a ketone as a solvent in a rate study involving amine as one of the reactants because of the possibility of its deactivation through the well known ketamine reaction:

$$RNH_2 + O{=}C\begin{matrix} \diagup R' \\ \diagdown R'' \end{matrix} \rightleftharpoons RN{=}C\begin{matrix} \diagup R' \\ \diagdown R'' \end{matrix} + H_2O$$

However, ketamine can exist only in a completely anhydrous system, and apparently in our work the above equilibrium was always heavily shifted to the left since addition of one mole of water (Table V, Item 75) to the mixture had no beneficial effect on the reaction rate. Besides, even if there was some retarding effect of MEK solvent on the reaction

Table I. Effect of Solvent Composition on the Rate of Reaction Between Phenyl Glycidyl Ether and Diethylamine Present in 1*N* Concentration at 25°C. Temperature

Conditions: Epoxide: Phenyl glycidyl ether, 1 molar (150 g./l.).
Amine: Diethylamine, 1 molar (73 g./l.).
Catalyst: None.
Solvent: Varied.

Solvent Used			*% Reacted at 25°C. in*	
Kind	*Moles per Liter*	*Sp. Gr. of Solution*	*24 hrs.*	*48 hrs.*
Toluene	7.14	0.8813	2.5	7.1
MEK	8.49	0.8350	4.0	11.7
Perchlor	7.45	1.4574	6.8	11.9
DMFA	9.87	0.9447	12.9	24.3
Ortho-dichloro-benzene	6.75	1.2138	20.2	37.9
Dimethyl sulfoxide	10.7	1.0608	30.6	50.5
Methylene chloride	11.82	1.2260	37.7	53.5
Isopropyl alcohol	10.0	.8250	91.5	96.0
Methanol	18.8	.8281	93.2	98.4

rates, the "relative changes" in these rates produced by the accelerators added (which was the subject of our study) would have remained unaffected.

Epoxide Component Selection. Inasmuch as most commercially important epoxy resins are polyglycidyl ethers of phenols, the simplest representative of this group of compounds, phenyl glycidyl ether itself, appeared to be the most logical choice and was selected for our study. In addition to being monofunctional, PhGE is also available in a very pure (distilled) state. Thus, its reactivity is not influenced by substituents, such as alcoholic hydroxyls, present in all other glycidyl ether type commercial epoxy resins.

In Table II the reader will find reaction rate data on a number of different epoxides which reacted with diethylamine.

It may be noted that the reaction rate became faster as the hydroxyl content of the epoxy molecules increased; the presence of halogens had a similar effect. On the other hand, the purest materials (at the top of the list) were also the slowest in reacting.

Amine Component Selection. For the purpose of this study it was thought desirable to select one amine representative from each of the alkyl and the aryl classes.

The alkyl amine selected was a monofunctional diethylamine which made it very convenient to use with all epoxides including the polyfunctional ones.

The choice of methylenedianiline as a representative aromatic amine was influenced by the facts that it is widely used in industry, and that, in view of its generally slow reactivity, information on accelerators for this amine would have immediate practical value.

Table II. Effect of Epoxide Nature on the Rate of Reaction with Amine

Conditions: Epoxide: Varied in kind, one eq. wt. per liter.
Amine: Diethylamine, 1 molar (73 g./l.).
Catalyst: None.
Solvent: Methyl ethyl ketone.

Epoxide Used		*Theoret. Eq. Wt. of Pure*	*Eq. Wt.*	*% Reacted at 25°C. in*	
Kind	*g./l.*	*Compd.*	*Differences*	*24 hrs.*	*48 hrs.*
Phenyl GE	150.0	150.0	—	4.0	11.7
Butyl GE	130.0	130.1	—	5.1	11.0
DER 332LC	172.0	170	2.0	5.7	14.6
Cresol GE	172.6	164	8.6	8.5	17.0
DER 332	172	170	2.0	9.0	18.5
DER 331	188	170	18.0	9.5	22.1
DER 736	193	125	68.0	12.2	20.8
DEN 431	158.5	156	2.5	13.7	24.4
Kopox 159	121.5	111	10.5	14.4	28.1
DEN 438	178.0	158.5	19.5	15.4	32.5
ERL 2774	208	170	38.0	20.9	36.1
Epon 812	162.0	86.7	75.3	25.5	42.3
Br_4BisPhA GE	384.0	328.0	56.0	25.6	44.1
o-Ph-Ph-GE	246.5	227	19.5	27.2	46.7
Hydroxyethyl glycid. ether	129	118	11.0	47.0	66.1
EPON 1031	284	156.5	127.5	56.5	72.3

Preliminary data obtained in deciding on the above amine selection are summarized in Table III. It is quite interesting and will be discussed in detail in the next section.

Catalyst Selection. Accelerators and catalysts already in use in the commercial epoxy resin technology (*1, 2, 3, 4, 5, 6, 7, 9, 11, 12, 13*) some of their homologues and derivatives, as well as several other compounds which we had reason to believe might be possibilities were tried.

These included alcohols, phenols, tertiary amines, acids, sulfur-containing compounds, and some other polar materials.

Details of Experimental Technique. TEST MIXTURE PREPARATION. Epoxide, curing agent, and accelerator were weighed into a tared 100-cc. volumetric flask and dissolved in a part of the solvent. After making up the volume the flask was reweighed and specific gravity of the solution calculated. The solutions were always 1*N* with respect to both reactants.

REACTION TEMPERATURE AND TEST DURATION. Reaction temperature was 25°C., and the flasks were kept in a water bath thermostatically controlled at this temperature. Small samples were removed and analyzed for epoxy group content at the time of mixing and after 24 and 48 hours at 25°C.

TESTING AND ANALYSIS. The progress of the reactions was followed by direct titration of small samples in an acetic acid medium in the presence of a large excess of tetraethylammonium bromide, to a crystal violet end point, using a standard 0.1*N* perchloric acid solution (also in glacial acetic acid). This is the method used by R. R. Jay (*8*). All tests were made in duplicate, and in case of disagreement between them, which was rare, the tests were repeated.

Because weighing is much more accurate than measuring by volume, the samples were analyzed on the weight basis. However, to bring the results to a common basis they were converted to the volume basis using specific gravity of the solutions for calculations.

Calculation of Results and Reporting. To save work and thus be able to cover more systems in a shorter time it was decided not to try to determine true reaction rate constants but to use the simple "percent reacted in 24 hours" data as our primary criterion for comparing reactivity of the test systems.

The data on percent reacted in 48 hours, also reported, may be considered as a check on the accuracy of the 24 hours figure and on the possibility of induction period, etc.; otherwise it is of no particular importance or interest.

Discussion of the Results and Conclusions

As I have already pointed out in the introduction and in my discussion of the experimental procedure, many factors can influence the epoxy group-amine reaction rate. I will now repeat and summarize them for emphasis. The reaction rates are influenced by:

1. The nature of the whole epoxy molecule, location of the oxirane group in it, and the presence of other polar groups in the same molecule.
2. The nature of the amine molecule and the presence of other functional or polar groups in it.
3. The presence and the nature of other molecular species such as catalysts, solvents, diluents, etc. and their relative proportion in the system.
4. Mobility factor of the reactants as affected by their molecular weight, configuration, functionality, presence of solvents, diluents and plasticizers, and temperature of the system.
5. The energy activating effect of temperature.

In practice, we must also keep in mind that when two or more of these rate-affecting factors are present at the same time, their combined effect is usually not only additive, but is synergystic, and therefore unpredictable. Thus, even a relationship found between individual members of a given group of catalysts in one system may not hold true in a different system or under a different set of conditions. For this reason the reader is cautioned that the results reported, and the conclusions reached from them apply rigorously only to the systems in which they were studied and that application of these data to other systems or for different sets of conditions should not be done without additional experimental verification.

Before proceeding with the discussion of our reported data on accelerators, I would like to digress a little and to point out a few interesting facts uncovered during the preliminary study of amine candidates, (Table III).

For instance, it was found that the reaction rate of diethylamine, a secondary amine, was more than twice that of the primary butylamine. This might be somewhat of a surprise, but really it should not be if one stops to examine the circumstances. First of all, reactivity of both the primary and the secondary amine hydrogens (unless the latter is hindered) is the same and there were twice as many DEA molecules present per given volume, which is an advantage according to the mass action law. Also, although initially the two amines had the same mol. wts. when the first hydrogen of the BuAm reacts and adds a molecule of PhGE, the mol. wt. of the secondary amine formed increases from 73 to 223, making it considerably larger and thus less mobile.

Another interesting observation is the greatly reduced reactivity of the primary alkylamines as a result of substitution: with hydroxyl, in the case of hydroxyethylamine, and cyano group, in the case of cyanoethyl ethylenediamine. The deactivating effect of the hydroxy group

Table III. Effect of Amine Molecule on the Rate of Primary Amine Group Reaction with PhGE

Conditions: Epoxide: PhGE 1 molar (150 g./l.).
Amine: Varied, one eqt. wt. per liter.
Solvent: Varied, as shown.

Amine Used			*% Reacted at 25°C.*	
Kind	*Gms./L.*	*Solvent*	*in 24 hrs.*	*in 48 hrs.*
Diethylamine	73.0	MEK	4.0	11.7
Diethylamine		CH_2Cl_2	37.7	53.5
Diethylamine		2-Propanol	91.5	96.0
Butylamine	36.5	MEK	1.4	3.3
		CH_2Cl_2	14.2	31.1
Hydroxyethyl-amine	30.5	MEK	0.5	1.2
		CH_2Cl_2	21.2	43.8
Cyanoethyl EDA (ZZL 0903)	49.7[a]	MEK	0	2.2
m-PhDA	27.0	MEK	0	0
MDA	49.5	MEK	0	0.1
MDA	49.5	2-Propanol	45.2	62.2

[a] The 49.7 gm./l. of cyanoethyl EDA is actually 1.31 equivalent (instead of 1.0 intended), an experimental error.

may be especially surprising to some readers in view of the well-known accelerating effect of hydroxyls in the epoxy-amine condensation reaction. However, that occurs only when the hydroxyl group is on the epoxy molecules, or on a separate one. On the amine, the hydroxyl group, being electronegative, reduces the basicity and hence also the reactivity of the amine. The same deactivating effect is produced by substitution with other electronegative groups such as cyano, halogens, and sulfone. The corollary that the more basic amines are also more reactive is also true.

Another property related to the basicity of amines is their toxicity to animals. In industrial practice this is taken advantage of in detoxifying alkylamines—*e.g.*, the ethyleneamine series—by allowing them to react with ethylene oxide, forcing hydroxyethyl group substituents.

To come back to our study of accelerators, because of the large differences in the relative effectiveness of catalysts depending on the amine's nature, the two systems studied will be listed (Tables IV and V) and discussed separately.

System I. Phenyl Glycidyl Ether-Diethylamine (Data in Table IV)

Alcohols. At 0.2 eqts per liter concentration alcohols produced from three to five times increase in reactivity, and from eight to 13 times increase at 1.0 eqts. per liter concentration. An interesting and unique property of the alcohol accelerators is that for the same equivalent hydroxyl concentration the accelerating effect increased as the number of hydroxy groups per molecule increased. Thus, for the same hydroxyl group concentration ethylene glycol was found to be more effective than methanol, and glycerol, in turn, was more effective than the glycol. Specifically, the percents of epoxide reacted in 24 hours were 11.4 *vs.* 16.6 *vs.* 20.3 for the 0.2 normal hydroxyl content and 30.8 *vs.* 41.7 *vs.* 53.3 for the 1.0*N* concentrations, respectively.

Phenols. Acceleration by phenols (for the same hydroxyl concentration) was about 3.0 times that of the alcohols and was independent of their functionality (compare items 12, 13, and 16, Table IV).

Substitution with electronegative groups such as halogens and especially the nitro group (items 17 and 26 in Table IV) greatly enhanced the accelerating effect of phenols. The effect was proportional to the number of substituent groups introduced. This effect was quite consistent—*e.g.*, *see* the chlorinated phenol series, items 19 to 23, inclusive.

Carboxylic Acids. Accelerating effect of benzoic acid was intermediate between that of alcohols and unsubstituted phenols. However, the presence of hydroxyl groups on the carbon adjacent to carboxyl (salicylic acid) brought the catalytic effect to that of pentachlorophenol.

Table IV. Effect of Catalysts on the Rate of Reaction of Phenyl Glycidyl Ether with Diethylamine

Condition: Epoxide: PhGE, 1 molar (150 g./l.).
Amine: Diethylamine, 1 molar (73 g./l.).
Catalyst: Varied in kind and concentration.
Solvent: Methyl ethyl ketone.

Catalyst Used			*% Reacted at 25°C. in*	
Kind	*Eqts./ Liter*	*g./l.*	*24 hrs.*	*48 hrs.*
A. *Control*				
1. no catalyst	—	—	4.0	11.7
B. *Alcohols*				
2. methanol	0.2	6.3	11.4	23.8
3. methanol	1.2	32.0	30.8	49.8
4. ethylene glycol	0.2	6.2	16.6	30.9
5. ethylene glycol	1.0	31.0	41.7	62.0
6. glycerol	0.2	6.1	20.3	36.1
7. glycerol	1.0	30.7	53.3	68.9
8. triethanolamine	0.2	9.9	23.3	41.7
9. triethanolamine	0.6	29.8	44.3	65.9
C. *Phenols*				
10. phenol	0.05	4.7	16.2	29.0
11. phenol	0.10	9.4	21.8	39.0
12. phenol	0.20	18.8	37.5	57.4
13. bisphenol A	0.20	22.8	35.1	55.1
14. resorcinol	0.05	2.8	15.1	28.6
15. resorcinol	0.10	5.5	22.6	37.7
16. resorcinol	0.20	11.0	34.9	57.0
17. *m*-nitro-PhOH	0.05	7.0	24.5	40.9
18. 2,4-dinitro-PhOH	0.05	9.2	49.7	68.6
19. 2-chloro-PhOH	0.05	6.6	17.5	33.5
20. 2,4-dichloro-PhOH	0.05	8.2	18.0	34.4
21. 2,4,5-trichloro-PhOH	0.05	9.9	21.0	36.0
22. 2,4,5,6-tetrachloro-PhOH	0.05	11.6	25.2	40.3
23. pentachloro-PhOH	0.05	13.3	32.6	48.3
24. *p*-chlororesorcinol	0.05	7.2	22.6	37.7
25. *p*-chlorophenol	0.20	25.7	45.8	66.4
26. *p*-bromophenol	0.20	34.6	46.0	66.9
D. *Carboxylic Acids*				
27. benzoic acid	0.05	6.1	10.9	21.9
28. benzoic acid	0.10	12.2	14.5	27.4
29. benzoic acid	0.20	24.4	17.6	31.7
30. salicylic acid	0.05	6.9	33.5	51.6
31. salicylic acid	0.10	13.8	44.9	62.5
32. salicylic acid	0.20	27.6	52.3	65.5
33. 85% lactic acid	0.20	21.0	33.5	50.3

Table IV. Continued

Catalyst Used			*% Reacted at 25°C. in*	
Kind	*Eqts./ Liter*	*g./l.*	*24 hrs.*	*48 hrs.*
E. Tertiary Amines				
34. BzDiMeAmine	0.20	27.0	7.4	16.8
35. $(Me)_4EDA$	0.20	11.6	9.5	19.9
F. Miscellaneous				
36. Thiokol LP-8	0.2	47.6	9.4	21.4
37. Thiokol LP-8	1.0	238.0	34.8	62.2
38. Mod-Epox	0.1	31.0	18.4	42.9
39. Mod-Epox	0.2	62.0	30.0	58.8
40. Mod-Epox	0.5	155.0	41.2	72.1

Lactic acid with the same vicinal location of hydroxyl and carboxyl groups was almost equally as effective as the salicylic acid, Part D of Table IV.

Tertiary Amines and Miscellaneous. As accelerators, the tertiary amines (items 34 and 35) were even less effective than methanol.

The sulfur-containing Thiokol LP–8 accelerator (for the same 0.2 eqts. concentration) gave a percent epoxide reacted similar to that given by the tertiary amines. However, even this may have been caused by its acting as a co-reactant rather than as a catalyst.

Mod-Epox (commercial triphenyl phosphite), which is frequently used as a viscosity reducing diluent, had a fairly strong accelerating effect, on par with that of unsubstituted phenol.

System II. Phenyl Glycidyl Ether-Methylenedianiline (Data in Table V)

Unlike that of the PhGE-DEA system, in the PhGE-MDA reaction, the catalysts derived from salicylic acid and not the substituted phenols showed the greatest accelerating effect under our conditions.

Because of the large differences in reactivity in the two systems studied, concentrations of accelerators were varied (by series) to keep their effects in a conveniently measurable range. For instance, while in PhGE-DEA system chlorinated phenols were added in 0.05 mole/liter concentration, in the PhGE-MDA experiments they were compared at 0.20 mole/liter concentration.

Alcohols. Alcohols were rather ineffective in PhGE-MDA system.

Phenols. On the hydroxyl equivalents basis, phenol and resorcinol were equal. There was a marked reduction in the catalytic effect of phenol, however, when a phenyl group was substituted in the ortho position. This might be attributed to the stearic hindrance by the bulky phenyl radical.

Table V. Effect of Catalysts on the Rate of Reaction of Phenyl Glycidyl Ether with Methylenedianiline

Epoxide: PhGE, 1 molar (150 g./l.).
Amine: MDA, one equivalent (49.5 g./l.).
Catalyst: Varied.
Solvent: Methyl ethyl ketone.

Catalyst Used			*% Reacted at 25°C. in*	
Kind	*Moles/ Liter*	*g./l.*	*24 hrs.*	*48 hrs.*
Control				
1. no catalyst	—	—	0.0	0.1
Alcohols				
2. glycerol	0.17	15.9	0.1	4.5
3. thioglycerol	0.17	18.0	3.4	9.1
Phenols				
4. phenol	0.20	18.8	4.8	8.2
5. *o*-phenyl-PhOH	0.20	34.0	0.6	3.0
6. resorcinol	0.10	11.0	4.6	8.1
Chlorinated Phenols				
7. 2-chloro-PhOH	0.20	25.7	3.5	6.0
8. 4-chloro-PhOH	0.20	25.7	2.4	6.0
9. 2,4-dichloro-PhOH	0.20	32.6	5.7	9.3
10. 2,5-dichloro-PhOH	0.20	32.6	3.8	9.5
11. 2,4,6-trichloro-PhOH	0.20	39.5	5.7	9.0
12. 2,4,5-trichloro-PhOH	0.20	39.5	11.6	19.6
13. tetrachloro-PhOH	0.20	46.4	8.6	14.4
14. pentachloro-PhOH	0.20	53.3	15.1	24.5
Nitrophenols				
15. 2-nitro-PhOH	0.20	27.8	1.3	2.8
16. 3-nitro-PhOH	0.20	27.8	3.4	5.9
17. 4-nitro-PhOH	0.20	27.8	9.3	14.9
18. 2,4-dinitro-PhOH	0.20	36.8	20.6	33.3
Miscellaneous Phenols				
19. 4-bromothiophenol	0.1	19.0	0.5	1.6
Non-Carboxylic Acids				
20. octylphosphoric	0.1	17.7	9.5	15.1
21. toluenesulfonic	0.1	17.2	6.5	10.8
22. phenolsulfonic	0.1	26.8	10.2	14.1
23. benzenesulfonyl chloride	0.1	17.7	8.1	19.5
Alkyl Carboxylic Acids				
24. lactic acid (85% soln)	0.1	10.5	8.3	18.0
25. lactic acid (85% soln)	0.2	21.0	23.6	30.8
26. propionic acid	0.2	14.8	7.8	11.9
27. succinic acid	0.1	11.8	9.2	15.5

Table V. Continued

Catalyst Used			% Reacted at 25°C. in	
Kind	*Moles/ Liter*	*g./l.*	*24 hrs.*	*48 hrs.*
Aromatic Carboxylic Acids				
28. benzoic acid	0.1	12.2	9.3	13.0
29. thiobenzoic acid	0.1	13.8	6.8	8.1
Hydroxy Benzoic Acids				
30. *o*-hydroxy-	0.1	13.8	37.1	52.0
31. *m*-hydroxy-	0.1	13.8	8.1	13.5
32. *p*-hydroxy-	0.1	13.8	6.0	13.0
33. 2,4-dihydroxy-	0.1	15.4	22.5	35.4
34. 2,5-dihydroxy-	0.1	15.4	26.1	42.8
Halogenated Benzoic Acid				
35. 2-bromo-	0.1	21.0	10.7	19.7
36. 2-chloro-	0.1	15.7	11.4	18.6
37. 4-chloro-	0.1	15.7	11.8	17.9
38. 2,4-dichloro-	0.1	19.1	17.9	29.3
39. 2,4,5-trichloro-	0.1	22.5	35.8	51.7
Miscellaneous Benzoic Acids				
40. 2-methyl-	0.1	13.6	2.9	7.8
41. 2-mercapto-	0.1	19.2	23.1	32.9
42. 2-nitro-	0.1	16.7	25.6	38.9
43. 3,5-dinitro-	0.1	21.2	38.3	55.8
44. 2-chloro,5-nitro-	0.1	20.2	31.4	45.6
Poly-Carboxylic Acids				
45. *o*-phthalic acid	0.1	16.6	1.6	2.4
46. *m*-phthalic acid	0.1	16.6	2.1	5.5
47. *p*-phthalic acid	0.1	21.0	not soluble in MEK	
48. trimellitic acid	0.1	21.0	not soluble in MEK	
Salicylic Acids				
49. salicylic acid itself	0.01	1.4	6.3	12.4
50. salicylic acid itself	0.05	6.8	21.1	34.0
51. salicylic acid itself	0.10	13.8	37.1	52.0
52. salicylic acid itself	0.20	27.6	46.7	66.3
53. 4-hydroxy-sal. acid	0.10	15.4	22.5	35.4
54. 5-bromo-sal. acid	0.10	21.7	46.5	62.7
55. 5-chloro-sal. acid	0.02	3.4	14.4	25.8
56. 5-chloro-sal. acid	0.05	8.6	31.8	50.1
57. 5-chloro-sal. acid	0.10	17.2	45.0	62.6
58. 5-chloro-sal. acid	0.20	34.1	58.7	74.8
59. 3,5-dichloro-sal. acid	0.1	20.7	53.2	71.5
60. 3-nitro-sal. acid	0.1	18.3	44.1	60.8
61. 5-nitro-sal. acid	0.1	18.3	44.3	58.5
62. 3,5-dinitro-sal. acid	0.1	22.8	17.9	33.5

Table V. Continued

Catalyst Used				% Reacted at 25°C. in	
	Kind	Moles/ Liter	g./l.	24 hrs.	48 hrs.
Tertiary Amines					
63.	BzDMA	0.2	27.0	2.7	3.9
64.	DMP-10	0.2	27.6	1.3	1.6
65.	DMP-30	0.2	44.8	5.6	13.5
66.	DMP-30	0.5	112.0	20.0	32.8
67.	DMP-30, without MDA	0.2	44.8	3.5	5.4
68.	DABCO (alone)	0.2	11.0	33.6	51.9
69.	DABCO with MDA	0.2	11.0	23.2	41.9
70.	DABCO with MDA	0.5	27.5	60.4	84.1
Sulfur-Containing Compounds					
71.	monothioglycerol	0.167	18.0	3.4	9.1
72.	Thiocol LP-8	0.2	47.6	0	0.1
73.	thiobenzoic acid	0.1	13.8	5.8	8.1
74.	*o*-mercapto-BzAcid	0.1	15.4	23.1	32.9
75.	thiosalicylic acid	0.1	15.4	18.1	25.4
76.	4-bromothiophenol	0.1	19.0	0.5	1.6
Miscellaneous					
77.	water	1.0	18.0	0.5	0.8
78.	Mod-Epox	0.5	155.0	0.8	2.1

Unlike the case of DEA-PhGE system, chlorine substitution on phenol showed no appreciable increase in catalytic activity until the number of chlorine atoms reached three. The increase in the accelerating effect by chlorine substitution, although small, was gradual and progressive, with the exception of that shown by the 2,4,5-trichlorophenol which was unexpectedly higher.

The relative increase in reactivity of phenol catalysts by nitro group substitution had position dependence the reverse of that produced by the halogen or carboxyl group substitution; namely, in this case, the para-nitrophenol had a much greater catalytic activity than the corresponding ortho isomer.

Acids, Non-Carboxylic. The strong non-carboxylic acids had only a modest activating effect in our system. This was probably owing, for one thing, to their limited solubility in MEK, and also perhaps because of their inactivation through salt formation with the amine.

Carboxylic Acids. In the absence of other polar, electronegative groups in the molecule, carboxylic acids have only a moderate accelerating effect; however, hydroxyl, halogen, or nitro group substitutions, either singly, or better yet, in combinations, resulted in very significant increase in their catalytic effect. Position of these other groups in relation to the carboxyl group also plays an important part. Thus, hydroxycarboxylic acids showed a high degree of activity only when both functional groups were on the adjacent carbons (items 25 and 30) but not when the two were further apart (compare items 31 and 32 with item 30. The second hydroxyl group in the salicylic acid, actually reduced its catalytic effect—*e.g.*, 2,4- and 2,5-dihydroxybenzoic acids (items 33 and 34 *vs.* 30 in Table V). The 2,6-dihydroxy isomer unfortunately was not available for testing at the time.

Single halogen substitution of benzoic acid (either chlorine or bromine) produced but slight improvement; however, increasing the number of chlorines to two and especially to three was markedly beneficial (items 35 to 39 incl.).

A single nitro group substitution, roughly speaking, was equal to two chlorine atoms, and the accelerating effect of two nitro groups or one nitro and one chlorine (on the same benzoic acid molecule) was quite high (items 43 and 44, Table V).

Aromatic polycarboxylic acids have no utility in the system under consideration, apparently either because of their poor solubility (in MEK and epoxides) or low order of activity, or both.

The most effective group of accelerators for the PhGE-MDA system was found to be halogen and nitro group-substituted salicylic acids. Of this group, items 49 through 62 in Table V, 3,5-dichlorosalicylic acid proved to be the most effective (item 59, tested in 0.1 mole/liter conc.). However, the 5-bromo, 5-chloro- and 3-, or 5-nitrosalicylic acids were close seconds in effectiveness.

Tertiary Amines. Generally speaking, tertiary amines are epoxy curing agents in their own right, so in studying the possible catalytic effect they might have on the MDA-PhGE system, runs were made both with and without MDA present (items 60 to 67, Table V). The conclusion was that they act both as curing agents and as activators for MDA condensation, and that the effect is synergystic since the extent of the overall epoxy group reaction when both amines were present together, was more than additive of that produced when they were reacted one at a time (compare item 62 with 64 and item 65 with 66).

The DABCO catalyst, which is triethylenediamine, with a rather unusual structure:

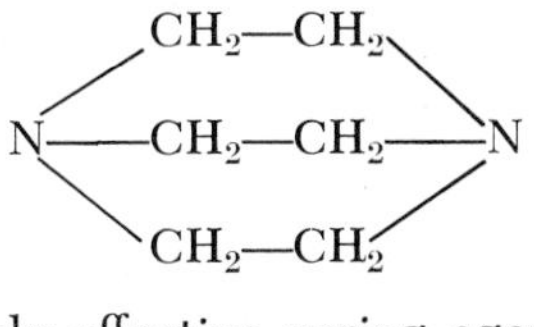

$$N\begin{matrix} \diagup CH_2\text{—}CH_2 \diagdown \\ \text{——}CH_2\text{—}CH_2\text{——} \\ \diagdown CH_2\text{—}CH_2 \diagup \end{matrix}N$$

proved to be an extremely effective curing agent for PhGE, surpassing, by a large margin, our model alkylamine, the diethylamine, as well as all other amines tried in the preliminary curing agent selection work (Table III). It was tempting, therefore, to test it and other tertiary amines as the principal curing agents for PhGE with the same accelerators as we used in the studies of MDA and DEA-PhGE reactions.

Results of these tests, shown in Table VI, however, were disappointing. Instead of acting as accelerators, both 5-chlorosalicylic acid and 2,4-dinitrophenol had a marked depressing effect on the DABCO reactivity (items 4 and 5 in Table VI), while in the case of DMP-30 their effect, if any, was very small and certainly within the limits of experimental error.

As a further follow up, the two accelerators used above, were also tested by themselves for a possible effect on self-condensation of PhGE, but found to have none (*see* the last two items in Table VI). This brought our thinking back to the question of the mechanism of the epoxy group reaction catalysis and the generally accepted assumption that the first step in the condensation reaction involving epoxides is the opening of the oxirane ring, and the function of the catalyst is to assist in bringing this about.

The above experimental facts—failure of the 5-chlorosalicylic acid to assist either in self condensation of an epoxy compound or in its cure

Table VI. Effect of Accelerators on the Rates of Phenyl Glycidyl Ether Condensation in the Presence of Tertiary Amines at 25°C.

Epoxide: PhGE, 1 molar (150 g./l.).
Amines: Tertiary, as given.
Catalyst: Varied, as given.
Solvent: Methyl ethyl ketone.

Amine			*Accelerators*			*% Reacted at 25°C. in*	
Kind	*Moles/ Liter*	*Gms./ Liter*	*Kind*	*Mols/ Liter*	*Gms./ Liter*	*24 hrs.*	*48 hrs.*
1. DABCO	0.25	27.5	None	—	—	60.4	84.1
2. DABCO	0.10	11.0	None	—	—	23.2	41.9
3. DABCO	0.05	5.5	None	—	—	9.5	14.6
4. DABCO	0.05	5.5	5-Cl-salicylic Ac.	.05	8.6	0.6	2.5
5. DABCO	0.05	5.5	2,4-DiNO$_2$PhOH	.05	9.2	0.1	1.6
6. DMP-30	0.20	44.8	None	—	—	3.5	5.4
7. DMP-30	0.10	22.4	None	—	—	0.2	2.5
8. DMP-30	0.10	22.4	5-Cl-salicylic Ac.	0.1	17.2	0.2	3.7
9. DMP-30	0.10	22.4	2,4-Di-NO$_2$PhOH	0.1	18.4	1.3	3.2
10. None	—	—	5-Cl-salicylic Ac.	0.2	34.4	1.1	0.7
11. None	—	—	2,4-Di-NO$_2$ · PhOH	0.2	36.8	0.0	0.2

by a tertiary amine, when it is so effective in the case of primary amine-epoxide reaction—casts some doubt on the correctness of the accepted mechanism of epoxide reaction catalysis.

Sulfur-Containing Compounds. As in the case of PhGE-DEA system and again contrary to expectations, the accelerating effect of sulfur-containing compounds was minor. The sulfur-containing salicylic acids (items 71 and 72) although when taken by themselves they may appear to be fairly effective, were actually not as good as the sulfur-free salicylic acid itself.

Miscellaneous Chemical Agents. Mod-Epox (triphenyl phosphite), the widely used diluent-plasticizer, even when added in an amount greater than PhGE itself (155 grams/liter) produced no increase in the reaction rate of the MDA-PhGE system (item 74, Table V). This is quite different from the DEA-PhGE system, where (items 38 through 40, Table IV) it proved to be among the best accelerators.

The lack of positive effect of water addition to the reaction mixture (item 74, Table V) was, in a way, most gratifying for it alleviated the fears of possible interference from MEK through ketamine formation reaction.

Table VII. Progress of Adiabatic Reaction Between D.E.R. 332 and DETA in the Presence of 2,4,6-Trichlorophenol Accelerator

Cl_3PhOH Content Gms./p.h.r.	Time, in Min., to Reach From 25° to 50°C.	From 50° to 100°C.	From 100°C. to Max.	Total Reaction Time, Min.	Max. Temp. Reached, °C.
None	48.3	5.3	3.1	56.1	250
0.7	23.0	2.8	3.2	29.0	246
1.8	14.4	2.1	3.9	23.4	252
3.6	8.0	2.4	4.1	14.5	257
7.2	4.0	2.0	3.4	9.4	252

Temperature. Temperature is a very effective accelerator for all chemical reactions, including that of epoxy-amine. Experiments designed to illustrate this effect of temperature are summarized in Table VII.

In these experiments, the system studied was solventless and consisted of D.E.R. 332 epoxy resin and DETA mixtures with different amounts of 2,4,6-trichlorophenol accelerator. The reaction was allowed to proceed adiabatically while temperature *vs.* time data were being recorded. The most interesting part of the results was that the effect of the accelerator was felt strongly only in the 25°–50°C. range, became minor in the 50°–100°C. range, and disappeared altogether above 100°C.!

In an oversimplified conjectural way, the observed apparent deactivation of catalysts at elevated temperature in our systems may be visualized as an inevitable consequence of the probable mechanism of their action. Going back to the diagrammatic scheme of catalysis shown earlier, we may think of the following sequence of events leading to the opening of the epoxy ring. To begin with, the accelerator molecule has to meet and attach itself to the oxirane oxygen (probably through the hydrogen bonding of its hydroxyl group), which results in loosening of one of the oxirane ring oxygen-carbon bonds. However, the hydrogen bonding forces that are holding the catalyst molecule at the oxirane ring are very weak and in a "hot" system the molecular movements (including that of atomic vibrations) are so vigorous that the catalyst molecule gets "shaken off" the epoxy group the instant it lands on it and before it can exert any influence on opening of the ring.

Summary

The rate of glycidyl group-amine reaction depends on many "internal and external" factors. Among them are:

1. Chemical nature of the whole epoxy molecule.
2. Presence and location of other functional and polar groups in it.
3. Chemical nature of the amine molecule.
4. Mobility factor.
5. Catalyst-activator addition.
6. Temperature of the system.

Of the many catalyst-activators studied, the halogen and nitro groups substituted phenol and salicylic acid proved to be the most effective, with the 3,5-dichlorosalicylic acid heading the list.

Key to the Abbreviations Used

Br_4BisPhA G.E.	Tetrabromo-bisphenol A glycidyl ether
Bz acid	Benzoic acid
BzDMA	Benzyl dimethylamine
CH_2Cl_2	Methylene chloride
DABCO	Triethylenediamine (Air Products and Chemicals)
D.E.R. 331	Standard epoxidized bisphenol A (Dow)
D.E.R. 332	Purified epoxidized bisphenol A (Dow)
D.E.R. 332 LC	D.E.R. 332 with very low ($<$ 0.01%) chlorine content (Dow)
D.E.R. 736	Epoxidized tetrapropylene glycol (Dow)
D.E.N. 431	Epoxide of dihydroxydiphenylmethane (Dow)
D.E.N. 438	Epoxidized novolak containing about 3.5 epoxy groups per mol. (Dow)
DETA	Diethylenetriamine
DEA	Diethylamine
DMFA	Dimethyl formamide, a solvent
DMP-10	4-Dimethylaminomethylphenol (Rohm & Haas)
DMP-30	2,4,6-Tris(dimethylaminomethyl)phenol (Rohm & Haas)

EDA	Ethylenediamine
EPON 812	Epoxydized glycerin (Shell)
EPON 1031	Epoxidized tetrakishydroxyphenylethane (Shell)
ERL 2774	Epoxidized bisphenol A, (U.C.C.C.)
G.E.	Glycidyl ether, usually preceded by an identifying word, like "phenyl G.E."
Kopox 159	Diepoxide of resorcinol (Koppers)
MDA	Methylenedianiline
$(Me)_4$EDA	Tetramethylethylenediamine
MEK	Methyl ethyl ketone
Mod-Epox	Triphenyl phosphite (Monsanto)
PhGE	Phenyl glycidyl ether
Sal. Acid	Salicylic acid
Thiokol LP-8	Low mol. wt. liquid polysulfide rubber (Thiokol Chemical)

Literature Cited

(1) British Patent **1,017,699** (Jan. 1966).
(2) British Patent **873,224** (July 1961).
(3) British Patent **929,373** (June 1963).
(4) British Patent **878,750** (Oct. 1961).
(5) Czech Patent **112,018** (*Chem. Abstr.* **62:** 16457f, 1965).
(6) de la Court, F. H., *Encres Imprimerie Continental Congr.* **1,** 154 (1964).
(7) Gough, L. J., Smith, I. T., *J. Oil & Chem. Assoc.* **43,** 409 (1960).
(8) Jay, R. R., *J. Anal. Chem.* **36,** 667 (1964).
(9) Netherlands Patent Application **No. 6,508,613** (*Chem. Abstr.* **65:** 9111c).
(10) Schechter, Leon, Wynstra, John, Kurkjy, Raymond P., *Ind. Eng. Chem.* **48,** 94 (1956).
(11) U. S. Patent **2,928,794** (March 1964).
(12) U. S. Patent **2,928,809** (March 1964).
(13) U. S. Patent **3,361,715** (Jan. 1968).

RECEIVED November 12, 1968.

5

Effect of Hydroxyl Compounds on Reactivity of Epoxy Resins

DAVID O. BOWEN and ROSS C. WHITESIDE, JR.

Resins Research Department, The Dow Chemical Co.,
Freeport, Tex. 77541

The following research was done to determine which types of hydroxyl accelerators are of practical value for improving reactivity of epoxy resins with amine curing agents. Unsubstituted monofunctional aliphatic alcohols appeared to be poor accelerators. More significant increases in reactivity were obtained with polyfunctional and substituted alcohols. Reactivity was found to be proportional to hydroxyl functionality. Mercapto and phenolic compounds gave the best acceleration. A near-linear relationship between additive acidity and acceleration was shown. Although compounds of high acidity gave the best acceleration, the use of these materials is not practical because of viscosity buildup during resin storage. Polyfunctional alcohols gave the best overall results. Reactivity differences between resins of varying purities were found to be caused by differences in aliphatic hydroxyl content from higher molecular weight resin homologs.

The fact that hydroxyl compounds will accelerate the reaction between epoxides and amine compounds is widely recognized. A generally accepted mechanism for reactions of this type is that of Shechter *et al.* (3), who have proposed that the reaction proceeds as shown

$$R_2NH + CH_2\overset{O}{\text{—}}CHR + HOX \rightarrow [R_2\overset{H}{N}\text{- - -}CH_2\overset{\overset{HOX}{\vdots}}{\overset{O}{\text{———}}}CHR]$$

$$\downarrow \quad OX^{\ominus}$$

$$[R_2\overset{H\oplus}{N}\text{—}CH_2\text{—}\overset{OH}{\overset{|}{CH}}\text{—}R] \rightarrow R_2N\text{—}CH_2\text{—}\overset{OH}{\overset{|}{CH}}\text{—}R + HOX$$

wherein hydroxyl-containing compounds aid in the opening of the epoxide ring by hydrogen bonding in the transition state.

The present work was carried out to determine which types of hydroxyl accelerators are of practical value for improving reactivity of epoxy resins with amine curing agents. A number of hydroxyl-containing compounds were screened for catalytic efficiency for this purpose. A further objective in this research was to explain differences in reactivity which occur among different liquid epoxy resins having a limited amount of variation in epoxide content and purity.

A method for determining reactivity was desired which could be used with conventional epoxy resins and curing agents, and in which the results would be directly related to the mechanical aspects of curing—*i.e.*, crosslinking and gelation. The gel time method used in the present work fulfilled the above requirements and was found to be considerably more accurate and less time consuming—because of the larger sample sizes used—than techniques involving the use of commercial gel time instruments. The procedure which was used is the "500-gram mass" method described in Dow sales literature (2) which is very similar to the ASTM D 2471 method. Details of the procedures are given below.

Samples of resin were weighed into one-pint metal cans along with appropriate additives. In some cases, heating was required to dissolve the additives, after which the mixtures were allowed to cool to room temperature. Appropriate stoichiometric amounts of D.E.H. 24 (Dow Chemical Co.) curing agent (triethylenetetramine) were weighed into separate containers so that when mixed the total resin/curing agent sample weight would be 500 grams. Resin and curing agent were allowed to come to equilibrium by placing the containers in a constant temperature chamber maintained at 25°C. for 24 hours. The curing agents then were poured into the pint cans containing the resin, and the mixtures were stirred mechanically until homogeneous blends were obtained. Thermocouples from a temperature recorder were lowered into the mixtures to monitor the temperature as the mixtures reacted, and gel time values were measured. The gel time was taken as the time elapsed between initial mixing and formation of a continuous "skin" across the top of the mixture in the can. To serve as a check, the time elapsed between initial mixing and attainment of peak exotherm temperature was measured. Duplicate samples were run for each additive tested, and resin-curing agent blanks containing no additive were run in each series of experiments. Normally each series of experiments consisted of measurements on 12 samples, including two blanks and duplicates of five different additives. The use of blanks in each series was necessary owing to slight variations in gel time between samples of the same composition when measured on different days; however, the difference in gel time between blanks and those samples with a particular additive at a given concentration did not vary significantly from day to day. For this reason, the difference in gel time between the modified resin and the blank (decrease in gel time) was taken as the best measure for resin reactivity.

Effect of Hydroxyl Additives on Resin Reactivity

A number of hydroxyl compounds were added to D.E.R. 332 (Dow Chemical Co.) epoxy resin at the 1.0 mole % level (based on epoxide content of the resin). D.E.H. 24 was added to the mixtures, and gel time measurements were performed by the procedure described above. Results are seen in Table I.

Table I. Effect of Additives on Gel Time of D.E.R. 332/D.E.H. 24

Compound	*Decrease In Gel Time (Min.)*[a]	*Compound*	*Decrease In Gel Time (Min.)*
Monoalcohols		*Phenols*	
Methanol	1	*o*-Cresol	9.5
Ethyl alcohol	2	*m*-Cresol	10.5
n-Propyl alcohol	1	*p*-Cresol	11
n-Butyl alcohol	2	Phenol	13
Diols			
Ethylene glycol	7	Bisphenol S	
Propylene glycol	8		
Triols		HO–C₆H₄–SO₂–C₆H₄–OH	13
Glycerin	12		
Trimethylolpropane	12		
Chlorohydrins			
Ethylene chlorohydrin	5.5	Tetrabromobisphenol A	14
1-Chloro-3-phenoxy-2-propyl alcohol	7	*o*-Chlorophenol	15
Glycerol dichlorohydrin	9	Bisphenol A	
Acids			
Acetic acid	12		
Dichloroacetic acid	14	HO–C₆H₄–C(CH₃)₂–C₆H₄–OH	16
Formic acid	18		
Miscellaneous			
Water	5		
Benzenethiol	17	*p*-Nitrophenol	20.5
Mercaptoethanol	14		

[a] Compared with D.E.R. 332 containing no additive.

Unsubstituted monofunctional aliphatic alcohols provide only small decreases in gel time in comparison with other compounds tested. More significant increases in reactivity were obtained with the use of multifunctional alcohols, substituted alcohols, and compounds containing phenolic hydroxyl groups. Two mercapto compounds (benzenethiol and mercaptoethanol) were also tested, and both compounds showed a high degree of activity.

A trend toward higher reactivity was noted in resins containing additives of higher acidity. In order to obtain a clearer relationship between additive acidity and resin reactivity, p*Ka* values were obtained for several additives from literature sources and plotted *vs.* gel time decrease for resins containing the additives at the 1.0 mole % level. Results are seen in Figure 1. A near-linear relationship between additive acidity and reduction in gel time is seen. These results are in agreement with the findings of Gough and Smith (*1*) from gel time measurements on amine-cured epoxy resins; Shecheter *et al* (*3*) also found that phenol was more effective in accelerating the reaction of diethylamine and phenyl glycidyl ether than aliphatic alcohols of lower acidity.

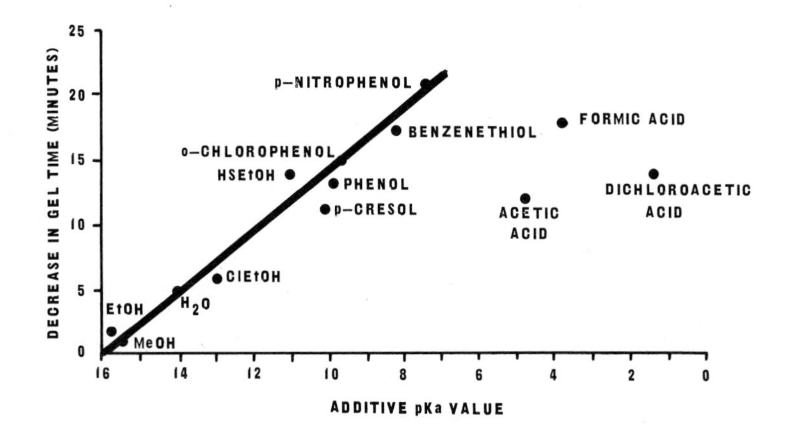

Figure 1. Effect of additive acidity on decrease in gel time of D.E.R. 332/D.E.H. 24. Additives present in resin at 1.0 mole % level, based on resin epoxide content

Although the resin reactivity increased in a linear fashion with additive acidity for the alcohols, phenols, and mercapto compounds, the carboxylic acids, which were of considerably higher acidity, did not follow this type of behavior. These materials displayed about the same degree of activity as some of the phenolic compounds. Shechter *et al.* (*3*) obtained similar results with acetic acid in their phenyl glycidyl ether-diethylamine studies, and noted that the reduced accelerative effect of the acid may have been caused by a higher level of salt formation with the amine, which would cause a corresponding reduction in concentration of acetic acid acting as the accelerator.

It is further seen from Table I that resin reactivity increases with increasing functionality of the hydroxyl additive. Glycerin was more effective as an accelerator than propylene glycol, which in turn was much more effective than *n*-propyl alcohol. The general increase in accelerative effect with increasing hydroxyl functionality can be explained on the basis of increase in molar concentration of hydroxyl groups added to the system. This has been demonstrated in the gel time studies of Gough and Smith (*1*). Results from the present studies are in agreement with the above work; in Figure 2, it is seen that reduction in gel time for D.E.R. 332/D.E.H. 24 is proportional to alcohol concentration for normal, secondary, and tertiary butyl alcohol. Dilution effects appear to exert an influence on reactivity at higher alcohol concentrations (4–5 mole %); such behavior would be expected according to Smith (*4*). A concentration/reactivity curve obtained with the use of bisphenol A as the accelerator is seen in Figure 3. A linear increase in reactivity is seen at lower concentrations (0–0.5 mole %). In this case, the break in the curve in the concentration region of 0.6 mole % is thought to be caused by partial loss of bisphenol A accelerator through an amine-catalyzed reaction with resin epoxide groups which would reduce the effective catalyst level.

Compatibility of the additive with the resin and/or curing agent also has a pronounced effect on the degree of reactivity attained in an epoxy resin system. A gel time reduction of 9.5 minutes in D.E.R. 332/D.E.H. 24 was obtained when neopentyl glycol was used as an accelerator at the 5 mole % hydroxyl level, but propylene glycol added to the same system to give the same hydroxyl concentration effected a 16.5 minute decrease in gel time. The neopentyl glycol was only partially soluble in the resin-curing agent blend. Similar results were obtained with pentaerythritol, which has very limited solubility in the system. A 17-minute reduction in gel time was obtained when glycerin was used as the additive at the 5 mole % hydroxyl level. This material is incompatible with the resin, but unlike neopentyl glycol and pentaerythritol the glycerin dissolves when the curing agent is blended into the resin.

Reactivity Differences among Different Liquid Epoxy Resins

A number of widely-used, general purpose liquid epoxy resins are commercially available. These resins may be generally characterized by

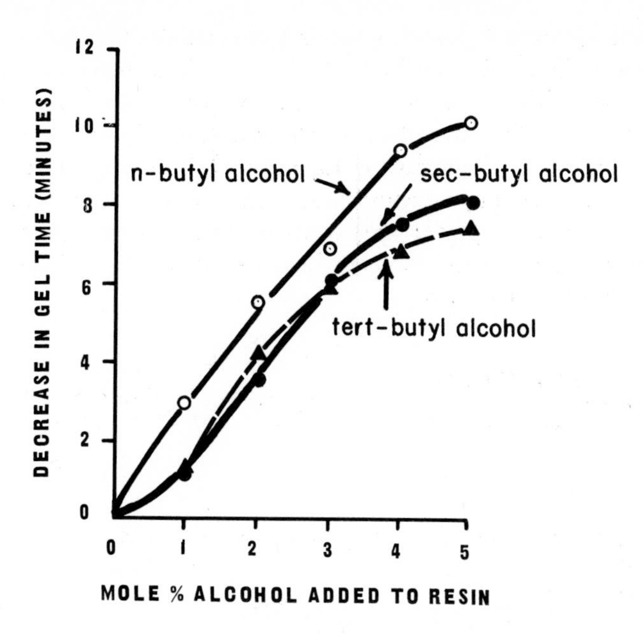

Figure 2. Effect of alcohol concentration on decrease in gel time of D.E.R. 332/D.E.H. 24

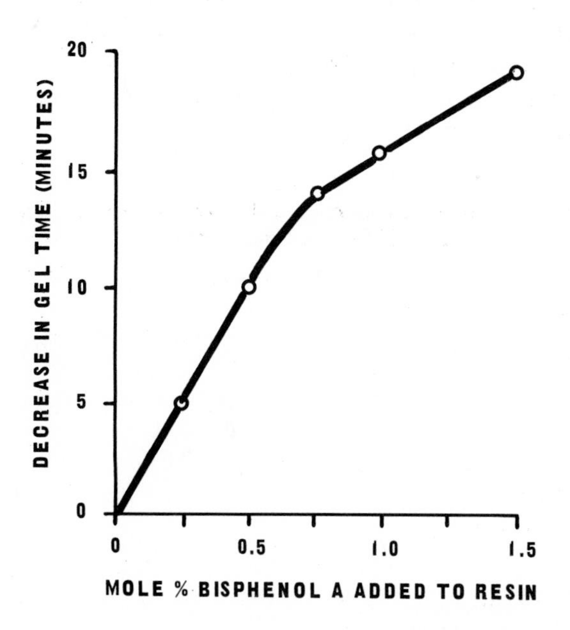

Figure 3. Effect of bisphenol A concentration on decrease in gel time of D.E.R. 332/D.E.H. 24

the structure given in Figure 4, wherein the average value for "n" is only slightly greater than zero. D.E.R. 331, for example, is the standard liquid epoxy resin of the Dow product line, and an average "n" value of about 0.12 would be considered typical for this material. However, a number of other liquid resins are available for use in certain applications where lower resin viscosity, higher epoxide content, premium electrical properties or very high resin purity are required. Differences in chemical reactivity among these products occur because of variations in processing required in their preparation.

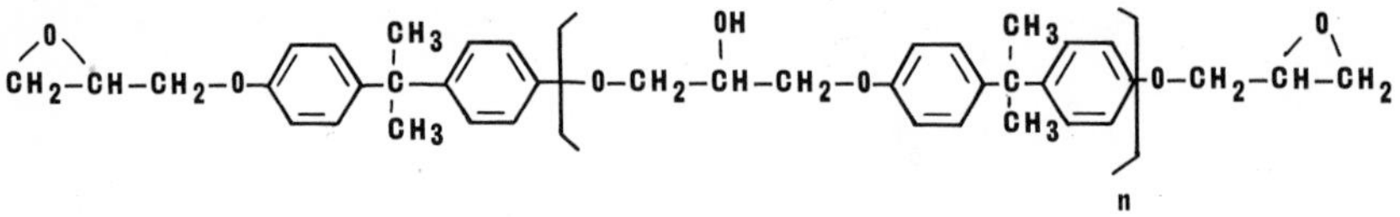

Figure 4. Structure for bisphenol A-type epoxy resins

Five different resins similar to commercially available products were used in the present work to study the effects of resin purity on chemical reactivity. Methods of preparation were adjusted so that the samples would have different epoxide contents and hydrolyzable chloride (residual chlorohydrin) contents. None of the products was modified with either reactive or non-reactive diluents.

Some general chemical properties and gel time values for the five resins are given in Table II.

Table II. Chemical Properties and Gel Time with D.E.H. 24 for Different Epoxy Resins

Resin	*Percent Epoxide*	*EEW*[a]	*Residual Chlorohydrin Content (as percent chlorine)*	*Gel Time (minutes)*
I	25.1	171	0.04	48
II	24.6	175	0.035	43
III	24.7	174	0.10	39
IV	23.0	187	0.046	29
V	22.8	189	0.14	27

[a] Epoxide equivalent weight.

Although variation in EEW for the different resins covers a relatively narrow range, considerable differences in reactivity are evident. The general trend toward longer gel time values at lower EEW values would indicate that reactivity decreases with increasing purity.

Liquid resins of the type under consideration are normally prepared from epichlorohydrin and bisphenol A. The reaction involves the formation of a chlorohydrin ether intermediate which is converted to the final glycidyl ether product by an alkaline dehydrohalogenating agent. By-products can include among others traces of unreacted phenolics, residual chlorohydrin groups from incomplete dehydrochlorination, and a certain amount of higher molecular weight resin homologs (oligomers with $n > 0$ having the structure seen in Figure 4).

Since these three extraneous components present in the resin are hydroxyl-containing materials then each component, if present in the resin in sufficient quantity, could affect the reactivity of the resin. A study was made to determine which of these materials make significant contributions toward the differences in reactivity which were observed; results are summarized below.

Various analytical methods revealed that all of the resins contained phenolic hydroxyl groups in trace quantities. The differences in phenolic OH among the resins, however, were not sufficient to account for the differences in reactivity which the resins displayed. For example, the difference in gel time between resins III and V was 12 minutes. Assuming that the phenolic OH groups behave in resin III similarly to bisphenol A in D.E.R. 332 (*see* Figure 3), then the additional phenolic material found in resin V could not account for as much as one minute of the total difference in gel time between the two resins.

It can be further shown that the residual chlorohydrin content is not the major cause of the differences in resin reactivity which were found. If this were not true, then one would expect resins I, II, and IV to have similar reactivity since these materials have approximately the same residual chlorohydrin content. Wide differences in reactivity which the resins display must obviously be caused by other influences. In a similar manner resins III and V displayed a notable difference in resin reactivity (12 minutes) although their chlorohydrin contents were somewhat similar. The difference in chlorohydrin content between the two resins amounts to about 0.2 mole % based on epoxide content of the resins. Assuming that the chlorohydrin in the resins behaves similarly to ethylene chlorohydrin or 1-chloro-3-phenoxy-2-propanol (*see* Table I), one might expect that the difference in chlorohydrin content between resins III and V might account for roughly a minute of the gel time difference found.

Since differences in phenolic OH and chlorohydrin among the resins apparently do not make major contributions toward the differences in resin reactivity which were found, then it must follow that these differences must arise mainly from differences in aliphatic hydroxyl content from higher molecular weight homologs ($n > 0$) in the resins. Data which support this hypothesis are presented below.

The relationship between hydroxyl content and epoxide content can be calculated by the use of the general structure for epoxy resins seen in Figure 4. The mole ratio of aliphatic hydroxyl groups to epoxide groups is directly proportional to the value for "*n*." Thus, a linear relationship between mole % aliphatic OH and EEW would exist, as is seen in Figure 5. The values for the plot were obtained by calculating theoretical epoxide and hydroxyl contents using the structure in Figure 4. Small values for "*n*" were used to cover the EEW range of the resins used in the present work. Using the plot in Figure 5, theoretical hydroxyl content from higher weight resin homologs may be obtained if the EEW for a particular resin is known, assuming other impurities—*e.g.*, chlorohydrin—are negligible.

In Figure 6, gel time is plotted *vs.* EEW and aliphatic hydroxyl content (OH values taken from the plot in Figure 5) for resins I, II, and IV, all of which have practically the same residual chlorohydrin content. The linear relationship between gel time and aliphatic hydroxyl content strongly suggests that differences in reactivity between these resins can be accounted for solely on the basis of differences in content of hydroxyl groups from the higher homologs. This has been confirmed in further experiments which are discussed below.

Using EEW values given in Table II and the plot in Figure 5, theoretical aliphatic hydroxyl contents for resins II and V were found to be about 1.7 and 6.7 mole %, respectively. Thus, a difference in hydroxyl content of about 5 mole % exists between the resins. According to Table II, the gel time of resin II would have to be reduced by 16 minutes to match the gel time of resin V. If this reactivity difference is caused by difference in aliphatic hydroxyl content as proposed above, then increasing the hydroxyl content in resin II to match that of resin V should make up for the difference in gel time. An experiment was carried out wherein the aliphatic hydroxyl content of resin II was increased 5 mole % by adding propylene glycol to the resin, and this effected a reduction in resin gel time of 16.5 minutes. Using glycerin as the additive at the 5 mole % hydroxyl level, gel time of resin II was reduced 17 minutes. Similar results were obtained using other aliphatic hydroxyl additives. It was determined from the plot in Figure 5 that the difference in aliphatic hydroxyl content between resins II and IV was about 4.3 mole %. From Table II, the gel time difference between the two resins was 14 minutes. Trimethylolpropane added to resin II at a level of 1.2 phr. increased the hydroxyl concentration by 4.5 mole %; this resulted in a reduction in gel time of 14.5 minutes.

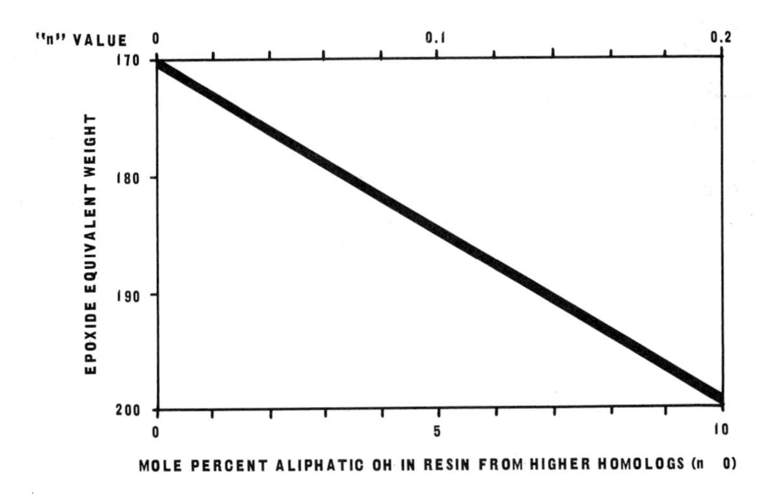

Figure 5. Relationship between epoxide content and aliphatic hydroxyl content in epoxy resins

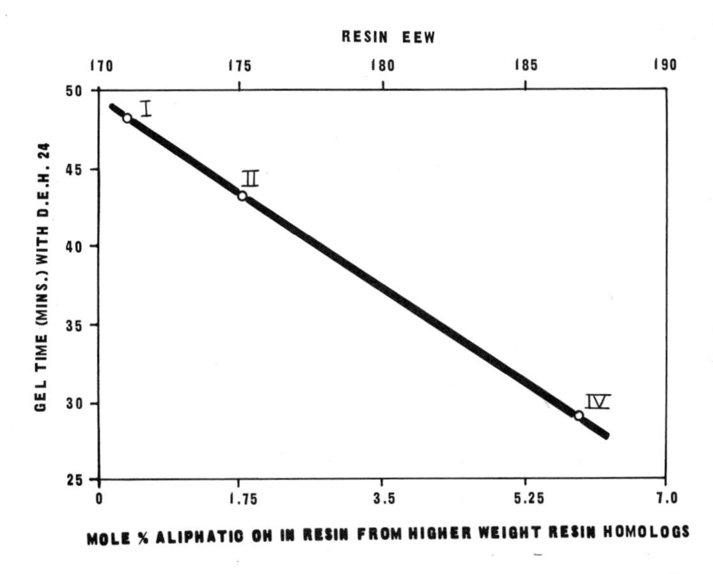

Figure 6. Effect of aliphatic hydroxyl content from higher weight homologs on reactivity of epoxy resins

Factors to Consider When Using Additives for Increased Resin Reactivity

Increased reactivity between epoxy resins and amine curing agents can be obtained by the addition of hydroxyl compounds to the epoxy formulation as has been shown above. The increase in reactivity obtained with the use of such additives depends upon the concentration and acidity of the compound which is used. There are several factors which should be considered when selecting an additive for altering resin reactivity.

The additive which is to be used must be miscible with the resin, curing agent, or final blend at the additive concentration required. This limits the use of certain additives. Trimethylolpropane, for example, has poor solubility in the resin, and concentrations greater than 1% by weight are difficult to maintain. Other compounds—*e.g.*, pentaerythritol—are, for practical purposes, insoluble in epoxy resins, and unless a co-solvent can be added to enhance additive solubility, such compounds are of little value as accelerators. Glycerine could not be used in applications where the additive must be blended into the resin prior to mixing and curing, but could be used if pre-blending into the curing agent is permissible.

The additive to be used should also have a relatively high boiling point, especially in vacuum casting and coating applications. Lower molecular weight monoalcohols would be of little value because of volatilization prior to and during the cure, and after curing if the cured product is used in elevated temperature applications.

Table III. Effect of Additives on Storage Stability of Epoxy Resins

			Viscosity (cp., 25°C.)	
Resin	*Additive*	*Concentration (Mole %)*	*Initial*	*After 7 Days Heating at 80°C.*
D.E.R. 332	Phenol	1.5	4320	5,000
D.E.R. 332	Mercaptoethanol	1.5	4280	5,970
D.E.R. 332	*p*-Nitrophenol	1.0	5200	7,300
II	Bisphenol A	3.0	7200	12,500

The additive must further be of sufficient activity to allow its use at low concentrations so as not to detract from other resin properties. The use of relatively high concentrations of low-activity additives leads to dilution effects and can interfere with mechanical properties. Polyglycols, for instance, may be used to increase resin hydroxyl content, but may also cause increased flexibility and decreased heat distortion temperature in the cured product.

When the additive must be pre-blended into the resin and stored, for extended periods, particularly at elevated temperatures, a low-acidity, aliphatic hydroxyl accelerator would be recommended. Viscosity buildup may occur during long-term storage of resins containing additives of higher acidity, as is seen in Table III. This effect is most probably caused by both reaction of the accelerator with the epoxide groups and epoxide homopolymerization accelerated by the acid nature of the additive; thus partial loss of epoxide functionality would be expected with the use of these compounds.

Strong organic acids are limited in their use as accelerators since they tend to react to some extent with amine groups before acting to catalyze the amine-epoxide reaction. In general, phenols and other intermediate-acidity compounds are probably the best additives to use when storage stability is not a problem. Provided that they meet the requirements discussed above, aliphatic hydroxyl compounds, preferably those of di- or trifunctionality, have also been found most useful in maintaining desired levels of reactivity in epoxy resin systems.

Literature Cited

(1) Gough, L. J., Smith, I. T., *J. Oil Color Chem. Assoc.* **43,** 409 (1960).
(2) The Dow Chemical Company, "Dow Liquid Epoxy Resins," Plastics Department, Midland, Mich.
(3) Shechter, L., Wynstra, J., Kurkjy, R. P., *Ind. Eng. Chem.* **48 No. 1,** 94 (1956).
(4) Smith, I. T., *Polymer* **2,** 95 (1961).

RECEIVED October 4, 1968.

6

The Kinetics of Gelation of Some Accelerated Acid Anhydride Cured Epoxy Resins

KING M. HOLLANDS and ILMAR L. KALNIN

Materials Research Department, Celanese Research Co., Summit, N. J.

The gelation kinetics of two epoxy resin systems (difunctional and tetrafunctional) cured with acid anhydrides was determined as function of time, temperature, and accelerator concentration by means of viscosity and gel time measurements. The activation energies for the initial viscosity and for the gelation process were calculated using an Arrhenius type equation. A simple reciprocal relationship between the gel time, determined by Tecam gel timer, and the gelation rate that was independent of temperature and acclerator (at low accelerator levels) was established. Equiviscosity curves were plotted by computer over the viscosity range of 10^2 to 10^5 centipoises and gelation time up to several thousand hours.

In the manufacture of molded composite products from reinforced epoxy resins the starting material, instead of being a raw blend of the reinforcing and the resinous components, is usually an extremely viscous intermediate—a "premix" or "prepreg." The resin matrix of such a prepreg has been polymerized to the so-called prepreg stage (or B-stage) by heating the initial resin-hardener melt until its viscosity gradually reached the desired value. The prepreg stage is primarily a practical concept intended to convey the idea that the prepreg resin will neither flow nor appreciably crosslink while in storage, but will do so during the hot molding cycle, imparting good cohesion and rigidity to the final part. The terminal point of the prepreg condition is the onset of substantial crosslinking that results in a very rapid increase in melt viscosity and the appearance of a readily measurable elastic modulus (5); this is known as the gel point. The polymerization process up to the gel point is commonly described as gelation. The time to gelation, known as the gel time, depends strongly on the temperature, resin composition, mass, and the initial state of the system and may range from less than a minute to hundreds of hours. The prepreg condition may be characterized by some empirical methods, such as the amount of resin exuded from a laminated reinforced plastic under a given temperature and pressure (*6*) or extraction with a solvent, usually dimethyl ketone (*1*). An understanding of the prepregging process, however, requires knowledge of the gelation kinetics which for many commercially important epoxy resin systems has not yet been investigated. The gelation kinetics would be characterized most thoroughly by determining the change in molecular weight and its distribution with time. A literature search, however, revealed no such study in epoxy resin-acid anhydride systems. In a few papers the gelation was investigated by measuring the decrease in the end-group contents by means of chemical titration. From this Tanaka and Kakiuchi (*7, 8*) concluded that the polymerization rate was first order with respect to each of the reactants, including the accelerator. Feltzin, *et al.* (*2*) and Fischer (*3*), however, found that the rate was first order with respect to the accelerator only, being independent of the resin and hardener concentrations. No attempts were made to determine the number-average molecular weight from the end-group analysis.

Another approach of interest to those concerned with resin rheology during processing is to measure the increase in melt viscosity during the gelation. The viscosity may be related to the molecular weight, since it is known that at not too high or too low or too polydisperse molecular weights and reasonably low shear rates the melt viscosity is proportional to a certain power of the weight-average molecular weight (*4*). Since no references were found in literature regarding the rheology of gelation in epoxy resin-acid anhydride systems, it was decided to investigate two typical systems, commonly used in the prepreg manufacture, by means of viscosity change as a function of time at a given accelerator concentration and temperature. Since the viscosity is very sensitive to temperature changes, every effort was made to maintain a constant temperature, within ±0.5°C., during the gelation.

Experimental

Materials. The two systems used were: Epi-Rez 508 (made by Celanese Coatings Co., Louisville, Kentucky), hardened with hexahydrophthalic acid anhydride (HHPA) (made by Allied Chemical Co., New York, N. Y.), and Epon 828/1031 (made by Shell Chemical Co., New York, N. Y.), hardened with methylbicyclo-(2,2,1) heptene-2,3-dicarboxylic anhydride (NMA) (made by Allied Chemical Co., New York, N. Y.).

The first one is a commercially pure diglycidyl ether of bisphenol-A (DGEBA), whereas the Epon system consists of a nearly equifunctional mixture of the difunctional DGEBA and tetrafunctional polyglycidyl ether of tetraphenyleneethane (50–50 wt. %). Benzyldimethylamine (BDMA) was used as accelerator. All of the components were characterized by

Table I. Composition of Epi-Rez and Epon Epoxy Systems

System	Composition pbw	Composition mol. %	Structure
Epi-Rez			
508—epoxy resin	100	38.4	Diglycidyl ether of bisphenol "A"
HHPA—curing agent	70	61.1	Hexahydrophthalic acid anhydride
BDMA—accelerator	0.0, 0.25, 0.5	0.0, 0.25, 0.5	Benzyldimethylamine
Epon			
828—epoxy resin	50	18.7	Diglycidyl ether of bisphenol A
1031—epoxy resin	50	8.5	Mixture of tetraglycidoxy-tetraphenylethane isomers
NMA—curing agent	90	71.8	Nadic methyl anhydride
BDMA—accelerator	0.0, 0.5, 1.0	0.0, 0.5, 1.0	Benzyldimethylamine

Table II. Properties of Epoxy

	Lot No.	Av. Molecular Wt. Mfg. Spec.	Av. Molecular Wt. Anal. Results	Epoxy Equivalent Mfg. Spec.	Epoxy Equivalent Anal. Results
Celanese Coatings Co. Epi-Rez					
508	SCR-4	340-360	350	171-177	175
508	SCR-16	340-360	340	171-177	171
Shell Chemical Co. Epon					
828	SCR-3	350-400	375	184-192	187
1031	SCR-2	840-960	880	210-240	220
Nadic methyl anhydride (NMA)	SCR-7	178.2	—	—	—
	SCR-8	178.2	—	—	—
Allied Chemical Co. hexahydrophthalic anhydride (HHPA)	SCR-11	154.2	—	—	—
	SCR-15	154.2	—	—	—

[a] Determined by x-ray fluorescence.

the appropriate standard analytical methods. Table I gives the compositions used; Table II—the manufacturers' specifications and the analytical results obtained.

The resins were heated to facilitate blending where necessary. Both the resin and the hardener were then brought separately to the desired temperature and mixed thoroughly. The time of mixing (with or without the accelerator) was considered as the zero-time. Regulated, water-cooled oil baths were used to maintain the desired temperatures: 40°, 60°, and 80° ± 1°C. Viscosity measurements were made at regular time intervals, by means of a Brookfield RVT viscometer (made by Brookfield Eng. Lab., Stoughton, Mass.), which was calibrated with standard oils. The viscosities were initially measured using several spindle sizes and speeds and were found to be essentially Newtonian in the range of study. The gel times were determined separately with a Tecam gelation timer (made by Techne, Ltd., Princeton, N. J.).

Discussion and Results

It was found that up to about 50,000 centipoises the change in viscosity prior to gelation was well represented by the exponential equation:

$$\eta = \eta_0 e^{kt} \tag{1}$$

The effect of temperature is two-fold: to decrease the viscosity of the system and to increase the gelation rate. It was found during the

Resins and Anhydrides

Hydrolyzable Cl		*Total Chlorine*		*Acid Upper Limit (%)*	
Mfg. Spec.	*Anal. Results*	*Mfg. Spec.*	*Anal.[a] Results*	*Mfg. Spec.*	*Anal.[b] Results*
0.05	0.04	0.2	0.25	—	—
0.05	0.04	0.2	0.25	—	—
0.1	0.02	—	0.22	—	—
—	0.03	—	0.82	—	—
—	—	—	—	—	1.5
—	—	—	—	—	0.78
—	—	—	—	—	1.2
—	—	—	—	—	2.7

[b] Determined by infrared spectroscopy.

processing of the accumulated data that in the temperature range used (40° to 80°C.) the effects of temperature on both the viscosity and the rate constant could be represented by Arrhenius type equations. Accordingly, the above equation was used in the logarithmic expanded form as follows:

$$\ln\eta = \ln\eta_{oo} + \Delta H_{\eta}/RT + k_{oo}t \exp(-\Delta H_k/RT) \qquad (1a)$$

in which k_{oo} is a function of accelerator content only, the resin and hardener contents remaining constant. The nomenclature is as follows:

η = viscosity of the system (centipoise, cp.)
η_o = initial (zero-time) viscosity = F (T, cp.)
η_{oo} = pre-exponential factor for the initial viscosity (cp.)
ΔH_{η} = apparent activation energy for the initial viscosity (kcal./mole)
R = gas constant (kcal./deg.)
k = rate constant of gelation = F (T, A) (hr.$^{-1}$)
k_{oo} = pre-exponential factor of gelation (hr.$^{-1}$)
ΔH_k = apparent activation energy for the gelation (kcal./mole)
T = temperature, (°K.)
t = time, (hr.)
A = accelerator (BDMA) content (mole %)

The pre-exponential factors, η_{oo} and k_{oo}, and the activation energies were obtained from computer-calculated least squares data. Each resin system was run at least twice at any given temperature and accelerator content.

As the polymerization proceeds beyond 10^4–10^5 cp., the epoxy system becomes viscoelastic and the viscosity increases faster than exponentially with time, even at constant temperature. At this point the viscosity then becomes too high to be measurable reliably and other methods of study

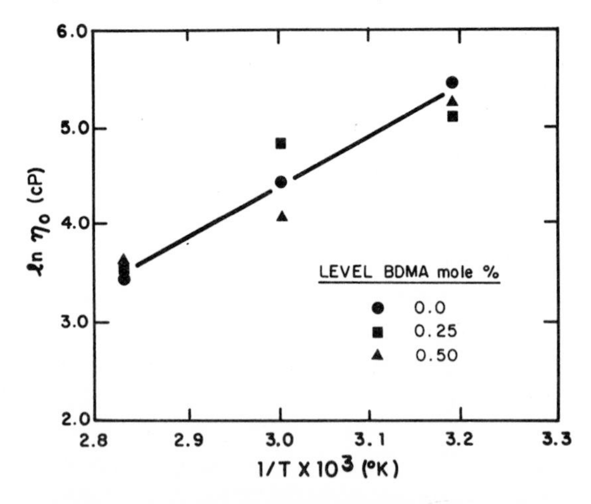

Figure 1. Initial viscosity vs. *reciprocal temperature for the Epi-Rez 508—HHPA system*

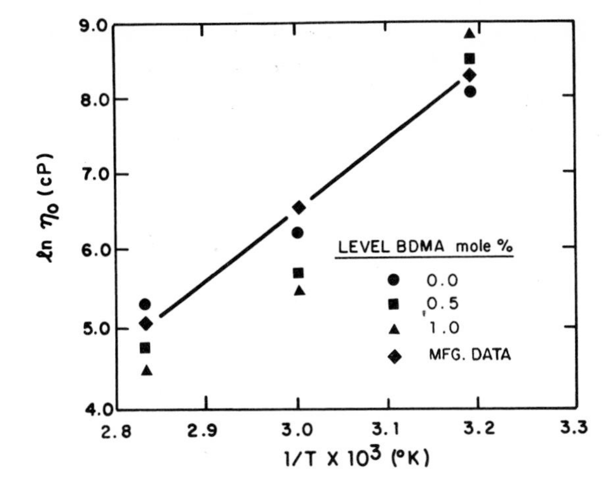

Figure 2. Initial viscosity vs. *reciprocal temperature for the Epon 828/1031—NMA system*

are advised which will not be considered here. In the viscous region (below $\sim 10^5$ cp.) it appears that the dependence of viscosity on the molecular weight is similar to that encountered in linear polymers—*i.e.*, $\eta_{00} \propto (\text{mol. wt.})^x$, in which x is a positive exponent. Further work is needed to determine the exact relationship between the viscosity and molecular weight during the crosslinking process.

The dependence of the initial viscosity on temperature for the two epoxy systems is shown in Figures 1 and 2, respectively. As expected, the initial viscosity is independent of the accelerator content. The activation energy for viscous flow is higher (18 kcal./mole) for the multifunctional Epon system than for the difunctional Epi-Rez (10.5 kcal./mole). The dependence of the gelation rates on temperature at various accelerator concentrations is shown in Figures 3 and 4. The DGEBA/HHPA system shows a large increase in both the rate constant and the activation energy upon introduction of even a small amount of accelerator. From then on, however, a first-order dependence on accelerator is indicated. The Epon system on the other hand has the same activation energy of gelation with or without the accelerator and does not show a low velocity reaction without accelerator. Further work is planned on similar systems using other hardeners and accelerators in order to elucidate further the role of the accelerator on the gelation kinetics. At present it can be said that the mixed tetrafunctional system is considerably more active without the tertiary amine accelerator than the wholly difunctional one.

The viscosity data obtained were used to make contour plots of equiviscosity curves over the range of 10^2 to 10^5 cp. up to 100°C. at various levels of accelerator. Data below 10^3 and above 10^4 were extrapolated using Equation 1a. The results for the two systems are given in Figure 5. The curves show a maximum at the point where the cross-linking reaction overtakes the effect of temperature on viscosity. The retrograde portion of the curve is, of course, not kinetically realizable in practice.

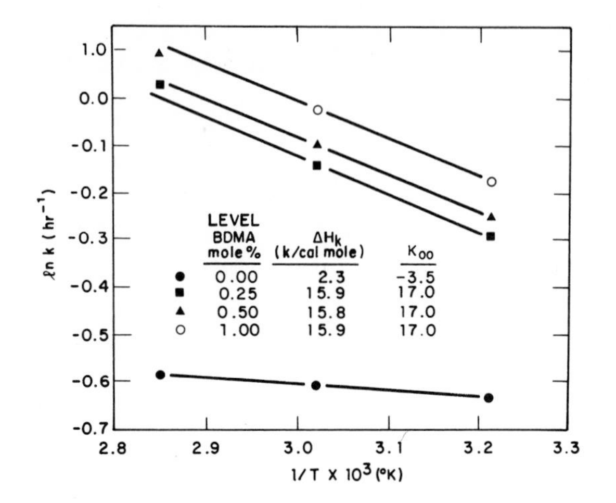

Figure 3. Rate constant vs. *reciprocal temperature for the Epi-Rez 508—HHPA system*

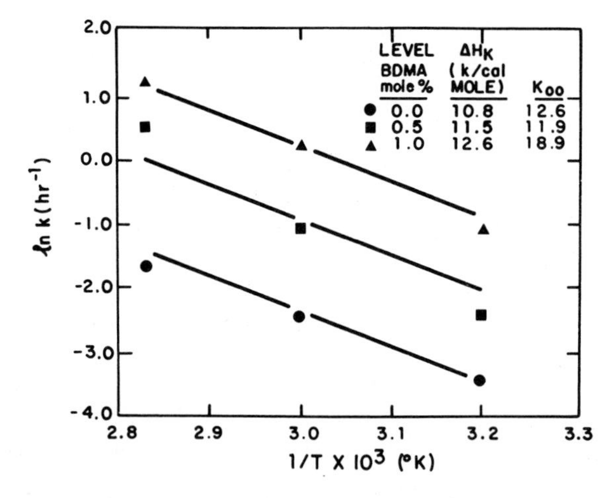

Figure 4. Rate constant vs. *reciprocal temperature for the Epon 828/1031—NMA system*

Gelation times for the two epoxy systems were obtained at several temperatures and levels of accelerator and are shown in Figures 6 and 7. Gel times determined on the Tecam gel timer are based on the appearance of a small, arbitrary elastic shear modulus, in the viscous system (5).

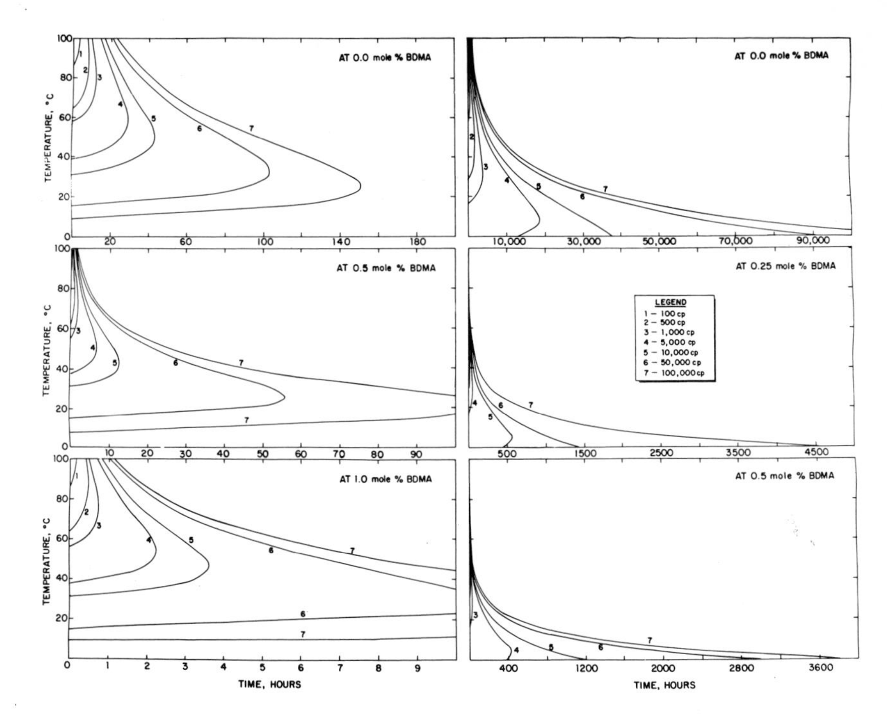

Figure 5. Equi-viscosity curves for Epi-Rez 508—HHPA (right) and the Epon 828/1031—NMA (left)

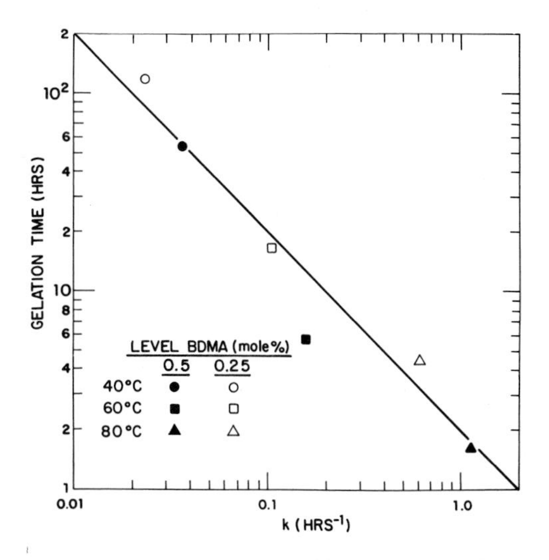

Figure 6. Gelation time vs. *rate constant at various temperatures and accelerator levels for Epi-Rez 508—HHPA*

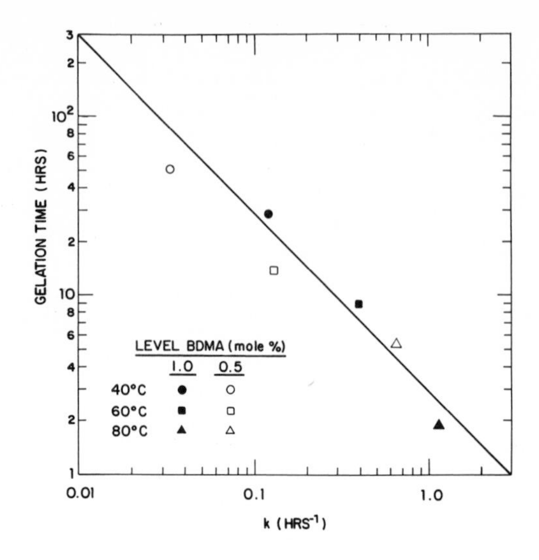

Figure 7. Gelation time vs. *rate constant at various temperatures and accelerator levels for Epon 828/1031—NMA*

The gel time, t_g, when plotted against the measured gelation rate, k, on a logarithmic scale was found to give a straight line, the slope of which is -1, indicating the applicability of Equation 1. Furthermore, the relationship apparently is independent of the temperature and level of accelerator (at low levels). The use of such a relationship can be quite useful in determining the pot life, gel time, resin advancement, and viscosity in the manufacture of reinforced epoxy resin composite intermediates. The pot life generally ends at a viscosity of about 5,000 centipoises, whereas the prepreg stage may extend to the gel point or even above. Knowledge of the viscosity and the extent of the reaction are both essential for characterization of partially crosslinked resins, yet the empirical characterization techniques mentioned before are limited in scope and application. Convenient characterizations of gelation kinetics of epoxy systems using this relationship in conjunction with one or two pairs of gel time–rate constant determinations now appear possible. Further work is in progress to extend gelation and gel time study to other epoxy resin systems.

Acknowledgment

Many valuable discussions with Kurt F. Wissbrun contributed much to the development of the approach presented in this paper.

Literature Cited

(1) ASTM, **D-2587-67T,** "Book of ASTM Standards," **27,** 738 (1967).
(2) Feltzin, J., Barsh, M. K., Peer, E. J., Petker, I., "Preprints of Papers," Organic Coatings and Plastics Chem. Div., 148th Natl. Meeting ACS, Chicago, Ill., **24** (2), 282 (1964).
(3) Fischer, R. F., *J. Polymer Sci.* **44,** 155 (1960).
(4) Miller, M. L., "The Structure of Polymers," p. 218, Reinhold Publishing Co., N. Y., 1966.
(5) Hills, B. A., *J. Oil Colour Chem. Assoc.* **45,** 257 (1962).
(6) SPI, Prepreg Test Method 2, Society of the Plastics Industry, New York, N. Y., Feb. 1960.
(7) Tanaka, Y., Kakiuchi, H., *J. Appl. Polymer Sci.* **7,** 1063 (1963).
(8) Tanaka, Y., Kakiuchi, H., *J. Polymer Sci.,* **Part A, 2,** 3405 (1964).

RECEIVED September 13, 1968.

7

Amine Functional Siloxanes as Epoxy Resin Hardeners

M. MARKOVITZ and L. S. KOHN

General Electric Co., Materials and Processes Laboratory,
Schenectady, N. Y. 12305

Amine functional siloxanes were synthesized from alkoxy functional siloxanes and hydroxy functional amines. These reaction products were readily soluble in liquid bisphenol A-diglycidyl ether epoxy resins and epoxy novolacs. The crosslinked resins ranged from transparent pale yellow to transparent amber tough solids. The cured resins had high tensile and flexural strengths. The heat distortion temperatures were relatively low owing to the presence of the flexibilizing polysiloxane chains. Tan δ at 60-cycle values were low at 25°C., and there was better retention of low tan δ values at elevated temperatures with the aromatic amine functional siloxanes than with the aliphatic amine functional siloxanes. Most of the resins immersed in water at 25° and 95°C. remained transparent after 56 days immersion.

Aliphatic and aromatic polyamines, amine adducts, heterocyclic nitrogen compounds, and amine functional polyamides have been widely used as epoxy resin hardeners (*6*). Low molecular weight amine functional polysiloxanes were synthesized in this laboratory to determine whether the presence of polysiloxanes in epoxy resins would improve heat resistance, water resistance, and electrical insulating properties over epoxy resins crosslinked with non-silicone containing amine hardeners.

There are several references in the literature concerning the synthesis and properties of alkanolamine silicon derivatives. Alkanolamine esters of orthosilicic acid were synthesized by heating orthosilicic esters with monoalkanolamines in the presence of water (*4*). These compounds were said to be biologically active. The synthesis and properties of di-*tert*-butyl diaminoalkyl silicates were described by DiGiorgio and co-workers (*2*); these compounds were synthesized by the reaction of di-*tert*-butyldichlorosilane with various alkanolamines. The synthesis, chemical properties, and uses of alkanolamine silicate derivatives such as diethoxydi-(β-diethylaminoethyl) silicate and diethyl(triethanolamine) silicate were described by Koehler and Lamprey (5). These compounds were used as dispersants and viscosity depressants in nonaqueous systems.

The reaction products of alkoxy functional siloxanes and hydroxy functional amines were investigated in our laboratory as hardeners for epoxy resins. Electrical and mechanical properties and the effects of heat aging on these properties were determined. All the amine functional siloxanes discussed in this report were readily soluble in epoxy resins.

The silicones used in this investigation were the commercially available Sylkyd 50 (Dow Corning) and diphenyldiethoxysilane (GE Silicone Products Dept., product No. XC-3709). Sylkyd 50 is a methoxylated polysiloxane having the average chemical structure of dimethyltriphenyltrimethoxytrisiloxane and contains 20% methoxy.

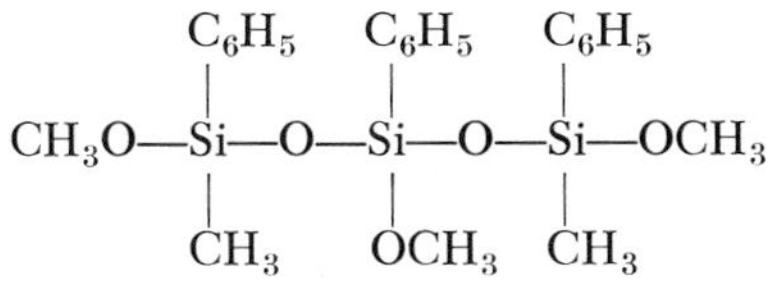

$$
\begin{array}{ccccccc}
 & C_6H_5 & & C_6H_5 & & C_6H_5 & \\
 & | & & | & & | & \\
CH_3O— & Si & —O— & Si & —O— & Si & —OCH_3 \\
 & | & & | & & | & \\
 & CH_3 & & OCH_3 & & CH_3 &
\end{array}
$$

Sylkyd 50

Experimental

Two to three moles of the hydroxyl functional amine per mole of Sylkyd 50 (average molecular weight 470) reacted by heating at 100°–240°C. and distilling the methanol formed in the reaction. After distillation of the alcohol stopped, the reaction mixtures were vacuum distilled to remove unreacted hydroxyamine. If aromatic hydroxy functional amines were used, the reaction mixtures were not vacuum distilled since the aromatic amines were not readily distillable even under vacuum.

Aliphatic hydroxy functional amines such as ethanolamine, *N*-ethylethanolamine or *N*-aminoethylethanolamine reacted faster with alkoxy siloxanes than did aromatic hydroxyamines such as *m*- or *p*-aminophenol. Attempts to promote a reaction between alkoxy siloxanes with amines having no hydroxy functionality were unsuccessful—*e.g.*, there was no apparent reaction after heating Sylkyd 50 and a eutectic of *m*-phenylenediamine and bis(*p*-aminophenyl) methane two hours at 145°–170°C.

The following are examples of several reactions investigated and the conditions necessary to effect reaction:

Sylkyd 50-Ethanolamine. A mixture of Sylkyd 50 (470 grams, 3.0 methoxy equivs.) and ethanolamine (183 grams, 3.0 moles) was stirred and heated. After 3.5 hours at 109°–154°C., 71 grams (2.2 moles) of methanol distilled from the reaction mixture, and the reaction mixture turned clear. The reaction mixture was then heated at 2–3 mm. to distill unreacted ethanolamine; 50 grams of ethanolamine were collected (theoretical is 54 grams). The clear yellow liquid product corresponded to an average structure of 2.2 amine groups per trisiloxane molecule and a functionality of 4.4. The product may be represented as a mixture of compounds:

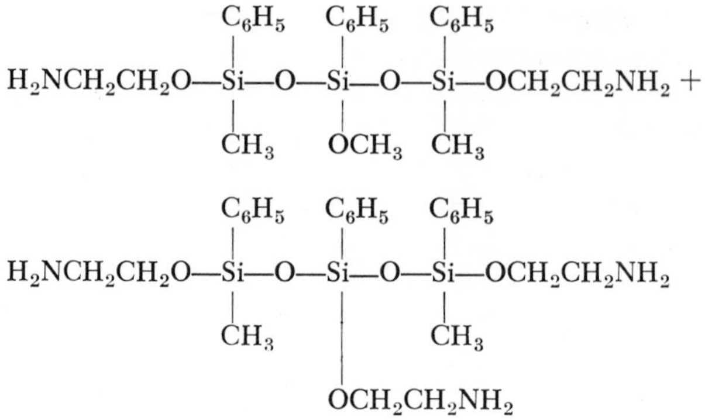

$$
\begin{array}{ccccccc}
 & C_6H_5 & & C_6H_5 & & C_6H_5 & \\
 & | & & | & & | & \\
H_2NCH_2CH_2O- & Si & -O- & Si & -O- & Si & -OCH_2CH_2NH_2 + \\
 & | & & | & & | & \\
 & CH_3 & & OCH_3 & & CH_3 &
\end{array}
$$

$$
\begin{array}{ccccccc}
 & C_6H_5 & & C_6H_5 & & C_6H_5 & \\
 & | & & | & & | & \\
H_2NCH_2CH_2O- & Si & -O- & Si & -O- & Si & -OCH_2CH_2NH_2 \\
 & | & & | & & | & \\
 & CH_3 & & | & & CH_3 & \\
 & & & OCH_2CH_2NH_2 & & &
\end{array}
$$

Sylkyd 50-*N*-aminoethylethanolamine. A mixture of Sylkyd 50 (470 grams, 3.0 methoxy equivs.) and *N*-aminoethylethanolamine (312 grams, 3.0 moles) was stirred and heated. Reaction began at 117°C., and after six hours at 117°–223°C., 82 grams (2.6 moles) of methanol distilled from the reaction mixture, and the reaction mixture was homogeneous. The reaction mixture was then heated two hours at 87°–163°C. and 2–3 mm. to distill unreacted *N*-aminoethylethanolamine. Thirty-eight grams of *N*-aminoethylethanolamine were collected (theoretical is 45 grams). The clear yellow liquid product corresponded to an average structure of 2.6 $H_2NC_2H_4NHC_2H_4O$-groups per trisiloxane and a functionality of 7.8. The product can be considered to consist of a mixture of compounds:

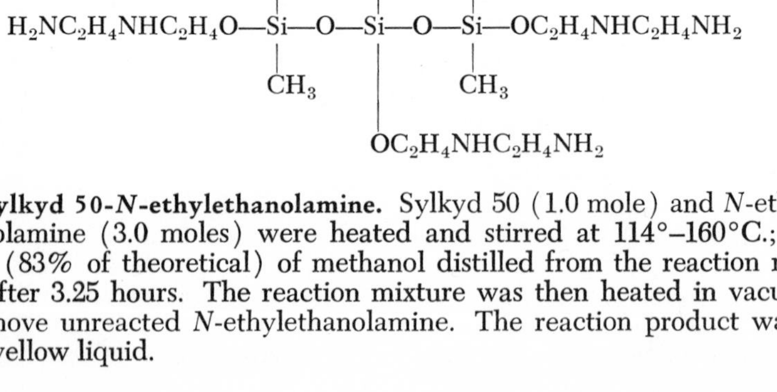

$$
\begin{array}{ccccccc}
 & C_6H_5 & & C_6H_5 & & C_6H_5 & \\
 & | & & | & & | & \\
H_2NC_2H_4NHC_2H_4O- & Si & -O- & Si & -O- & Si & -OC_2H_4NHC_2H_4NH_2 + \\
 & | & & | & & | & \\
 & CH_3 & & OCH_3 & & CH_3 &
\end{array}
$$

$$
\begin{array}{ccccccc}
 & C_6H_5 & & C_6H_5 & & C_6H_5 & \\
 & | & & | & & | & \\
H_2NC_2H_4NHC_2H_4O- & Si & -O- & Si & -O- & Si & -OC_2H_4NHC_2H_4NH_2 \\
 & | & & | & & | & \\
 & CH_3 & & | & & CH_3 & \\
 & & & OC_2H_4NHC_2H_4NH_2 & & &
\end{array}
$$

Sylkyd 50-*N*-ethylethanolamine. Sylkyd 50 (1.0 mole) and *N*-ethylethanolamine (3.0 moles) were heated and stirred at 114°–160°C.; 2.5 moles (83% of theoretical) of methanol distilled from the reaction mixture after 3.25 hours. The reaction mixture was then heated in vacuum to remove unreacted *N*-ethylethanolamine. The reaction product was a clear yellow liquid.

Sylkyd 50-*m*-Aminophenol. Sylkyd 50 (1.0 mole) and *m*-aminophenol (2.0 moles) reacted for six hours at 174°–217°C.; 1.8 moles (90% of theoretical)of methanol distilled from the reaction mixture. In another experiment, Sylkyd 50 (1.0 mole) and *m*-aminophenol (2.2 moles) reacted at 192°–200°C. After 5.5 hours, 1.75 moles (80% of theoretical) of methanol distilled from the reaction mixture. The reaction products were solids at room temperature.

Sylkyd 50-*p*-Aminophenol. Sylkyd 50 (1.0 mole) and *p*-aminophenol (2.0 moles) reacted 4.5 hours at 178°–240°C.; 1.6 moles (80% of theoretical) of methanol distilled from the reaction mixture. The reaction product was a solid at room temperature.

Sylkyd 50-*p*-Aminophenethyl alc. Sylkyd 50 (1.0 mole) reacted with *p*-aminophenethyl alcohol (2.0 moles). After six hours at 135°–200°C., the theoretical quantity of 2.0 moles of methanol distilled from the reaction mixture. A representative structure of the product is:

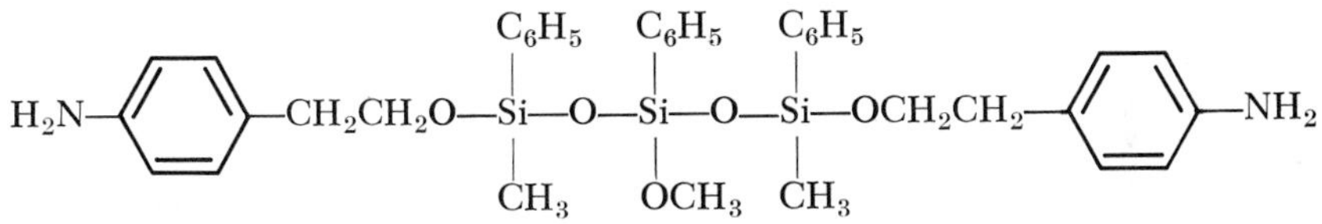

$$H_2N-C_6H_4-CH_2CH_2O-\underset{CH_3}{\overset{C_6H_5}{Si}}-O-\underset{OCH_3}{\overset{C_6H_5}{Si}}-O-\underset{CH_3}{\overset{C_6H_5}{Si}}-OCH_2CH_2-C_6H_4-NH_2$$

If 2.2 moles of *p*-aminophenethyl alcohol were used, the theoretical 2.2 moles of methanol distilled after eight hours at 135°–200°C. The reaction products solidified at room temperature.

Diphenyldiethoxysilane Ethanolamine. Diphenyldiethoxysilane (1.0 mole) reacted with ethanolamine (2.0 moles) by heating at 120°–160°C. After six hours, 1.4 moles (70% of theoretical) of ethanol distilled from the reaction mixture.

Diphenyldiethoxysilane *m*-Aminophenol. Diphenyldiethoxysilane (1.0 mole) and *m*-aminophenol (2.0 moles) reacted at 200°–218°C. Ethyl alcohol (1.5 moles, 75% of theory) distilled from the reaction mixture after 11 hours.

The alkanolamine-alkoxy siloxane and phenolic amine-alkoxy siloxane reactions are general reactions and they are not limited to the above examples. In place of Sylkyd 50 or diphenyldiethoxysilane, other alkoxy functional silicones can be used to modify the properties and vary the silicone content of the epoxy-silicone amine resins. Silicones with higher alkoxy content will form amine functional silicones having higher amine functionality and result in more rigid products when used to crosslink epoxy resins. The following alkoxy functional polysiloxanes are examples of commercially available materials.

SR-196, 10% methoxy	(GE Silicone Products Dept.)
SR-191, 15% methoxy	(GE Silicone Products Dept.)
XR-6188, 15% methoxy	(Dow Corning)
XC-3923 (phenyl triethoxysilane), 56% ethoxy	(GE Silicone Products Dept.)

The epoxy resins used in this investigation were commercial bisphenol A-diglycidyl ether epoxy resins or epoxy novolacs. The properties of these resins are:

Epon 826—bisphenol A-diglycidyl ether epoxy, epoxide equiv. wt. 180–188, viscosity 65–95 poises at 25°C., Shell Chemical Company.

Epon 828—bisphenol A-diglycidyl ether epoxy, epoxide equiv. wt. 185–192, viscosity 100–160 poises at 25°C., Shell Chemical Company.

D.E.R. 332—bisphenol A-diglycidyl ether epoxy, epoxide equiv. wt. 172–178, viscosity 40–64 poises at 25°C., Dow Chemical Company.

D.E.N. 431—epoxy novolac, epoxide functionality 2.2, epoxide equiv. wt. 175–182, viscosity 300–900 poises at 52°C., Dow Chemical Company.

Data on tan δ at 60 cycles, heat distortion temperature, tensile and flexural strength, thermal degradation and water resistance are given in this report. Each test result is the mean value of a number of test samples. Tan δ was based on one or two samples, two or three samples for heat distortion temperature, four to six samples for tensile and flexural properties, and four to eight samples for thermal degradation and water

Table I. Tan δ *vs.* Temperature

	Bisphenol A-diglycidyl ether epoxy resins							
Epon 828	188[a]	188	188	188	188	188	188	188
Sylkyd 50-ethanolamine	116							
Sylkyd 50-*N*-aminoethyl-ethanolamine		87						
Sylkyd 50-*m*-aminophenol			149					
Sylkyd 50-*m*-aminophenethyl alc.				159				
Sylkyd 50-*p*-aminophenol					156			
Sylkyd 50-*N*-ethyl-ethanolamine						49(.2)	98(.4)	123(.5)
Shell's curing agent Z						30(.8)	23(.6)	19(.5)
Temperature, °C.	*Tan δ (60 cycles 10 VPM)*							
25	.0046	.0085	.0057	.002	.001	.0041	.0030	.0041
75	.031	.0077	.0063	.003	.001	.0040	.043	.058
100	.36	.032	.030	.035	.027	.015	.10	.26
125			.011	.013	.012	.14		
150			.091	.055	.042			

[a] The quantities of epoxy resins and hardeners, in parts by weight, correspond to 1.0 epoxy equivalent per amine hydrogen equivalent. Where two hardeners are used, the amine hydrogen equivalents contributed by each hardener are given in parentheses.

Table II. Tan δ *vs.* Temperature

	Epoxy Novolacs								
D.E.N. 438	178[a]	178	178	178	178	178			
D.E.N. 431							176	176	176
Sylkyd 50-ethanolamine	116								
Sylkyd 50-*N*-aminoethyl-ethanolamine		87					87		
Sylkyd 50-*m*-aminophenol			149					149	
Sylkyd 50-*p*-aminophen-ethyl alcohol				170					170
Sylkyd 50-*N*-ethyl-ethanolamine					141(.5)	56(.2)			
Shell's curing agent Z					19(.5)	30(.8)			
Temperature, °C.	*Tan δ (60 cycles, 10 VPM)*								
25	.0065	.0085	.0056	.003	.0075	.0076	.0084	.005	.0043
75	.014	.0098	.0068	.003			.0095	.008	.0099
100	.083	.020	.088	.009	.016	.012	.024	.013	.034
125		.11	.023	.020		.041	.45	.023	.065
150		.87	.023	.021		.29		.094	.65
175				.142					

[a] The quantities of epoxy resins and hardeners, in parts by weight, correspond to 1.0 epoxy equivalent per amine hydrogen equivalent. Where two hardeners are used, the amine hydrogen equivalents contributed by each hardener are given in parentheses.

Table III. Heat Distortion Temperature (at 264 p.s.i.)

	Aliphatic Silicone Amines							
Epon 828	188[a]	188						
D.E.R. 332			175	175				
D.E.N. 431					176	176		
D.E.N. 438							178	178
Sylkyd 50-ethanolamine	116		116		116		116	
Sylkyd 50-*N*-aminoethyl-ethanolamine		87		87		87		87
Mils Deflection	*Temperature, °C.*							
1	53	81	50	83	54	86	61	94
5	60	89	58	93	61	95	73	110
10 (HDT)	62	92	60	96	65	98	78	117

[a] The quantities of epoxy resins and hardeners, in parts by weight, correspond to 1.0 epoxy equivalent per amine hydrogen equivalent.

Table IV. Heat Distortion Temperature (at 264 p.s.i.)

	Aromatic Silicone Amines							
Epon 828	188[a]	188						
D.E.R. 332			175	175				
D.E.N. 431					176	176		
D.E.N. 438							178	178
Sylkyd 50-*p*-aminophenethyl alcohol	170		170		170		170	
Sylkyd 50-*m*-aminophenol		145		145		145		145
Mils Deflection	*Temperature, °C.*							
1	55	67	51	68	55	68	57	72
5	63	77	61	78	62	78	75	87
10 (HDT)	67	80	65	82	68	82	82	93

[a] The quantities of epoxy resins and hardeners, in parts by weight, correspond to 1.0 epoxy equivalent per amine hydrogen equivalent.

Table V. Tensile Strength, Tensile

	Bisphenol A-diglycidyl	
Epon 828	188[a]	188
Sylkyd 50-*N*-aminoethylethanolamine	87	
Sylkyd 50-*m*-aminophenol		149
Sylkyd 50-*p*-aminophenethyl alc.		
Sylkyd 50-*N*-ethylethanolamine		
Curing Agent Z		
15 hrs. @ 160°C.		
Tensile Strength, p.s.i.	9200	11,400
% Elongation at break	5.8	7.1
Tensile modulus, p.s.i.	1.9×10^5	2.3×10^5
28 days @ 135°C. in air		
Tensile Strength, p.s.i.	6400	5400
% Elongation at break	1.8	1.6
Tensile modulus, p.s.i.	2.3×10^5	2.2×10^5
56 days @ 135°C. in air		
Tensile Strength, p.s.i.	5590	6050
% Elongation at break	1.5	1.7
Tensile modulus, p.s.i.	2.5×10^5	2.3×10^5
28 days @ 160°C. in air		
Tensile Strength, p.s.i.	7500	6300
% Elongation at break	1.9	1.9
Tensile modulus, p.s.i.	2.2×10^5	2.2×10^5
56 days @ 160°C. in air		
Tensile Strength, p.s.i.	4800	5900
% Elongation at break	2.1	1.6
Tensile modulus, p.s.i.	2.0×10^5	2.8×10^5

[a] The quantities of epoxy resins and hardeners, in parts by weight, correspond to 1.0 epoxy equivalent per amine hydrogen equivalent. Where two hardeners are used, the

resistance. ASTM test methods D648-56, D790-61, and D638-58 were used for determining heat distortion temperature, flexural and tensile properties, respectively.

Results and Discussion

The amine functional siloxanes were readily soluble in epoxy resins. Liquid siloxane amines were dissolved in liquid epoxy resins at room temperature and were deaerated in vacuum to remove air bubbles. The solid siloxane amines—*i.e.*, those based on aromatic amines—were heated at 100°–120°C. until they became fluid and then were mixed with the epoxy resin. The epoxy novolacs were heated to 60°–80°C. to decrease their viscosity and facilitate the blending of the siloxane amine. No compatibility problems were encountered in all the combinations of

Modulus, and Elongation at 25°C.

ether epoxy resins

188	188	188	188
159			
	49(.2)	98(.4)	123(.5)
	30(.8)	23(.6)	19(.5)
8700	11,300	8200	4100
9.3	7.2	4.6	3.0
1.8×10^5	2.1×10^5	2.1×10^5	1.8×10^5
6000	5900	7200	6700
2.0	1.9	3.0	2.0
1.0×10^5	2.2×10^5	2.2×10^5	2.2×10^5
5900	5600	7100	5100
1.9	1.7	2.1	1.5
2.1×10^5	2.2×10^5	2.1×10^5	2.2×10^5
5900	6400	7600	7400
1.8	3.0	2.7	2.7
2.4×10^5	2.3×10^5	2.2×10^5	2.1×10^5
6300	6100	5100	5600
1.9	1.9	1.3	1.7
2.4×10^5	2.1×10^5	2.3×10^5	2.4×10^5

amine hydrogen equivalents contributed by each hardener are given in parentheses.

Table VI. Tensile Strength, Tensile Modulus, and Elongation at 25°C.

	Epoxy Novolacs			
D.E.N. 438	178[a]	178	178	
D.E.N. 431				176
Sylkyd 50-ethanolamine	116			
Sylkyd 50-*N*-aminoethyl-ethanolamine		87		87
Sylkyd 50-*m*-aminophenol			149	
15 hrs. @ 160°C.				
Tensile strength, p.s.i.	10,400	6,800	9,950	10,700
% Elongation at break	6.0	4.1	5.9	6.0
Tensile modulus, p.s.i.	2.0×10^5	1.9×10^5	2.3×10^5	2.2×10^5
28 days @ 135°C. in air				
Tensile strength, p.s.i.	6,200	4,700	6,400	6,300
% Elongation at break	2.0	1.4	1.6	1.9
Tensile modulus, p.s.i.	2.6×10^5	2.4×10^5	2.7×10^5	2.0×10^5
56 days @ 135°C. in air				
Tensile strength, p.s.i.	6,900	2,700	4,400	4,500
% Elongation at break	2.1	0.8	1.3	1.4
Tensile modulus, p.s.i.	2.3×10^5	2.1×10^5	2.2×10^5	2.2×10^5
28 days @ 160°C. in air				
Tensile strength, p.s.i.	5,500	4,500	5,500	6,100
% Elongation at break	2.7	1.5	1.8	2.0
Tensile modulus, p.s.i.	2.4×10^5	2.2×10^5	2.4×10^5	2.1×10^5
56 days @ 160°C. in air				
Tensile strength, p.s.i.	5,200	3,100	4,700	4,000
% Elongation at break	2.0	1.2	1.2	1.2
Tensile modulus, p.s.i.	2.5×10^5	3.4×10^5	2.6×10^5	2.1×10^5

[a] The quantities of epoxy resins and hardeners, in parts by weight, correspond to 1.0 epoxy equivalent per amine hydrogen equivalent.

epoxy resins and siloxane amines investigated. The high solubility of these siloxane amines is probably caused by their relatively short polysiloxane chain length.

The Sylkyd 50-*N*-ethylethanolamine has a relative low amine H functionality. Shell's curing agent Z was used with the Sylkyd 50-*N*-ethylethanolamine hardener to increase the crosslink density. Curing agent Z is a eutectic of the aromatic amines *m*-phenylenediamine and bis(*p*-aminophenyl)methane. The number of epoxy equivalents was equal to the sum of the amine hydrogen equivalents contributed by the amine hardeners.

The Sylkyd 50-aliphatic hydroxyamine reaction products reacted as typical slow aliphatic polyamines, *i.e.*, mild exotherm 0.5–1 hour after mixing followed by hardening, however, an elevated temperature cure was necessary to achieve optimum physical and electrical properties. The aromatic amine siloxanes were less reactive. These gelled at room temperature after approximately 8 hours, and an elevated temperature cure was necessary.

Cure. To reduce the number of variables, all samples were cured two hours at 25°–140°C. plus 15 hours at 160°C. Shorter cure times and lower temperatures are probably adequate for the aliphatic amine siloxane cured epoxy resins.

Tan δ *vs.* Temperature. Tan δ at 60 cycles *vs.* temperature of the bisphenol A epoxy resin Epon 828 cured by various siloxane amines was determined (*see* Table I). The weights of resin and hardener were based on approximately stoichiometric quantities—1.0 epoxy equivalent per amine H equivalent. The amine H equivalent weight was based on the total amount of hydroxyamine which reacted with or was present in the Sylkyd 50-hydroxyamine reaction product. Tan δ at 25°C. was 0.01 for all samples., but tan δ at elevated temperatures was lower for the aromatic amine cured samples. Tan δ decreased as the Shell's curing agent Z content was increased in resins containing Epon 828 and the hardeners Sylkyd 50-*N*-ethylethanolamine and curing agent Z.

Tan δ at 25°–175°C. of epoxy novolacs cured by siloxane amines are summarized in Table II. Tan δ of epoxy novolacs followed the same general trend displayed by bisphenol A epoxy resins—*i.e.*, lower tan δ values for aromatic than for aliphatic siloxane amines. The lower softening temperatures of the D.E.N. 431 samples accounted for the more rapid increase in tan δ at elevated temperatures of the D.E.N. 431 samples compared with the D.E.N. 438 samples.

In general, tan δ at 60 cycles *vs.* temperature of epoxy resins crosslinked by siloxane amines were similar to the values obtained with epoxy resins crosslinked with conventional aliphatic and aromatic amines. The presence of polysiloxane groups in these resins does not contribute to retention of low tan δ values at elevated temperatures.

Heat Distortion Temperature. The heat distortion temperature at 264 p.s.i. of epoxy resins cured by aliphatic siloxane amines (Table III) and aromatic siloxane amines (Table IV) were determined. Samples 5 inches × 1/2 inch × 1/2 inch were used.

The heat distortion temperatures of Epon 828 and D.E.R. 332 crosslinked by the same siloxane amine were similar because both epoxy resins had similar epoxide functionality and epoxide equivalent weights. The heat distortion temperatures of D.E.N. 431 samples were slightly higher owing to the higher epoxide functionality of D.E.N. 431 (functionality 2.2). There was a significant increase in the heat distortion temperature of the D.E.N. 438 (functionality 3.6). Higher heat distortion temperatures resulted from epoxy resins cured by Sylkyd 50-*N*-aminoethylethanol-

Table VII. Flexural Strength

	Bisphenol A-diglycidyl	
Epon 828	188[a]	188
Sylkyd 50-*N*-aminoethylethanolamine	87	
Sylkyd 50-*m*-aminophenol		149
Sylkyd 50-*p*-aminophenethyl alc.		
Sylkyd 50-*N*-ethylethanolamine		
Curing agent Z		
15 hrs. @ 160°C.		
Flexural Strength, p.s.i.	18,400	25,500
Flexural modulus, p.s.i.	4.2×10^5	5.6×10^5
28 days @ 135°C. in air		
Flexural Strength, p.s.i.		12,200
Flexural modulus, p.s.i.		5.7×10^5
56 days @ 135°C. in air		
Flexural Strength, p.s.i.	7,200	9,200
Flexural modulus, p.s.i.	5.2×10^5	5.1×10^5
28 days @ 160°C. in air		
Flexural Strength, p.s.i.	11,500	11,300
Flexural modulus, p.s.i.	5.1×10^5	5.4×10^5
56 days @ 160°C. in air		
Flexural Strength, p.s.i.	10,200	9,000
Flexural modulus, p.s.i.	5.5×10^5	5.3×10^5

[a] The quantities of epoxy resins and hardeners, in parts by weight, correspond to 1.0 epoxy equivalent per amine hydrogen equivalent. Where two hardeners are used, the amine hydrogen equivalents contributed by each hardener are given in parentheses.

amine than by Sylkyd 50-ethanolamine because of the higher amine H functionality of the former.

The heat distortion temperature of epoxides crosslinked with Sylkyd 50-*p*-aminophenethyl alcohol were lower than those crosslinked with Sylkyd 50-*m*-aminophenol (*see* Table IV). There was an 11–17 degree increase in heat distortion temperature on using the 3.6 functionality epoxy novolac in place of liquid bisphenol A-diglycidyl ether epoxies. The heat distortion temperatures in Table IV are relatively low compared to the > 150°C. heat distortion temperatures that were obtained with aromatic polyamines (*6*). Low heat distortion temperature is a consequence of modifying amines with polysiloxanes.

Tensile Strength, Tensile Modulus, and Elongation. Tensile strength, tensile modulus, and elongation at break were determined at 25°C. for Epon 828 and epoxy novolacs crosslinked by various siloxane amines. The results are presented in Tables V and VI. The effects of heat aging on these properties were also determined. The tensile samples were aged at 135° and 160°C. in air circulating ovens. Samples were removed for testing after 28 and 56 days.

Castings of Epon 828 crosslinked with siloxane amines had the combination of high tensile strength and high elongation. The tensile strength

and Modulus at 25°C.

ether epoxy resins

188	188	188	188
159			
	49(.2)	98(.4)	123(.5)
	39(.8)	23(.6)	19(.5)
19,800	20,600	14,200	9,900
4.3×10^5	4.3×10^5	5.0×10^5	3.9×10^5
10,800	11,400	11,700	7,800
5.6×10^5	7.7×10^5	6.1×10^5	6.7×10^5
9,500	9,600	12,000	7,100
5.0×10^5	5.3×10^5	5.2×10^5	5.2×10^5
11,100	9,800	14,400	8,800
5.4×10^5	5.4×10^5	4.8×10^5	5.4×10^5
9,600	9,600	9,400	8,000
5.0×10^5	5.3×10^5	5.0×10^5	5.2×10^5

Table VIII. Flexural Strength and Modulus at 25°C.

Epoxy Novolacs

D.E.N. 438	178[a]	178	178	
D.E.N. 431				
Sylkyd 50-ethanolamine	116			176
Sylkyd 50-*N*-aminoethyl-ethanolamine		87		87
Sylkyd 50-*m*-aminophenol			149	
15 hrs. @ 160°C.				
Flexural Strength, p.s.i.	19,300	17,400	14,700	18,500
Flexural modulus, p.s.i.	4.4×10^5	5.0×10^5	4.2×10^5	4.4×10^5
28 days @ 135°C. in air				
Flexural Strength, p.s.i.	13,900	12,000		12,100
Flexural modulus, p.s.i.	6.3×10^5	5.3×10^5		7.1×10^5
56 days @ 135°C. in air				
Flexural Strength, p.s.i.	12,300	10,100		9,500
Flexural modulus, p.s.i.	5.5×10^5	5.4×10^5		5.3×10^5
28 days @ 160°C. in air				
Flexural Strength, p.s.i.	10,900	11,200		10,700
Flexural modulus, p.s.i.	5.6×10^5	5.7×10^5		6.3×10^5
56 days @ 160°C. in air				
Flexural Strength, p.s.i.	9,800	7,500		7,900
Flexural modulus, p.s.i.	5.6×10^5	5.3×10^5		5.6×10^5

[a] The quantities of epoxy resins and hardeners, in parts by weight, correspond to 1.0 epoxy equivalent per amine hydrogen equivalent.

and especially the elongation decreased, while the modulus generally increased during heat aging. The initial tensile strength increased as the curing agent Z content was increased in castings of Epon 828 cured by solutions of Sylkyd 50-*N*-ethylethanolamine and curing agent Z.

Epoxy novolacs crosslinked with siloxane amines also had high initial tensile strengths and elongation (*see* Table VI). These properties were affected during heat aging in air. Decrease of tensile strength and elongation during heat aging is more characteristic of non-aromatic polymers and conventional amine cured epoxy resins than of polysiloxanes.

Flexural Strength and Flexural Modulus. Flexural strength and flexural modulus and the effect of heat aging on these properties were determined (*see* Tables VII and VIII). High flexural strengths were obtained after an overnight cure at 160°C. Flexural strength increased as the curing agent Z content was increased in Epon 828 Sylkyd 50-*N*-ethylethanolamine-curing agent Z castings. The initial flexural strengths were generally higher for D.E.N. 438 than for Epon 828 samples.

Flexural strength decreased and flexural modulus generally increased during heat aging in air at 135° and 160°C. The rate of decrease of flexural strength was rapid in the first four weeks of heat aging, but the rate decreased after this initial rapid drop in flexural strength.

Table IX. Thermal Degradation (% weight change)

Sample	Aging Temp. °C.	% Weight Loss in Air		
		7 days	*28 days*	*56 days*
Epon 828 (188[a]), Sylkyd 50-*N*-aminoethylethanolamine (87)	135	1.05	3.23	4.04
	160	3.27	6.36	7.91
Epon 828 (188), Sylkyd 50-*m*-aminophenol (149)	135	1.12	2.56	2.73
	160	2.55	3.89	4.47
Epon 828 (188), Sylkyd 50-*p*-aminophenethyl alc. (159)	135	1.60	2.85	3.06
	160	2.91	4.07	4.45
Epon 828 (188), Sylkyd 50-*N*-ethylethanolamine (49), Z(30)	135	1.04	1.49	1.52
	160	1.79	3.12	3.85
Epon 828 (188), Sylkyd 50-*N*-ethylethanolamine (98), Z(23)	135	2.02	3.29	3.68
	160	3.40	6.04	7.49
Epon 828 (188), Sylkyd 50-*N*-ethylethanolamine (123), Z(19)	135	2.47	4.38	5.14
	160	4.07	7.39	9.33
D.E.N. 438 (178), Sylkyd 50-ethanolamine (116)	135	1.96	3.91	4.76
	160	4.11	7.63	8.88
D.E.N. 438 (178), Sylkyd 50-*N*-aminoethylethanolamine (87)	135	0.66	0.87	1.09
	160	1.61	3.13	4.47
D.E.N. 431 (176), Sylkyd 50-*N*-aminoethylethanolamine (87)	135	0.83	1.54	1.59
	160	1.83	3.50	5.48

[a] The quantities of epoxy resins and hardeners, in parts by weight, correspond to 1.0 epoxy equivalent per amine hydrogen equivalent. Where two hardeners are used, the sum of the amine hydrogen equivalents contributed by the hardeners is equal to the number of epoxy equivalents.

Table X. Water Resistance

Sample	*Water Temp.*	*Weight Change,[b] %* 28 days	56 days
Epon 828 (188[a]), Sylkyd 50-*N*-aminoethyl-	25°C.	+0.80 (a)	+1.23 (a)
ethanolamine (87)	95	+4.08 (a)	+4.62 (a)
Epon 828 (188), Sylkyd 50-	25	+0.48 (a)	+0.62 (a)
m-aminophenol (149)	95	+2.57 (a)	+2.75 (a)
Epon 828 (188), Sylkyd 50-	25	+0.43 (a)	+0.82 (a)
p-aminophenethyl alc. (159)	95	−0.73 (c)	−0.58 (c)
Epon 828 (188), Sylkyd 50-*N*-ethyl-	25	+0.66 (a)	+0.95 (a)
ethanolamine (49), Z (30)	95	+3.53 (a)	+2.50 (a)
Epon 828 (188), Sylkyd 50-*N*-ethyl-	25	+0.73 (a)	+1.11 (a)
ethanolamine (98), Z (23)	95	+3.92 (b)	+5.75 (b)
Epon 828 (188), Sylkyd 50-*N*-ethyl-	25	+0.60 (a)	+1.07 (a)
ethanolamine (123), Z (19)	95	+0.64 (b)	+3.92 (b)
D.E.N. 438 (178), Sylkyd 50-*N*	25	+0.79 (a)	+1.06 (a)
ethanolamine (116)	95	+1.81 (a)	
D.E.N. 438 (178), Sylkyd 50-*N*-amino-	25	+0.91 (a)	+1.41 (a)
ethanolamine (87)	95	+4.74 (a)	+4.81 (a)
D.E.N. 431 (176), Sylkyd 50-*N*-amino-	25	+0.73 (a)	+1.15 (a)
ethanolamine (87)	95	+4.40 (a)	+4.36 (a)

[a] The quantities of epoxy resins and hardeners (pbw) correspond to 1.0 epoxy equivalent per amine hydrogen equivalent. Where two hardeners are used, the sum of the amine hydrogen equivalents contributed by the hardeners is equal to the number of epoxy equivalent.
[b] + = weight gain, − = weight loss, (a) = transparent, (b) = translucent, (c) = translucent and pitted.

Thermal Degradation. Samples 4 inches (length) × 1 inch (width) × 0.09 inch (thickness) were aged eight weeks at 135°C. and 160° in air circulating ovens. The percent weight loss was determined after one, four, and eight weeks of heat aging (*see* Table IX). It should be noted that the samples were prepared in sealed molds, and any volatiles present either in the epoxy resin or in the siloxane amine hardener could not escape cure.

The Sylkyd 50-*N*-aminoethylethanolamine reaction product was used to crosslink both Epon 828 and D.E.N. 438, but the weight losses were significantly lower for the D.E.N. 438 samples. The weight losses also increased in Epon 828-Sylkyd 59-*N*-ethylethanolamine-curing agent Z resins as the curing agent Z content was decreased.

The overall weight losses were high compared with aliphatic polyamine and polyamide crosslinked epoxy resins—*e.g.*, D.E.R. 332 crosslinked by triethylenetetramine loses 1.42% of its weight after 21 days at 160°C., and D.E.R. 331 crosslinked by the liquid polyamide D.E.H. 14 loses 1.73% of its weight after 21 days at 160°C. (3).

Water Resistance. Samples 2 inches (length) × 1 inch (width) × 0.09 inch (thickness) were immersed in water at 25° and 95°C., and weight changes after four and eight weeks were determined. The results are presented in Table X.

The samples aged in water at 25°C. retained their original transparency. Most of the samples aged in water at 95°C. also retained their original appearance, but two of the samples turned translucent and one sample was pitted. Surface deterioration of the pitted sample resulted in overall weight loss.

The weight changes in water at 25°C. compared favorably with epoxy resins cured by conventional hardeners. For example, the following weight changes were recorded after 28 days in water at 25°C. for D.E.R. 331 cured by various hardeners; triethylenetetramine, +0.80; methylenedianiline, +1.06; Nadic methyl anhydride, +0.80, BF_3-MEA, +1.04; liquid polyamide D.E.H. 14, +1.10 (*3*).

Conclusions

Amine functional siloxanes were synthesized from alkoxy functional siloxanes and hydroxy functional amines. These reaction products were readily soluble in liquid bisphenol A-diglycidyl ether epoxy resins and epoxy novolacs. The crosslinked resins ranged from transparent pale yellow to transparent amber hard tough solids.

The cured resins had high tensile and flexural strengths. The heat distortion temperatures were relatively low because of the presence of the flexibilizing polysiloxane chains. Tan δ at 60-cycle values were low at 25°C., and there was better retention of low tan δ values at elevated temperatures with the aromatic amine functional siloxanes than with the aliphatic amine functional siloxanes. Most of the resins immersed in water at 25° or 95° remained transparent after 56 days immersion.

Epoxy-siloxane amine resins do not generate any volatiles during cure and can be used in casting, adhesive, potting, laminating, filament winding, and pre-preg applications. Epoxy-siloxane amine compositions should be useful in coatings where the good weathering performance of siloxanes is desirable (*1*). These coatings can also be formulated as solventless systems where heavier coatings are required and volatile solvents cannot be tolerated.

Acknowledgments

We gratefully acknowledge the assistance of R. Borkowski, C. J. Reinhardt, and G. P. Wadsworth for their contributions to the electrical and physical testing, and the General Electric Research and Development Center for their interest and partial support of this work.

Literature Cited

(1) Chatfield, H. W., "The Science of Surface Coatings," D. Van Nostrand Company, Inc., New York, 1962.
(2) DiGiorgio, P. A., Sommer, L. H., Whitmore, F. C., *J. Am. Chem. Soc.* **71,** 3254 (1949).
(3) Dow Chemical Company, "Dow Liquid Epoxy Resins," Bulletin No. 170-141A.
(4) Klein, G., Neinburg, H., *German Patent* **637,532** (1936).
(5) Koehler, J. O., Lamprey, H., ADVAN. CHEM. SER. **23,** 217 (1959).
(6) Lee, H., Neville, K., "Handbook of Epoxy Resins," McGraw-Hill, New York, 1967.

RECEIVED May 31, 1968.

8

High Performance Cycloaliphatic Epoxy Resins for Reinforced Structures with Improved Dynamic Flexural Properties

A. C. SOLDATOS, A. S. BURHANS, L. F. COLE, and W. P. MULVANEY

Union Carbide Corp., Bound Brook, N. J. 08805

The combination of tensile strength and modulus of the matrix epoxy resin relate to the edgewise compressive and flexural strengths of the composites, while the combination of tensile strength, modulus, and elongation are reflected in dynamic flexural fatigue. Epoxy resins with improved toughness have produced laminates with significantly improved fatigue properties under dynamic stressing beyond the levels obtainable with high modulus/low elongation epoxies, by reducing crack initiation and crack propagation. These improvements were obtained by curing the high performance bis(2,3-epoxycyclopentyl) ether/ethylene glycol copolymer with amine hardeners varying in molecular distance between the functional amine groups.

In recent years, there has been considerable progress in the development of higher strength reinforcements for use in structural composites. With the realization that the maximum potential of these higher strength glass, boron, and graphite filaments could be obtained only with high performance matrix materials, Union Carbide undertook a long range fundamental program under military funded contracts to upgrade the performance of epoxy resins.

The major objectives of this investigation were:

1. The development of new types of epoxy resins with cast properties substantially higher than those of the state-of-the-art materials.

2. The development of resin-hardener systems which could be used for the fabrication of practical reinforced structures and which would retain their properties under dynamic stressing, both in air and water. This phase of the program is supported by the U. S. Naval Research Laboratories.

From this work the cycloaliphatic epoxide ERLA-4617 has emerged as the leading candidate, and has, to a large extent, met the above objectives.

ERLA-4617, is the copolymer of bis(2,3-epoxycyclopentyl) ether and ethylene glycol, catalyzed with a tertiary amine.

The bis(2,3-epoxyclopentyl) ether, designated ERR-4205, shown in Figure 1 consists of a mixture of liquid and solid isomers, in a ratio of approximately 35/65.

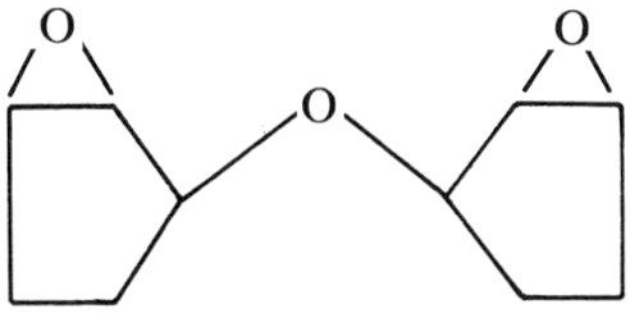

Figure 1. Bis(2,3-epoxycyclopentyl) ether ERR-4205; 65% Solids—35% liquid isomers

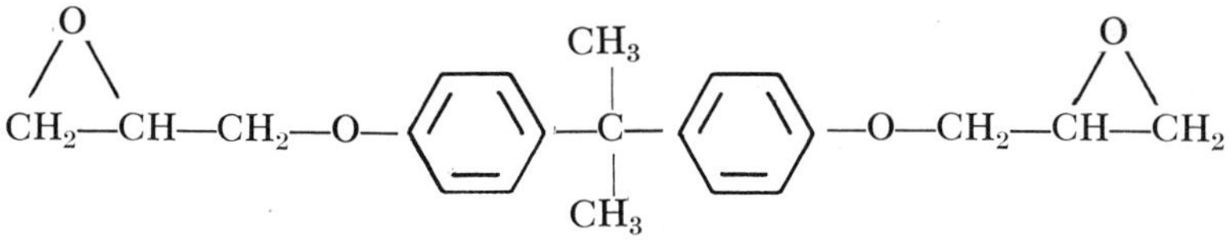

Figure 2. ERL-2772

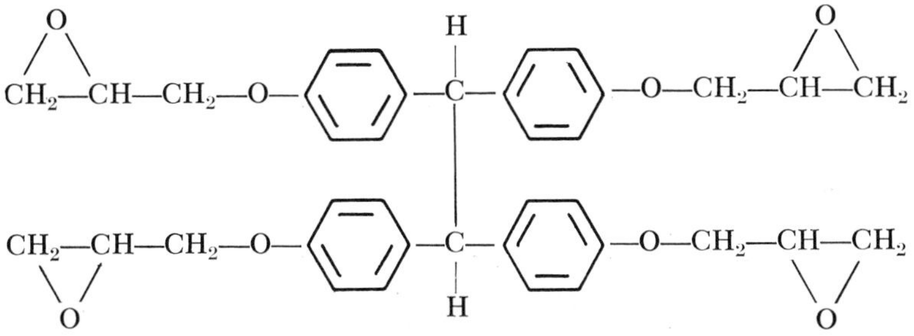

EPON 1031

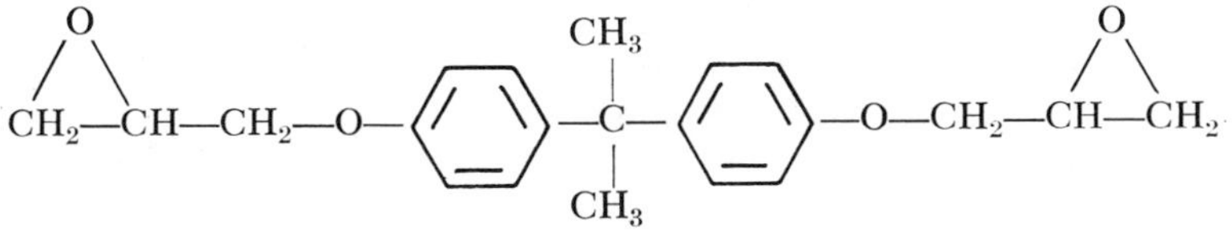

EPON 828

Figure 3. Epon 828/Epon 1031

ERLA-4617 is a very low viscosity material (80-100 centipoises at 25°C.) with an epoxy assay of 113-120 grams/equivalent of epoxide. The chemistry of this resin, including a postulated reaction mechanism, was discussed in detail in a previous paper (*1*).

The two state-of-the-art epoxy resins used for comparison purposes in this paper are ERL-2772 and Epon 828/1031; their structures are shown in Figures 2 and 3 respectively.

The typical cast resin properties of ERLA-4617 cured with stoichiometric amount of *m*-phenylenediamine are compared with the properties of ERL-2772 and Epon 828/1031 cured with stoichiometric amounts of *m*-PDA and MNA/BDMA respectively, as shown in Table I. These data demonstrate the substantially higher cast tensile, flexural, and compressive properties of ERLA-4617 compared with those of the state-of-the-art materials.

Table I. Cast Resin Properties

	ERLA-2772 m-*PDA*[e]	*Epon 828/1031* *MNA*[f]/*BDMA*	*ERLA-4617* m-*PDA*
Compressive Modulus, p.s.i.[a]	441,000	551,000	890,000
Compressive Strength, p.s.i.	19,200	21,600	32,800
Tensile Modulus, p.s.i.[b]	458,000	507,000	783,000
Tensile Strength, p.s.i.	12,900	9,100	19,200
Flexural Modulus, p.s.i.[c]	462,000	597,000	815,000
Flexural Strength, p.s.i.	17,500	16,400	31,000
Heat Distortion Temp., °C.[d]	158	143	175

Cure Cycle: 4 hours at 85°C., + 3 hours at 120°C., + 16 hours at 160°C.

[a] ASTM D695-63T.
[b] ASTM D638-64T.
[c] ASTM D790-66.
[d] ASTM D648-56.
[e] *m*-Phenylenediamine.
[f] Methyl nadic anhydride.

The work with glass cloth laminates produced from the ERLA-4617/*m*-phenylenediamine system, using "wet-lay-up" or "prepreg" techniques, demonstrates that the high cast resin properties are indeed translated into high performance composites. The properties shown in Table II are from laminates assembled by "wet-lay-up," and those shown in Table III are from prepregs uncatalyzed and catalyzed with $BF_3 \cdot$ MEA. The fabrication and properties of these ERLA-4617 glass cloth composites were discussed in a previous presentation.

Retention of Properties Under Dynamic Fatigue Conditions. An important prerequisite to practical design of advanced composite structures, in addition to the need for initially high mechanical properties, is retention of these properties under dynamic fatigue stressing. Therefore, a major objective of the present investigation was the development of matrix resin systems which would provide high retention of composite properties under simulated use conditions.

Table II. Properties of "Wet-Lay-Up" Laminates, 181-S-994-HTS Cloth

	ERLA-2772 m-*PDA*	*ERLA-4617* m-*PDA*
Edgewise Compressive Strength, p.s.i.	65,000	85,000
Modulus, p.s.i.	3,950,000	4,380,000
Flexural Strength @ 75°F., p.s.i.	—	140,900
Modulus @ 75°F., p.s.i.	—	4,360,000

Cure Cycle: 16 hours at 85°C. and + 16 hours at 160°C.

Table III. ERLA-4617/*m*-PDA Laminate Properties with and without Catalyst

	ERLA-4617/m-*PDA*[a]	*ERLA-4617*/m-*PDA*[b] *1.5%* BF_3MEA[c]
Edgewise Compressive Strength, p.s.i.	88,400	87,200
Flexural Strength, p.s.i.	149,000	124,000
Cure Cycle	16 hours at 85°C. + 16 hours at 160°C. 32 hours total	1 hour at 110°C. + 2 hours at 120°C. + 2 hours at 160°C. 5 hours total

[a] Prepreg uncatalyzed.
[b] Prepreg catalyzed with BF_3MEA.
[c] Based on the epoxy resin.

Under dynamic stressing, in contrast to static loadings, stationary cracks in the composites can propagate rapidly, and the toughness of the matrix system should be a measure of its ability to resist extension of the crack. The edgewise compressive and flexural strengths of composites under static loadings increase with increasing cast resin tensile strength. Glass cloth laminates based on the ERLA-4617/*m*-phenylenediamine system exhibit edgewise compressive strengths at the level of 85–88,000 p.s.i., compared with state-of-the-art bis A-diglycidyl ether at 65,000 p.s.i. as shown in Tables II and III. The elongation of the ERLA-4617/*m*-PDA system is approximately 2.5%. Improvements in elongation, therefore, while retaining high tensile strength and modulus (greater toughness), was thought to be the most promising route to providing composites with very high retention under dynamic fatigue in both air and water.

Effect of Amine Hardeners. Throughout the earlier work, *m*-phenylenediamine (*m*-PDA) was used as the hardener for ERLA-4617. Recently, this investigation was extended to include other diamine hardeners varying in molecular distance between the active amine groups in an attempt to improve further the cast resin and composite properties.

The amines tested were *m*-aminobenzylamine (*m*-ABA), methylenedianiline (MDA), and a long chain aliphatic diamine designated ZZL-0822 (Union Carbide proprietary hardener).

Their chemical configurations and the molecular distance between the active sites, expressed in angstroms, are shown in Figure 4.

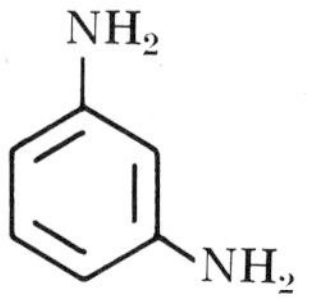

NH_2 / NH_2

Meta-phenylenediamine

Distance between active nitrogen sites–5.2 A.

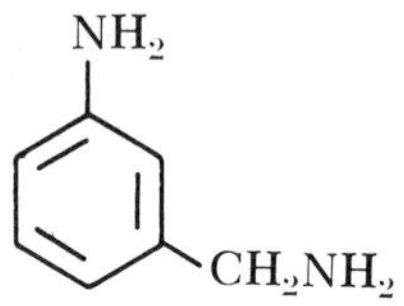

NH_2 / CH_2NH_2

Meta-aminobenzylamine

Distance between active nitrogen sites–7 A.

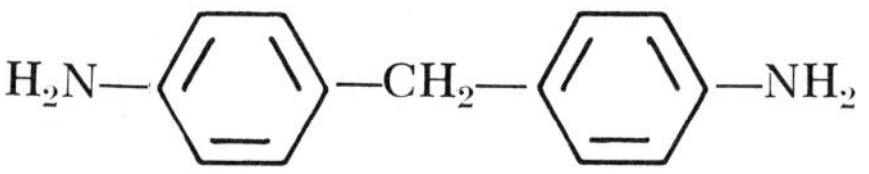

H_2N—⟨benzene⟩—CH_2—⟨benzene⟩—NH_2

Methylenedianiline

Distance between active nitrogen sites–10.6 A.

Long chain aliphatic diamine (ZZL-0822)

Distance between active nitrogen sites, 15-25 A.

Figure 4. Amine hardeners

Cast Resin Properties

The cast properties of ERLA-4617 cured with the various amine hardeners are shown in Table IV. These data clearly indicate that most resin properties are a function of the molecular distances between the active sites of the hardener.

(1) In tension, the modulus decreases as the distance between the amine groups increases. The highest modulus (820,000 p.s.i.) was obtained with the *m*-phenylenediamine (5.2A.) and the lowest (550,000 p.s.i.) was obtained with the long chain diamine, ZZL-0822. The

elongation, however, as might be expected, followed exactly the reverse pattern. ZZL-0822 produced the highest elongation (greater than 12.5%) and *m*-phenylenediamine, the lowest (2.8%). The properties obtained with the other two hardeners, *m*-aminobenzylamine and methylenedianiline, were intermediate to those of *m*-phenylenediamine and ZZL-0822. The strengths showed virtually no trend with the exception of ZZL-0822 which had a strength of only 14,000 p.s.i. The strength values obtained with other hardeners are considered to be equivalent, for all practical purposes since tensile values normally fluctuate fairly widely, owing to failures initiated by undetected flaws. For example, values for the ERLA-4617/*m*-PDA system range from 17,500 to 19,200 p.s.i.

(2) In flexure, high modulus was again obtained with *m*-PDA, (860,000 p.s.i.); the lowest modulus and strength were obtained with the ZZL-0822 hardener.

(3) The compressive modulus also followed the same pattern. The highest value (890,000 p.s.i.) was obtained with *m*-PDA and the lowest 600,000 p.s.i.) with ZZL-0822.

(4) The heat distortion temperature data suggest that the aliphatic nature of ZZL-0822 and the hybrid nature of the *m*-aminobenzylamine (one aromatic and one aliphatic amine groups) influence the heat distortion temperature more than molecular spacing.

Since modulus and strength, and particularly the heat distortion temperature of the aliphatic diamine ZZL-0822, were significantly lower than those obtained with the other three hardeners, a blend of ZZL-0822 with *m*-PDA was used to upgrade properties. The cast properties of ERLA-4617 cured with a 70/30 blend of *m*-PDA/ZZL-0822 (based on amine equivalent rather than the actual amine weight) are shown in Table IV. As was expected, all of the properties are between those obtained with either *m*-PDA or ZZL-0822 alone.

Glass Reinforced Composites. We have already shown that glass cloth laminates with exceptional properties (Tables II and III) have been produced from the ERLA-4617/*m*-phenylenediamine system using both "wet-lay-up" or "prepreg" techniques.

Four additional "wet-lay-up" laminates were fabricated based on ERLA-4617/*m*-phenylenediamine, ERLA-4617/*m*-aminobenzylamine, ERLA-4617/methylenedianiline, and ERLA14617/*m*-phenylenediamine-ZZL-0822 (70–30 blend). S-994-HTS glass cloth was used. These laminates were prepared in order to establish whether there is a relationship between the toughness of the resin and retention of mechanical properties under dynamic loadings.

Dynamic Flexural Fatigue. The screening test chosen for this study was dynamic flexural fatigue of the composites in both air and water, run on a Baldwin Sonnatag SF-I-OU, 1800 c.p.m. constant stress fatigue machine under standard conditions at room temperature.

To date, only flexural fatigue data in air have been developed.

Table IV. ERLA-4617 Cast Properties

	m-*Phenylene-diamine*	m-*Amino-benzylamine*
Heat Distortion, Temp., °C.	170	152
Tensile Modulus, p.s.i.	820,000	700,000
Tensile Strength, p.s.i.	18,500	17,900
% Elongation	2.8	3.2
Flexural Modulus, p.s.i.	860,000	780,000
Flexural Strength, p.s.i.	31,500	29,500
Compressive Modulus, p.s.i.	890,000	850,000
Compressive Strength, p.s.i.	31,500	30,000
% Deformation	7.5	7.0

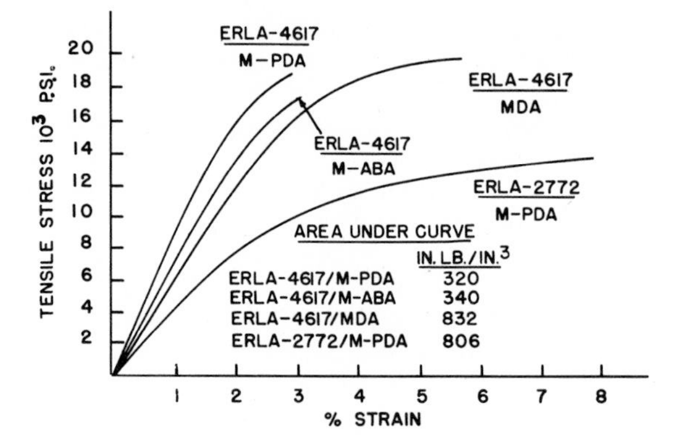

Figure 5. Cast resin tensile stress-strain curve

Effect of Toughness on Dynamic Flexural Fatigue. The most recently developed data have shown indeed that improvements in elongation, while retaining high tensile strength, improve retention of properties under dynamic fatique.

A resin system with high elongation and high tensile strength should have greater toughness as measured by the energy to break (area under the stress-strain curve).

The tensile stress-strain curves for the cast resin systems ERLA-4617/*m*-phenylenediamine, ERLA-4617/*m*-aminobenzylamine, ERLA-4617/methylenedianiline and ERLA-2772/*m*-phenylenediamine are shown in Figure 5. The area under the curve of the ERLA-4617/methylenedianiline system is considerably higher (832 in. lb./in.^{3}) than that of the ERLA-4617/*m*-phenylenediamine (320 in. lb./in.^{3}) which was accomplished by increasing the elongation from 2.8 to 6.0% while retaining high tensile strength. The tougher ERLA-4617/methylenedianiline system, in turn, produced glass cloth composites with flexural fatigue properties superior to the ERLA-4617/*m*-phenylenediamine system, as shown

Cured with Various Amine Hardeners

Methylene-dianiline	*ZZL-0822*	m-*Phenylenediamine/ ZZL-8022 (70/30)*
162	80	128
610,000	550,000	660,000
18,800	14,000	17,000
6.0	>12.5	4.0
690,000	580,000	730,000
30,000	17,500	29,500
750,000	600,000	840,000
27,000	17,000	27,000
8.0	—	6.0

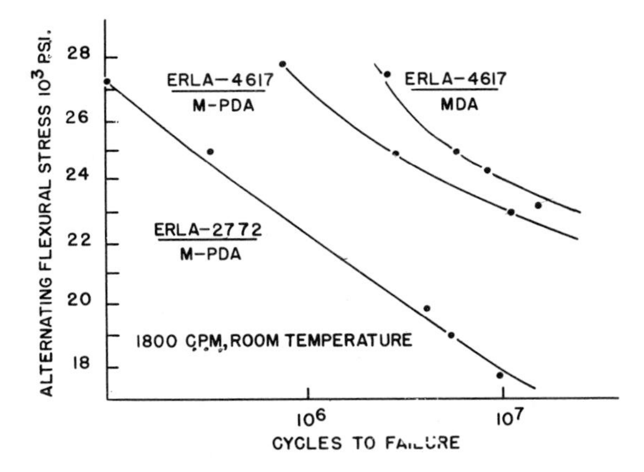

Figure 6. Fatigue results on ERLA-4617 and ERLA-2772 in air

in Figure 6. While the area under the ERLA-2772/*m*-phenylenediamine curve is quite large (800 in. lb./in.^{3}) the performance of this system in laminates, both under static and dynamic conditions, is significantly inferior to either ERLA-4617/*m*-phenylenediamine or ERLA-4617/methylenedianiline systems. Although the tensile strength of this resin is low, the area under the curve is large owing to the high (8%) elongation. Therefore, high elongation, *per se*, is not the answer to increasing laminate performance; the resin must also have high tensile strength and high tensile modulus.

Water Resistance

Fatigue data of composites in water have not been obtained as yet, but substantial indications on the water resistance of the resin/hardener system itself have been obtained by using a simple screening test.

Test for Water Resistance. Cast resin cylinders (0.5 inch in diameter and approximately 1 inch long) were boiled for 24 hours in water. Each specimen was weighed before and after boiling. The weight per cent increase was calculated as follows:

$$\text{Weight \% Increase} = \frac{\text{Weight after boil—Original Weight}}{\text{Original Weight}} \times 100$$

Finally, each specimen was allowed to stand in air and examined periodically for signs of cracking or crazing. The results of the boiling water test of ERLA-4617 cured with *m*-phenylenediamine, *m*-aminobenzylamine, methylenedianiline and 70/30 *m*-phenylenediamine/ZZL-0822 blend are shown in Table V.

Table V. Cast Resin Cylinders of ERLA-4617 Cured with Various Amine Hardeners, after 24 Hours in Boiling Water

Amine Hardener 100% Stoichiometry	*Cure Cycle*	*Weight %, Increase*	*Remarks On Drying in Air*
m-PDA/ZZL-0822 (70/30)	24 hrs. @ 100°C. + 16 hrs. @ 160°C.	4.8	One crack after one week.
m-Aminobenzylamine	4 hrs. @ 85°C. + 3 hrs. @ 120°C. + 16 hrs. @ 160°C.	3.0	No cracks.
m-Phenylenediamine	4 hrs. @ 85°C. + 3 hrs. @ 120°C. + 16 hrs. @ 160°C.	3.0	No cracks.
Methylenedianiline	4 hrs. @ 85°C. + 3 hrs. @ 120°C. + 16 hrs. @ 160°C.	1.9	No cracks.

The results indicate that water resistance may be related to the type of hardener used. By this test, ERLA-4617/*m*-ABA and ERLA-4617/*m*-PDA absorbed 3.0% water; ERLA-4617/MDA absorbed only 1.9%, and none of the specimens developed any cracks.

The ERLA-4617/MDA system appears to be the least sensitive of all in water and is expected to provide composites with high retention of properties under dynamic stressing in water.

In summary, it appears that the combination of tensile strength and modulus of the matrix resin relate to the edgewise compressive and flexural strengths of composites, while the combination of tensile strength, modulus and elongation are reflected in dynamic flexural fatigue in air. The improvement in boiling water resistance of the ERLA-4617/MDA cast resin system will hopefully be translated into high retention of composite properties under dynamic fatigue stress in water.

Acknowledgment

The authors wish to express their appreciation to U. S. Naval Research Laboratories, Washington, D. C. for sponsoring the above investigation.

The authors also acknowledge the contributions of C. M. Eichert, R. F. Sellers, and S. G. Smith, Jr., who have been associated with this project.

Literature Cited

(1) Soldatos, A. C., Burhans, A. S., *Ind. Eng. Chem. Prod. Res. Develop.* **5**, 225 (1967).

RECEIVED May 24, 1968.

9

Dynamic Mechanical Properties of Epoxies' β-Transition Mechanism

EDWARD CUDDIHY and JOVAN MOACANIN

Jet Propulsion Laboratory, Oak Grove Drive, Pasadena, Calif. 91103

A study was made of the β-transition in bisphenol-A based epoxy resins prepared with five different curatives. A consistent interpretation of the transition mechanism could be made in terms of the mobility of the diether linkage of bisphenol-A, a grouping common to all the studied resins. This interpretation could be extended to include polycarbonates. For the epoxy resins, a quantitative correlation was observed between the concentration of DGEBA and the magnitude at maximum of the β-transition loss tangent peak. For resins prepared with anhydride curatives, additional mobile groups are introduced into the backbone structure resulting in an additional contribution to the maximum in the loss tangent peak.

In investigating the dynamic mechanical properties of epoxy resins, previous investigators (*8, 10, 13, 15, 19, 22*) have consistently observed the presence of a β-transition between −60° and −100°C. Accepting that this transition arises from mobility of segmental groups in the polymer, these investigators designated certain groups as being responsible for the β-transition. These designations, however, fail to give a unified interpretation of the transition mechanism.

In this study we investigated the effect on the β-transition of diglycidyl ether of bisphenol-A (DGEBA) based epoxy resins whose structures were varied systematically by employing five different curatives. Examination of molecular models of each of the epoxies were used to aid in identifying mobile segments. These results along with loss tangent data allowed us to arrive at a consistent interpretation of the β-transition mechanism.

Experimental

DGEBA (Epon 828) purified by molecular distillation was used to prepare the five resins with one of the following curatives: aliphatic

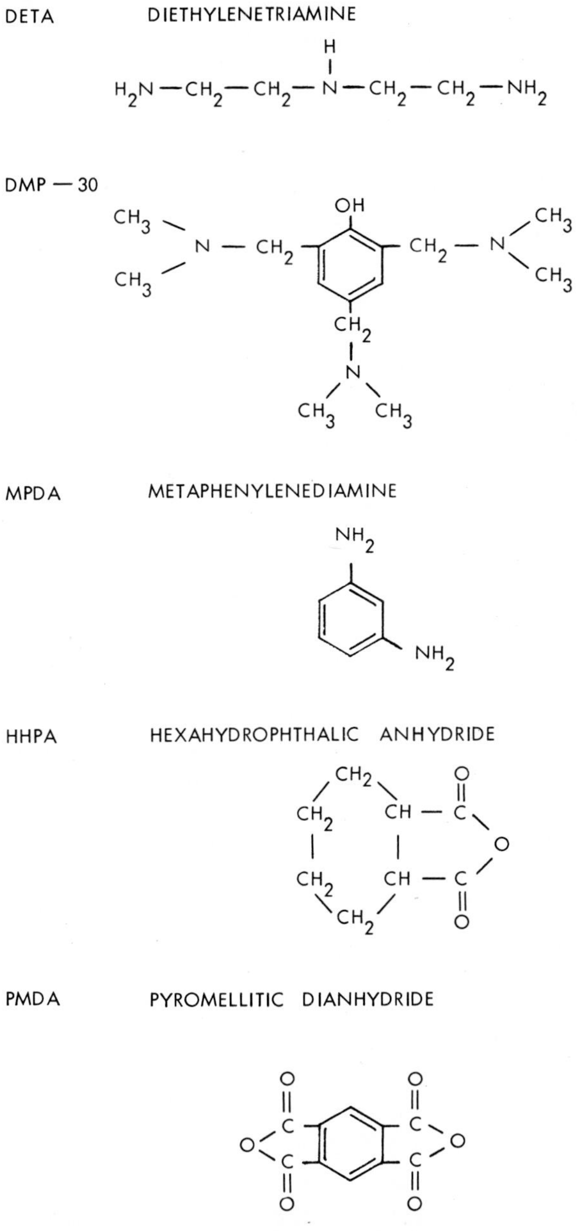

DETA DIETHYLENETRIAMINE

$$H_2N-CH_2-CH_2-\underset{|}{\overset{H}{N}}-CH_2-CH_2-NH_2$$

DMP — 30

MPDA METAPHENYLENEDIAMINE

HHPA HEXAHYDROPHTHALIC ANHYDRIDE

PMDA PYROMELLITIC DIANHYDRIDE

Figure 1. Chemical structures of epoxy curatives

polyamine (DETA), tertiary amine (DMP-30), aromatic diamine (MPDA), alicyclic anhydride (HHPA), and an aromatic dianhydride (PMDA). The chemical structure of each curative is shown in Figure 1, while the compositions and cure conditions for each of the resins are given in Table I.

A free oscillating torsion pendulum (*11*) (about 1 Hz.) was employed to measure the dynamic mechanical properties between −196° and 200°C.

Table I. Compositions and Cure Conditions for the Epoxy Resin[a]

Curative Type	*Composition,*[b] *p.h.r.*	*Cure Conditions*
DETA	10	Gelled at 25°C., postcured 4 hrs. at 150°F.
DMP-30	2	4 hrs. at 250°F.
MPDA	18	4 hrs. at 250°F.
HHPA	74	4 hrs. at 250°F.
PMDA	40	4 hrs. at 250°F.

[a] Prepared employing a DGEBA purified by distillation.
[b] Parts of curative based on one-hundred parts of DGEBA.

Results

The dynamic mechanical properties for the five epoxy resins are shown in Figure 2 respectively, as plots of the loss tangent, the shear modulus, G', and the creep compliance, J'. All five resins exhibited above room temperature a major transition α corresponding to the glass transition and a low temperature transition β. These are seen as peaks in the loss tangent curves and as inflections in G' and J'. Table II summarizes T_g, and the temperature and value at the maximum for the β-transition. The table includes literature Izod impact values which are seen to correlate with the magnitude of the β-transition. Figure 3 gives a plot taken from the literature (*17*) of the loss tangent for four polycarbonates all based on bisphenol-A. These materials which are chemically similar to the epoxy resins also exhibit a similar low temperature β-transition.

Discussion

β-Transitions for DETA cured epoxies were found by Kaelble (*8*) who reported a maximum tan δ value of 0.055 in close agreement with our value of 0.062 (Table II). β-Transitions for MPDA were reported by May and Weir (*15*) and Kline (*10*) but were not observed by Kaelble

(*8*). A β-transition was found for the HHPA resin by Shito and Sato (*19*) but not by May and Weir (*15*). No literature reports on DMP-30 or PMDA could be found.

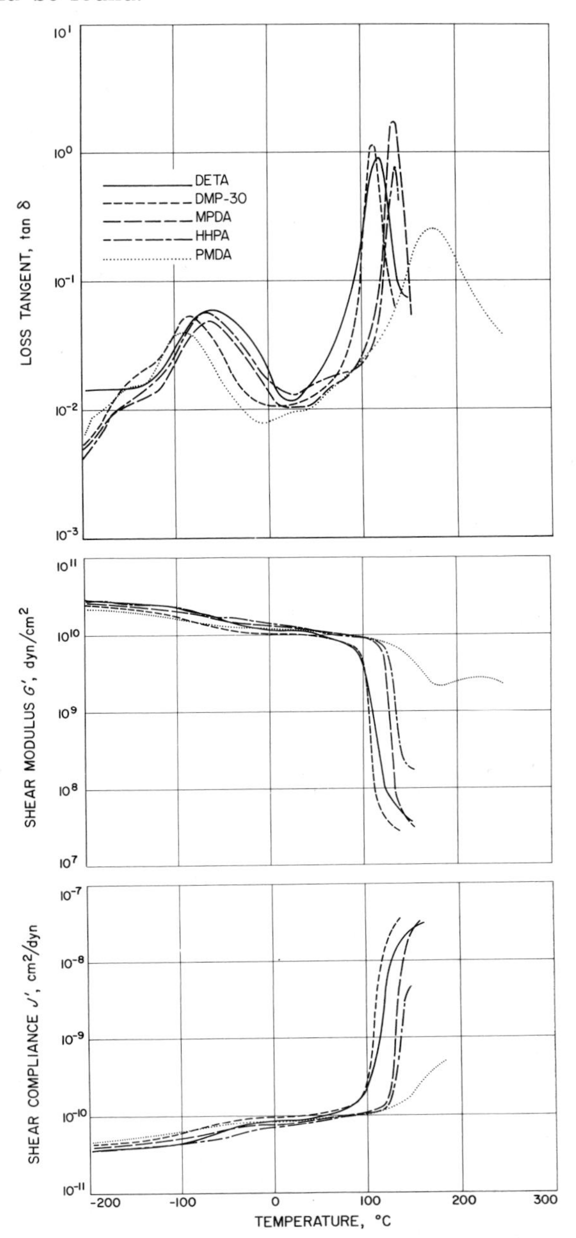

Figure 2. Dynamic mechanical properties as a function of epoxy curatives

Table II. **Properties of the Cured Epoxy Resins**

Curative	T_g,[a] °C.	*β-Transition* T_{max}, °C.	*β-Transition* $(tan\ \delta)_{max}$	*IZOD*[b] *Impact, ft. lb./in.*
DETA	112	−68	0.0626	0.3-0.4
DMP-30	108	−85	0.0525	?
MPDA	130	−64	0.0489	0.207
HHPA	134	−65	0.0563	0.3
PMDA	148	−95	0.0415	0.1

[a] Taken as the temperature corresponding to a modulus value of 3×10^9 dynes/cm.^{2} (Ref. 21).
[b] Reference 14.

Shito and Sato ascribed the β-transition to a chair-boat rearrangement of the cyclohexane ring of HHPA. For MPDA, May and Weir considered the rotation of the following structure enclosed in brackets

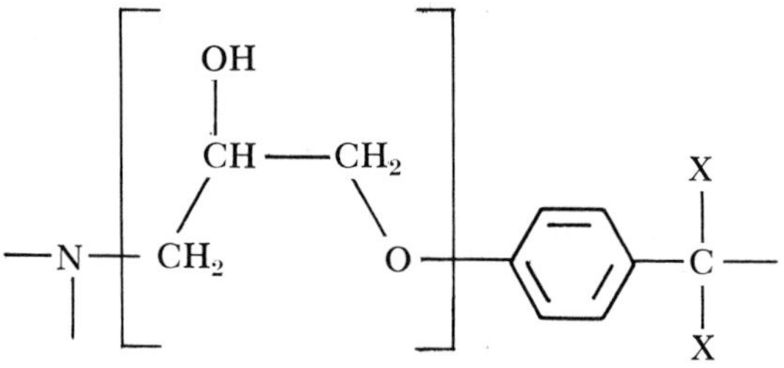

$$-\underset{|}{N}-\left[CH_2-\underset{\underset{OH}{|}}{CH}-CH_2-O\right]-C_6H_4-\underset{X}{\overset{X}{\underset{|}{\overset{|}{C}}}}-$$

but could not explain the β-transition for a phthalic anhydride cured epoxy since it does not contain a similar structure. A recent paper by Van Hoorn (22) employing other curatives with DGEBA reported β-transitions for the 19 systems he studied and also ascribed the transition to mobility of the above group. In this study a β-transition was observed for all the systems and their structures as introduced into the epoxy-backbone by the curatives are given in Figure 4. For comparison, Figure 5 shows the structures of the four polycarbonates whose loss tangent curves are given in Figure 3.

Structure A of the epoxides (Figure 4) is typical for cures with primary and secondary amines such as DETA and MPDA and is the same as the structure given above. Structure B deriving from tertiary amine cures such as DMP-30 bears no similiarity to Structure A, yet the DMP-30 cure exhibits a strong β-transition. Further, the chain segments

$$-CH_2-O-$$

between tie points in the structure are too short to provide the requisite mobility as at least three or four contiguous methylene groups are required to result in an observable transition (*23*).

Structures C and D are from cures with difunctional anhydride HHPA and tetrafunctional anhydride PMDA, respectively. The rigid structure imparted to the epoxy backbone by PMDA is reportedly (*14*) responsible for the high glass-transition temperature (*see* Table II), but despite the rigidity of the curative introduced-structure, a pronounced β-transition is observed.

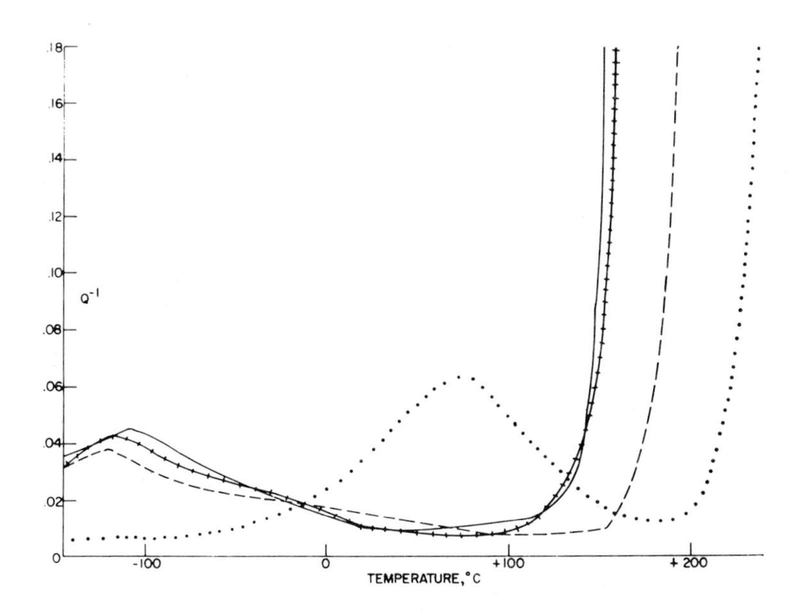

Figure 3. Loss tangent for various polycarbonates (Reference 9)

Poly(bisphenol A carbonate) ———
Poly(bisorthocresol A carbonate) –|—|—|–
Poly(bisphenol of acetophenone carbonate) — —
Poly(orthotetrachlorobisphenol A carbonate) . . . .

Examination of Hirschfelder models of Structures A, B, and D revealed no possibility for rotational or significant mobility of groupings introduced by the curative. (It should be emphasized again that the grouping in A between the nitrogen and the phenyl ring has been previously considered as being responsible for the β-transition.) However, examination of the models did reveal the existence of four freely rotating backbone segments. These are shown in Figure 6 as: (A) the dimethylene ether linkage of bisphenol-A, (B) *p*-dioxane ring, (C) central section of DETA, and (D) the diether bridges from anhydride cures which is also Structure C in Figure 4.

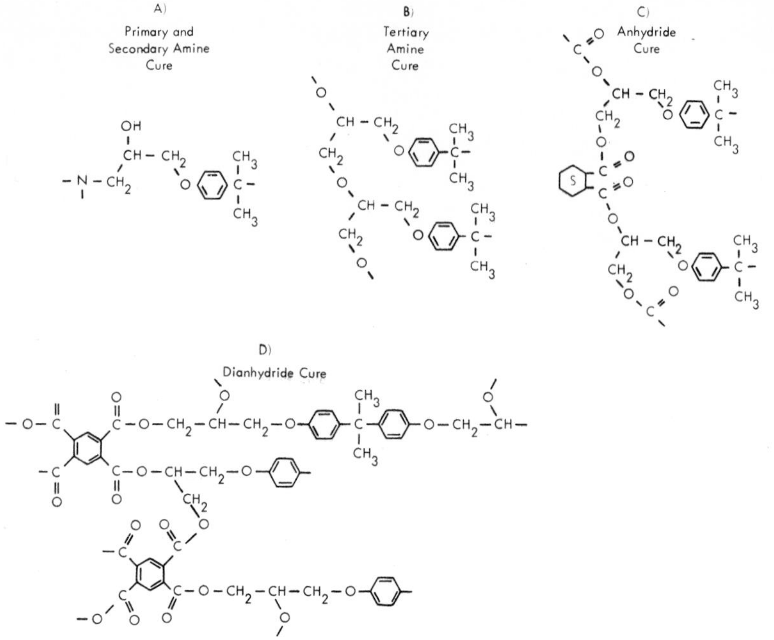

A) Primary and Secondary Amine Cure

B) Tertiary Amine Cure

C) Anhydride Cure

D) Dianhydride Cure

Figure 4. *Curative-introduced structures in the epoxy resins*

These considerations could be extended to polycarbonates based on bisphenol-A (Figure 5) where previous investigations have assigned for the β-transition the following carbonyl grouping.

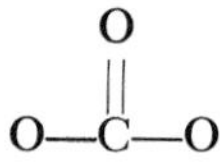

$$\mathrm{O{-}\overset{\overset{\displaystyle O}{\|}}{C}{-}O}$$

Again, examination of the models showed that motion of the group is highly restricted but that the ether linkage of bisphenol A can rotate. Thus, despite the great disparity in curative-introduced structural groupings in epoxies along with the carbonyl grouping in the polycarbonates, all systems exhibiting a β-transition have in common bisphenol A.

Stretch Induced Mobility. In order to have free mobility of the diether linkage of bisphenol A, it was found *via* molecular models that the backbone chain containing the segment must be in a stretched or extended configuration. Any moderate coiling or bending of the chain provided sufficient steric interference to prevent movement. Evidence that backbones of epoxy resins are indeed in a stretched conformation was given by Katz and Tobolsky (*9*). Improvements in strength of polycarbonates owing to stretching have been discussed (*3, 6, 12, 16, 18, 20*). Specifically, Golden *et al.* (*3*) concluded that stretching freed for rotation additional chain segments in the amorphous region. They also observed improvements in strength of polycarbonates owing to heat treatment—*i.e.*, annealing—presumably by freeing for rotation chain segments in amorphous regions. Since annealing produced no change in crystallinity, they argued for an ordering of the amorphous phase which would allow chain extension and thus permit additional segmental rotation. Extending chains of polycarbonates based on bisphenol A should allow the diether linkage, as in the epoxy resins, to rotate freely. This effect may be quite general since evidence for "stretched-induced-transition" was recently observed for poly(ethylene terephthalate) (*1*) at cryogenic temperatures.

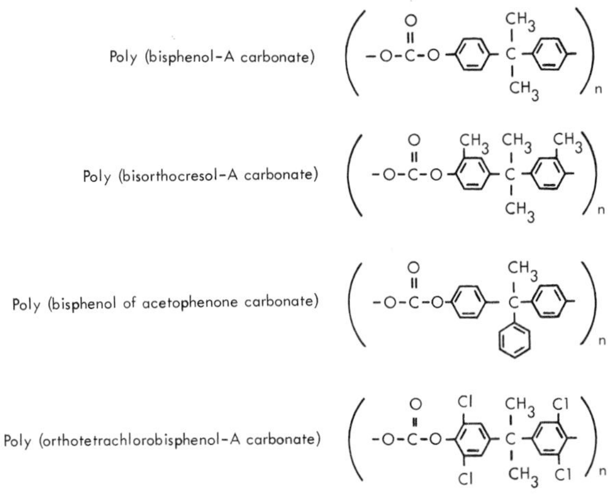

Poly (bisphenol-A carbonate)

Poly (bisorthocresol-A carbonate)

Poly (bisphenol of acetophenone carbonate)

Poly (orthotetrachlorobisphenol-A carbonate)

Figure 5. Structures of the polycarbonates of Figure 3

Correlation of β-Transition Intensity with Rotational Modes. In Table II is demonstrated the excellent correlation between the magnitude of the β-transition and Izod impact for the five resins. Heijboer (*4, 5*) has presented evidence that impact strength will be improved if the low temperature transition arises from motions in the backbone chain rather than from motions of side groups. In view of Heijboer's observations, the β-transition for the epoxy resins must arise from backbone rotations, the magnitude being determined by the presence and concentration in the epoxy backbone of the four rotational modes given in Figure 6.

Rotational modes A, C, and D are associated with segments which are known to occur in the backbone of cured epoxy resins, while *p*-dioxane rings (rotational mode B) can be introduced into the backbone by epoxy-epoxy reactions catalyzed by tertiary amines. Although the presence of *p*-dioxane rings in cured epoxy resins has not been demonstrated, their formation from epoxy groups is known (*6*), and this reaction step is shown in Part B of Figure 6. Thus, only resins cured with tertiary amines or where tertiary amines are generated during cure would be expected to have the *p*-dioxane ring.

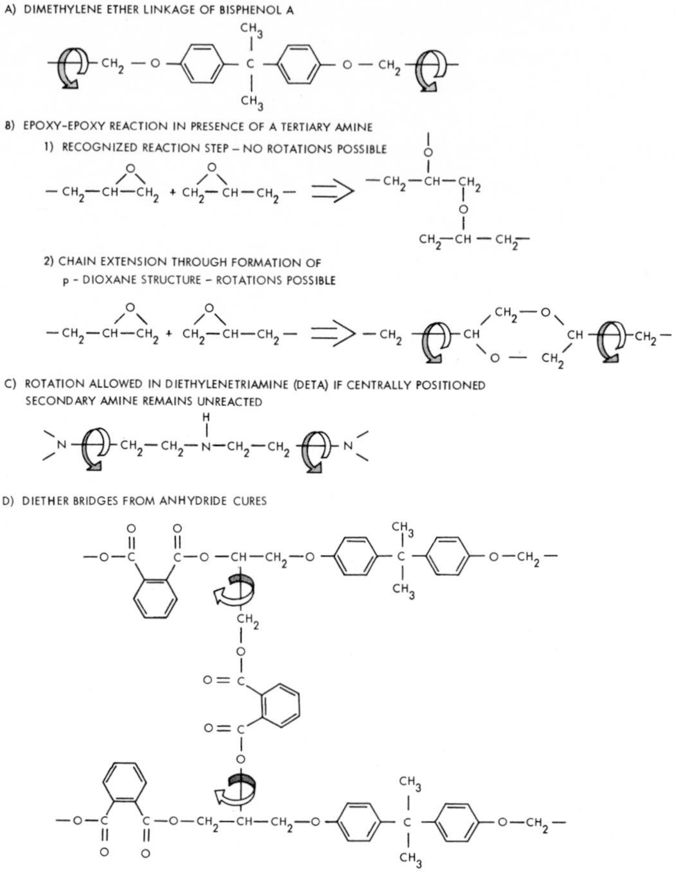

A) DIMETHYLENE ETHER LINKAGE OF BISPHENOL A

B) EPOXY-EPOXY REACTION IN PRESENCE OF A TERTIARY AMINE

1) RECOGNIZED REACTION STEP – NO ROTATIONS POSSIBLE

2) CHAIN EXTENSION THROUGH FORMATION OF p - DIOXANE STRUCTURE – ROTATIONS POSSIBLE

C) ROTATION ALLOWED IN DIETHYLENETRIAMINE (DETA) IF CENTRALLY POSITIONED SECONDARY AMINE REMAINS UNREACTED

D) DIETHER BRIDGES FROM ANHYDRIDE CURES

Figure 6. Rotational modes in cured epoxy resins

The DETA cured epoxy resin (Table II) has the highest magnitude for the β-transition and the Izod impact and has three rotational modes. In addition to the dimethylene ether linkage of bisphenol A which is present in all five resins, this polyfunctional diamine generates tertiary amines during polymerization which could catalyze epoxy-epoxy reaction to yield *p*-dioxane rings. Finally, if the central secondary amine of DETA failed to react, then the entire section between the terminal diamines can contribute a backbone rotational mode. This is a very probable possibility as this material's cure schedule included an initial room temperature gelation. It is known (*14*) that this can result in incomplete chemical conversion because of steric hindrance. The mobility of the diamine segment may be responsible for the loss tangent plateau below the β-transition which is conspicuously absent (Figure 2) from the other epoxies. Recent work by Dammont and Kwei (2) has demonstrated the presence of a transition near −125°C. for epoxies containing a segment of contiguous methylene groups of the size of the central section of DETA.

The other amine curatives are the tertiary amine DMP-30 and the aromatic diamine MPDA, both having the rotational mode A and the possibility of rotational mode B (Figure 6). Finally, HHPA can have rotational modes A and D while PMDA, a tetrafunctional curative is only allowed the rotational mode A. Hence, comparing the anhydrides, HHPA has the higher magnitude for its β-transition as compared with PMDA.

Since rotational mode A (the ether linkage of bisphenol A) is common to all the epoxies, its contribution to the magnitude of the β-transition and the Izod impact value should be proportional to the concentration of DGEBA in the cured epoxy resin. As PMDA contains only rotational mode A, dividing the magnitude of its β-transition by the concentration of DGEBA in the PMDA cure (Table III) will yield the contribution to the β-transition per unit concentration of DGEBA. From Table III, a value of 0.045 is calculated for the PMDA cure.

Table III. Correlation of DGEBA Concentration with the Maximum Value of the β-Transition

Curative	*Density Cured Epoxy Resin gm./ml.*	*Concentration of DGEBA C = gms./ml. Resin*	*tan δ max/C*	*IZOD Impact ft.-lb./in.*	*Allowed Rotational Modes*[a]
PMDA	1.283	0.9169	0.0452	0.1	A
DMP-30	1.186	1.1625	0.0452	?	A, B[b]
MPDA	1.214	1.0289	0.0475	0.207	A, B[b]
HHPA	1.211	0.6960	0.0809	0.3	A, D
DETA	1.195	1.0864	0.0576	0.3-0.4	A, B,[b] D

[a] *See* Figure 6.
[b] Presence of *p*-dioxane rings in epoxy resins have not been confirmed.

For DMP-30 and MPDA, values of 0.045 and 0.047 respectively are obtained in almost exact agreement with PMDA cure, thus implying the absence of *p*-dioxane rings and that therefore the β-transition and its magnitude derives exclusively from the DGEBA.

HHPA and DETA yielded higher values of 0.080 and 0.057 respectively which reflect that these curatives contained additional rotational modes. For DETA, the additional mode is apparently only the central section of DETA considering the absence of evidence for the *p*-dioxane rings in the other two amine curatives. HHPA in having the highest ratio suggests that a significant contribution to the β-transition and impact derives from the diether bridges introduced by the anhydride curatives. Additional evidence for increased impact properties from anhydride cures is provided by noting that the phthalic anhydride cures, the unsaturated analog of HHPA, have Izod impact values near 0.42 (*14,* compare with Table II).

Conclusion

The β-transition in bisphenol A based epoxy resins and polycarbonates can be consistently interpreted in terms of mobility of the diether linkage of bisphenol A. The mobility of groupings previously assumed for the β-transition were found *via* molecular models to be immobile owing to either inherent inflexibility or steric hindrance. For those epoxy resins containing only the possibility of mobility within DGEBA, an excellent correlaton was found between the magnitude of the β-transition and DGEBA concentration. Epoxy resins having other groupings capable of mobility, specifically diether bridges from anhydride cures, exhibited β-transitions whose magnitudes were higher than those calculated on the basis of DGEBA. Finally, inspection of Figure 3 shows for the polycarbonates that the magnitude of the β-transitions at the maximum is comparable with the epoxy resins, yet polycarbonates have impact values about eight times those of epoxies. As it was found that the diether linkage of the bisphenol A in polycarbonates, as in the epoxies, is capable of mobility, perhaps the magnitude of the β-transition is a measure of total impact potential while the actual impact value may be influenced by factors each such as thermal treatment, amorphous phase changes, stretching, crosslinking, or crystallinity.

Acknowledgment

This paper represents one phase of research performed by the Jet Propulsion Laboratory, California Institute of Technology sponsored by the National Aeronautics and Space Administration, Contract NAS7-100.

Literature Cited

(1) Armeniades, C. D., Kuriyama, I., Roe, J. M., Baer, E., *J. Macromol. Sci. Phys.* **B1** (**4**), 777 (1967).
(2) Dammont, F. R., Kwei, T. K., *J. Polymer Sci.* **A-2, No. 6,** 457 (1968).
(3) Golden, J. H., Hammant, B. L., Hazell, E. A., *J. Appl. Polymer Sci.* **11,** 1571 (1967).
(4) Heijboer, J., *Ned. Rubberind* **No. 21, Vol. 27** (1966).
(5) *Ibid.,* **No. 22, Vol. 27** (1966).
(6) I. G. Farben Industries, *British Patent* **346550** (1930).
(7) Ishida, Y., Matsuoka, S., *Am. Chem. Soc. Polymer Reprints* **6,** 795 (1965).
(8) Kaelble, D., *SPE J.* **15,** 1071 (1959).

(9) Katz, D., Tobolsky, A. V., *Polymer* **4,** 417 (1963).
(10) Kline, D., *J. Polymer Sci.* **47,** 237 (1960).
(11) Koppelmann, V. T., "Kolloid-Zeitschrift," **144,** 12 (1955).
(12) Krum, F., Muller, F. H., *Kolloid-2.* **164,** 81 (1959).
(13) Kwei, F. K., *J. Polymer Sci.* **A-2, 4, No. 6,** 943 (1966).
(14) Lee, M., Neville, K., "Handbook of Epoxy Resins," Chap. 6, p. 7, McGraw-Hill Book Co., New York, 1967.
(15) May, C. A., Weir, F. E., *SPE Trans.* **2,** 207 (1962).
(16) Mercier, J. P., Aklonis, J. J., Litt, M., Tobolsky, A. V., *J. Appl. Polymer Sci.* **9,** 447 (1965).
(17) Reding, F. P., Faucher, J. A., Whitman, R. D., *J. Polymer Sci.* **54,** S56 (1961).
(18) Robertson, R. E., *J. Phys. Chem.* **5,** 1575 (1965).
(19) Shito, N., Sato, M., *J. Polymer Sci.* **C, No. 16, Part 2,** 1069 (1967).
(20) Stern, E., Vasilescu, V., Schrob, I., *Mater. Plastics* **2,** 80 (1965).
(21) Tobolsky, A. V., "Properties and Structure of Polymers," p. 74, John Wiley and Sons, Inc., New York (1960).
(22) Van Hoorn, H., *J. Appl. Polymer Sci.* **12,** 871 (1968).
(23) Willbourn, A. H., *Trans. Faraday Soc.* **54,** 717 (1958).

RECEIVED July 18, 1968.

10

Some Basic Properties of Carboxy-Terminated Polyisobutylene-Epoxy Resin Systems

ROMAN SLYSH

Enjay Polymer Laboratories, P. O. Box 45, Linden, N. J. 07036

Carboxy-terminated polyisobutylene (CTPIB) is a viscous prepolymer capable of producing flexible, crosslinked structures at both room and elevated temperatures with epoxides, isocyanates, and aziridines. Although CTPIB can be prepared in various molecular weights, the polymer investigated had a number average molecular weight, $\overline{M}_n$*, of about 1800 and an average functionality of about two carboxyl groups per molecule. This study discusses the preparation of CTPIB, curing reactions, and various CTPIB–epoxy compositions with regard to cure, stress–strain relationship, adhesion, and durability. The most significant features of CTPIB–epoxy products are high flexibility (up to 500% elongation) and high ozone, heat, and water resistance. For these reasons they may be advantageous, compared with the presently available flexible epoxies, such as the epoxy–polyamide and epoxy–polysulfide. CTPIB products also exhibit good adhesion to such materials as aluminum, stainless steel, glass, wood, and concrete.*

Carboxy-terminated polyisobutylene (CTPIB) is a low molecular weight prepolymer containing polyisobutylene backbone and carboxyl groups which are located at the ends of the polymeric chains. Because of the presence of reactive terminal groups, CTPIB is capable of chain extending and crosslinking with suitable curing agents to produce thermosetting products of high strength.

CTPIB falls into the category of telechelic (22) prepolymers (Greek "telos," end, and "chele," claw)—*i.e.*, prepolymers possessing two reactive terminal groups capable of producing strong elastomeric structures. These structures are considerably stronger than those obtained from randomly functional polymers of the same molecular weight because of the absence of free chain ends which do not participate in network formation. Telechelic polymers are usually liquids, which makes their handling and processing much easier than other high molecular weight polymers.

Various telechelic polymers are available. The polymer chain can include polysulfide, polybutadiene, butadiene–acrylonitrile copolymer, polyamide, polyether, or polyester. Reactive terminal groups can be thiol, carboxyl, hydroxyl, amine, epoxide, isocyanate, or olefin. One of the oldest prepolymers is thiol-terminated polysulfide, which is the most widely used material in various sealant applications. The chemistry and technology of polysulfide polymers have been discussed thoroughly by Bertozzi (*2*). The functionally terminated butadiene polymers are primarily used as binders in solid propellants. Their preparation, properties, and curing characteristics are discussed by French (*8*). The carboxyl- and thiol-terminated butadiene–acrylonitrile copolymers are described by Drake and McCarthy (*7*). These materials react with epoxy resins and are used in adhesives and sealants. Excellent physical properties can be obtained from urethane elastomers which are derived from hydroxyl-terminated polyethers or polyesters and isocyanates. These products, discussed by Saunders and Frisch (*17*), are used in such diverse applications as castings, coatings, caulks, sealants, adhesives, encapsulants, and potting compounds.

Although telechelic prepolymers are being used in various applications, many of them suffer disadvantages which limit their growth. Of particular interest is their stability to heat, oxidation, and water. Low stability in these areas is frequently responsible for many failures encountered in various industrial applications. Carboxy-terminated polyisobutylene was developed to provide a product that would exhibit superior ozone, thermal, and water stability. This study discusses the preparation of CTPIB, curing reactions, and various CTPIB–epoxy compositions with regard to cure, stress–strain relationship, adhesion, and durability. The effect of plasticizers and fillers on the basic properties of these systems is also included. In most cases flexible epoxies, such as epoxy–polyamide and epoxy–polysulfide, were compared directly to assess better the potential of CTPIB products in adhesive and coating applications.

Preparation of CTPIB

CTPIB is prepared by degradative ozonization of the high molecular weight copolymer of isobutylene and about 4% piperylene in the presence of pyridine (*1*) as shown on p. 110.

The high molecular weight copolymer is prepared by the conventional cationic polymerization used in isobutylene–diene systems. The polymer is dissolved in hexane, pyridine is added at 20–40 wt. % of the

$$-\!\!\left[\left(CH_2-\underset{CH_3}{\overset{CH_3}{\underset{|}{\overset{|}{C}}}}-\right)_n CH_2-CH=CH-\overset{CH_3}{\overset{|}{CH}}-\right]_m\!\!-$$

$$\downarrow O_3 \quad \text{Pyridine}$$

$$m\ HOOC-\overset{CH_3}{\overset{|}{CH}}-\!\left(-CH_2-\underset{CH_3}{\overset{CH_3}{\underset{|}{\overset{|}{C}}}}-\right)_n CH_2-COOH$$

CTPIB

polymer, and the ozonization is carried out at room temperature using an ozone–oxygen mixture.

Ozonization in the presence of a nucleophilic reagent such as pyridine results in the production of acids, peracids, and aldehyde. The formation of ozonides and peroxides, which are difficult to convert to useful terminal functionality, is thus avoided. The process consists of three steps: (a) double bond cleavage with the formation of aldehyde and acid groups, (b) oxidation of aldehyde to acid and peracid, and (c) reduction of peracid to acid. The polymer produced has the number average molecular weight, $\overline{M}_n$, of about 1800. The carboxy assay can vary, depending upon the process conditions and the finishing step. The product used in this study had an average functionality of about two carboxyl groups per molecule.

CTPIB of molecular weights other than 1800 can also be prepared, simply by using copolymers of different piperylene–isobutylene ratios. Piperylene concentrations lower than 4% will produce CTPIB of higher molecular weights, while the opposite is true at higher levels of unsaturation. This study is based exclusively on the prepolymer with the molecular weight of about 1800. A detailed synthesis of CTPIB is given by Baldwin *et al.* (*1*).

Curing Reactions of CTPIB

CTPIB, like other carboxyl-containing polymers, can be cured with various agents. As early as 1955 Brown and Gibbs (*4*) stated that carboxylic elastomers can produce vulcanizates by salt formation, esterification with polyfunctional alcohols or diepoxides, amide formation with polyamines and anhydride formation. A rather extensive and excellent discussion on crosslinking reactions of carboxylic elastomers has been published by Brown (*5, 6*). These reviews, in addition to the reactions indicated above, also include hydrogen bonding, ester formation with polyimines, reaction with polycarbodiimides, amide formation with polyisocyanates, and radiation decarboxylation. This study deals exclusively with epoxy resin cures, primarily because epoxy resins can react with carboxylic polymers at room temperature to produce useful products.

CTPIB reacts with epoxy resins in the presence of tertiary amine catalysts most probably according to the following reactions.

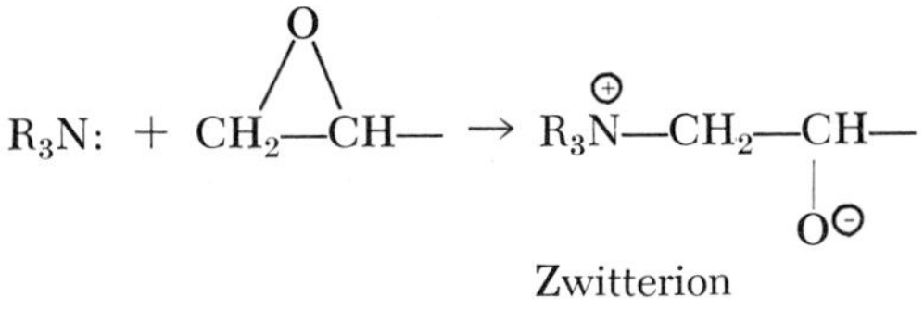

$$R_3N{:} + \underset{\text{(epoxide, O bridging)}}{CH_2\text{—}CH\text{—}} \rightarrow R_3\overset{\oplus}{N}\text{—}CH_2\text{—}\underset{\substack{|\\ O^{\ominus}}}{CH}\text{—} \qquad (1)$$

Zwitterion

$$R_3\overset{\oplus}{N}\text{—}CH_2\text{—}\underset{\substack{|\\ O^{\ominus}}}{CH}\text{—} + \underset{\text{CTPIB}}{HOOC\text{—}\overset{\substack{CH_3\\|}}{CH}\text{—}\left(CH_2\text{—}\overset{\substack{CH_3\\|}}{\underset{\substack{|\\CH_3}}{C}}\right)\text{—}CH_2\text{—}COOH} \rightarrow$$

$$HOOC\text{—}\overset{\substack{CH_3\\|}}{CH}\text{—}\overset{*}{R}\text{—}CH_2\text{—}COO^{\ominus} + R_3\overset{\oplus}{N}\text{—}CH_2\text{—}\underset{\substack{|\\ OH}}{CH}\text{—} \qquad (2)$$

$$HOOC\text{—}\overset{\substack{CH_3\\|}}{CH}\text{—}\overset{*}{R}\text{—}CH_2\text{—}COO^{\ominus} + \underset{\text{(epoxide, O bridging)}}{CH_2\text{—}CH\text{—}} \rightarrow$$

$$HOOC\text{—}\overset{\substack{CH_3\\|}}{CH}\text{—}\overset{*}{R}\text{—}CH_2\text{—}COOCH_2\text{—}\underset{\substack{|\\ O^{\ominus}}}{CH}\text{—} \qquad (3)$$

$$\downarrow \text{CTPIB}$$

$$HOOC\text{—}\overset{\substack{CH_3\\|}}{CH}\text{—}\overset{*}{R}\text{—}CH_2\text{—}COO^{\ominus} +$$

$$HOOC\text{—}\overset{\substack{CH_3\\|}}{CH}\text{—}\overset{*}{R}\text{—}CH_2\text{—}COOCH_2\text{—}\underset{\substack{|\\ OH}}{CH}\text{—} \qquad (4)$$

$$\overset{*}{R} = \text{—}\left(CH_2\text{—}\overset{\substack{CH_3\\|}}{\underset{\substack{|\\CH_3}}{C}}\right)_n\text{—}$$

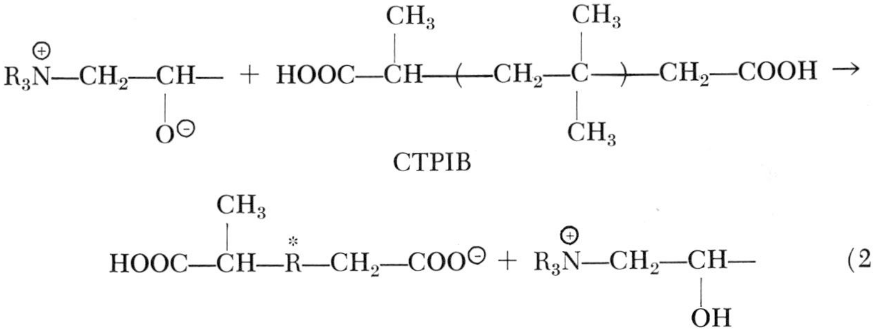

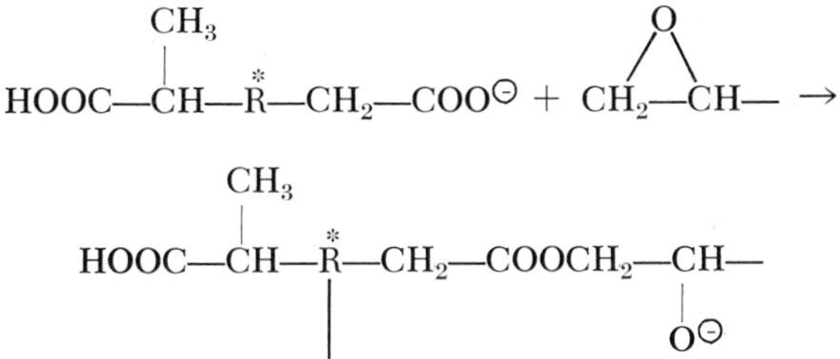

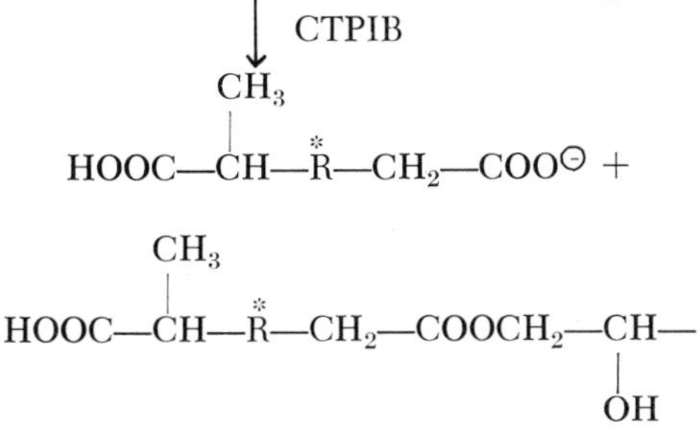

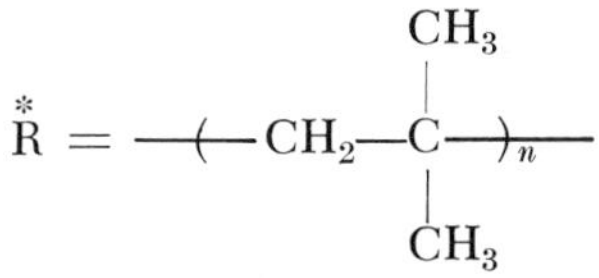

Reaction 1 was suggested by Mika (*13*) and Brown (*5*); however, they did not explain how the subsequent addition of acid to the zwitterion takes place. Schechter and Wynstra (*18*) suggested the formation of a salt as a first step in the amine catalyzed epoxy–acid reaction followed by the carboxylate ring opening of epoxide to form an alkoxide ion as shown in Reaction 3. Hydrogen abstraction from another acid molecule by alkoxide will generate a new carboxylate anion which will propagate the reaction until all acid is exhausted. Schechter and Wynstra also found that tertiary amine, such as benzyldimethylamine, is a much more powerful catalyst than potassium hydroxide. However, they gave no explanation for these results. Similar observations were also made by Oswald (*15*). In view of these results it appears that the zwitterion formed in Reaction 1 is an important intermediate in the CTPIB–epoxy reaction. Reaction 2 should occur readily because of the basic character of the zwitterion and the large separation of charges between the products. The carboxylate anion formed in Reaction 2 is believed to open the epoxide ring, as suggested by Schechter and Wynstra. After all acid has reacted, any epoxide remaining will probably react with nascent hydroxyl groups to produce stable ether linkages (*9*):

$$\underset{\displaystyle OH}{\underset{|}{-CH-}} + \overset{O}{\overbrace{CH_2-CH}}- \rightarrow \underset{\displaystyle O-CH_2-\underset{\displaystyle OH}{\underset{|}{CH}}-}{\underset{|}{-CH-}} \qquad (5)$$

At high temperatures crosslinking reactions may involve carboxyl groups from CTPIB and nascent hydroxyl groups, as implied by Mika (*13*) and Brown (*6*).

$$-\overset{\displaystyle O}{\overset{||}{C}}-OH + \underset{\displaystyle OH}{\underset{|}{-CH-}} \rightarrow \underset{\displaystyle O-\underset{\displaystyle O}{\underset{||}{C}}-}{\underset{|}{-CH-}} + H_2O \qquad (6)$$

At high epoxide–CTPIB ratios homopolymerization of epoxide may take place to form crosslinked structures (*14*).

$$R_3\overset{\oplus}{N}-CH_2-\underset{\displaystyle O^{\ominus}}{\underset{|}{CH}}- + \overset{O}{\overbrace{CH_2-CH}}- \rightarrow R_3\overset{\oplus}{N}-CH_2-\underset{\displaystyle OCH_2-\underset{\displaystyle O^{\ominus}}{\underset{|}{CH}}-}{\underset{|}{CH}}- \qquad (7)$$

The polymerization continues, resulting in a three dimensional network containing ether linkages.

The extent of the reactions indicated will depend upon the concentration of various ingredients and the reaction conditions. The addition esterification *via* epoxy–carboxyl (Reactions 1–4) is believed to predominate in the presence of a tertiary amine. Other reactions indicated are probably also taking place to various degrees during the curing of CTPIB with epoxy resins.

Discussion of Results

CTPIB–epoxy resin compositions were evaluated for possible applications in the adhesive, sealant, and coating fields. A wide range of formulations, all containing CTPIB from a single preparation, was studied. The variables included:

Epoxy resin type and concentration (20–100 p.h.r.)
Catalyst concentration (1.8–15 p.h.r.)
Curing temperature (75° and 195°F.)
Type of plasticizer and filler

Epoxy resins used as curing agents for CTPIB were Epon 828 and 830 (bisphenol A type, Shell Chemical) and ERLA-0500 (*N,N*-Diglycidyl-*p*-aminophenyl glycidyl ether, Union Carbide). All compositions were cured in the presence of tri-2,4,6-(dimethylaminomethyl)phenol, known as DMP-30, which acted as a catalyst.

Cure Rate. Catalyzed CTPIB–epoxy systems cure well at 195°F. (1–3 hours) to produce tack-free surfaces. At room temperature curing time varies from a few days to several weeks, depending upon the

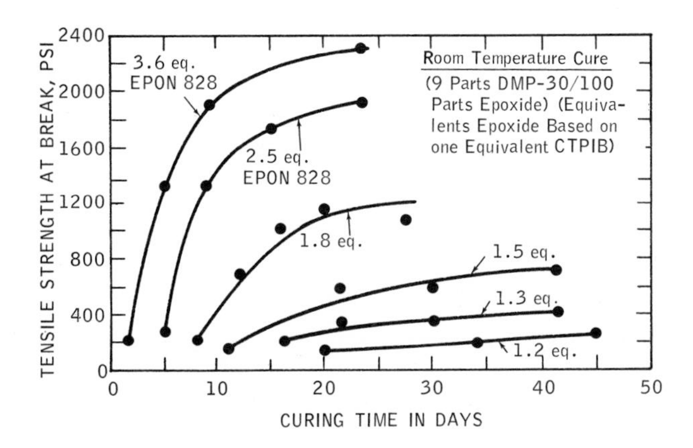

Figure 1. Effect of Epon 830 resin concentration and curing time upon the tensile strength of CTPIB

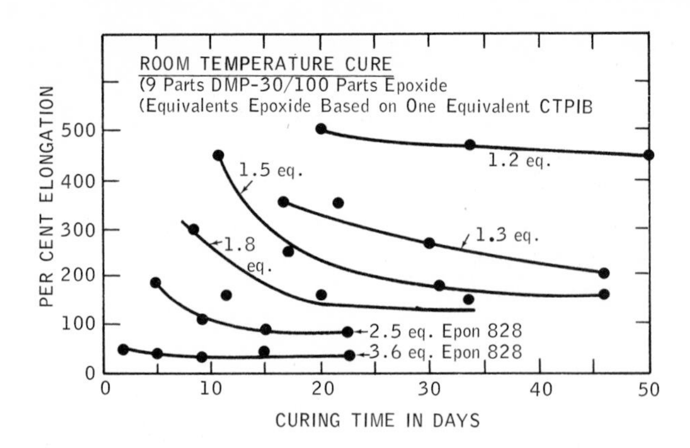

Figure 2. Effect of Epon 830 resin concentration and curing time upon the elongation CTPIB

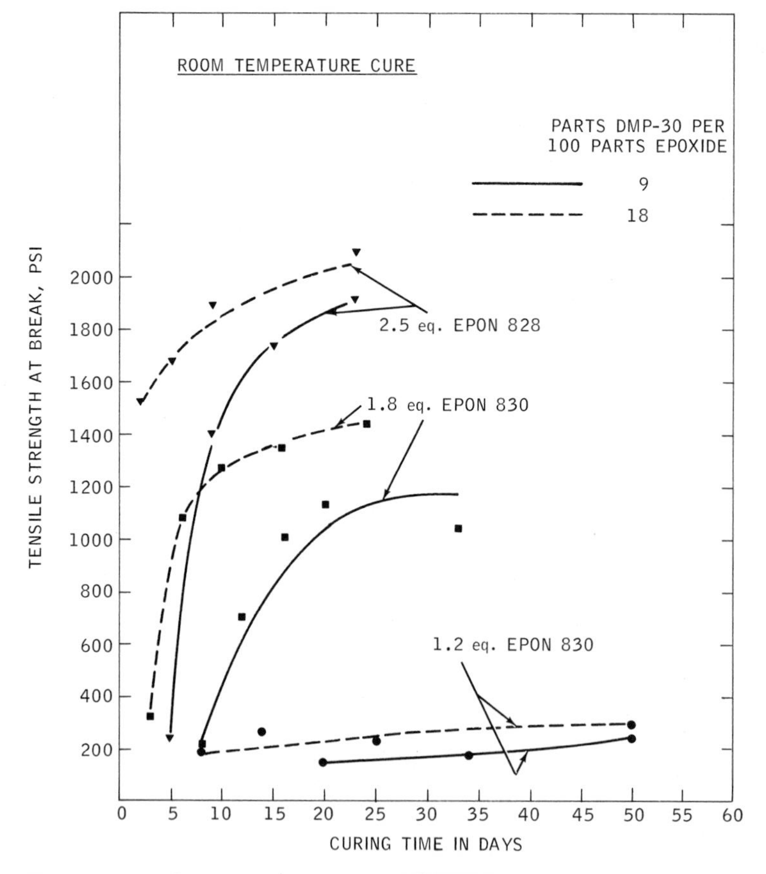

Figure 3. Effect of epoxy resin and DMP-30 concentrations upon the tensile strength of CTPIB compositions

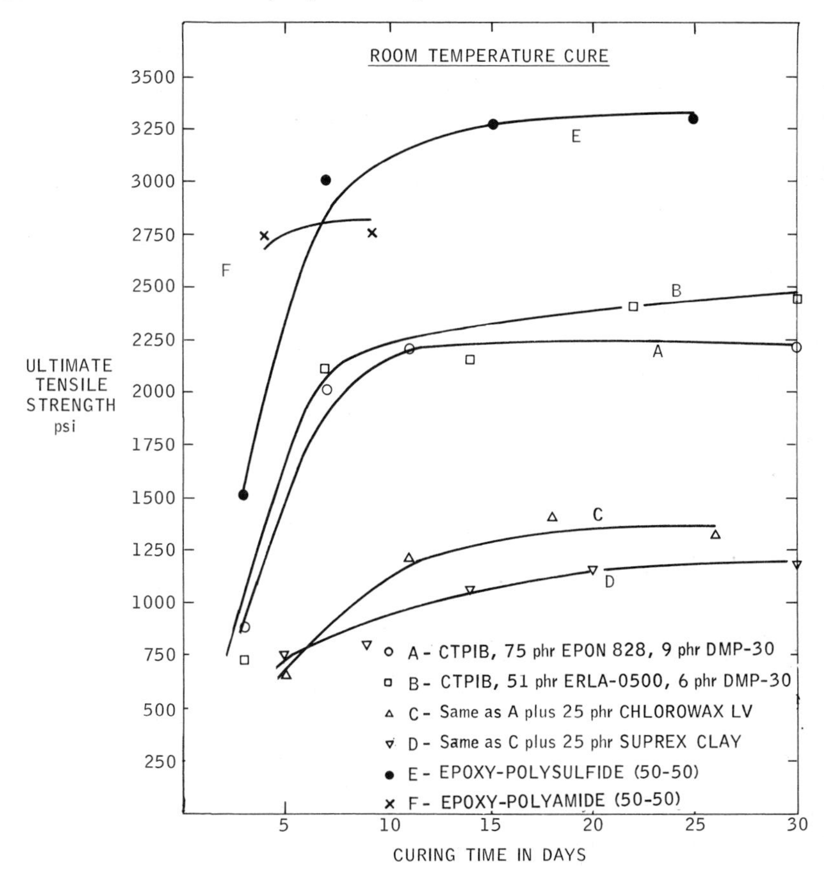

Figure 4. Effect of curing time upon the tensile strength of various compositions

concentration of epoxide and the catalyst. In general, faster cures are obtained with higher concentrations of epoxide (> 50 p.h.r.). A rather slow reaction between CTPIB and epoxy resin at room temperature is not surprising since it is well known that carboxyl groups react relatively slowly with epoxides at these conditions.

Stress–Strain Relationship of CTPIB–Epoxy Resin Systems. Tensile strength measurements at various curing times were used to follow the cure rate of CTPIB–epoxy products at room temperature. Although this type of measurement does not represent an absolute method for determining the state of cure, it provides a good relative value concerning the rate of cure. Stress–strain data were obtained using microdumbell-shaped specimens (2-11/16 inches long, 20 mils thick) at a crosshead speed of 10 inches/min.

The results presented in Figures 1 and 2 show that reasonably rapid cures can be obtained with CTPIB systems containing over 2.5 equivalents of Epon 828 per one equivalent CTPIB. The data shown in Figure 3 indicate that even faster cures will result with increasing concentration of the catalyst. All compositions containing > 1.8 equiv. epoxide/equiv. CTPIB exhibit a high degree of network perfection as indicated by the high percent insolubles (> 90%) in cyclohexane measured after immersion for 72 hours. High elongations are obtained with systems containing < 2.5 equiv. epoxide, indicating highly flexible products (Figure 2).

Tensile strength and elongation results of CTPIB–epoxy compositions are compared with those of epoxy–polysulfide and epoxy–polyamide in Figures 4 and 5, respectively. (The amount of epoxide used in the CTPIB mixtures corresponds to 3.6 equiv./equiv. CTPIB. The polysulfide– and polyamide–epoxy ratios constitute the upper limit according to their respective manufacturers). In general, the CTPIB systems com-

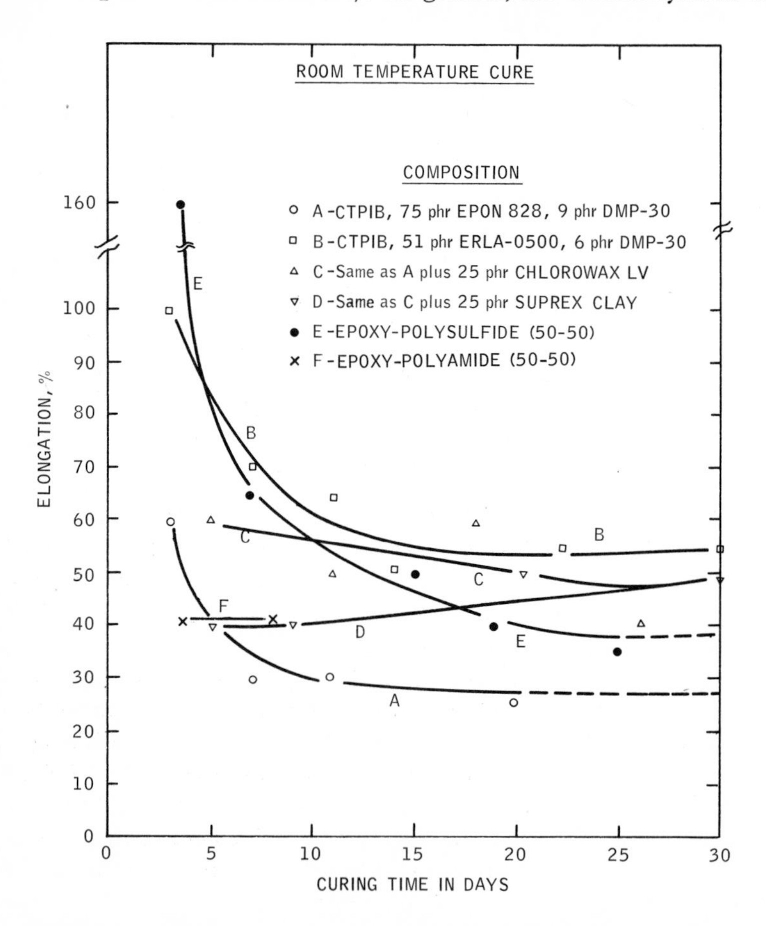

Figure 5. Effect of curing time upon the elongation of various compositions

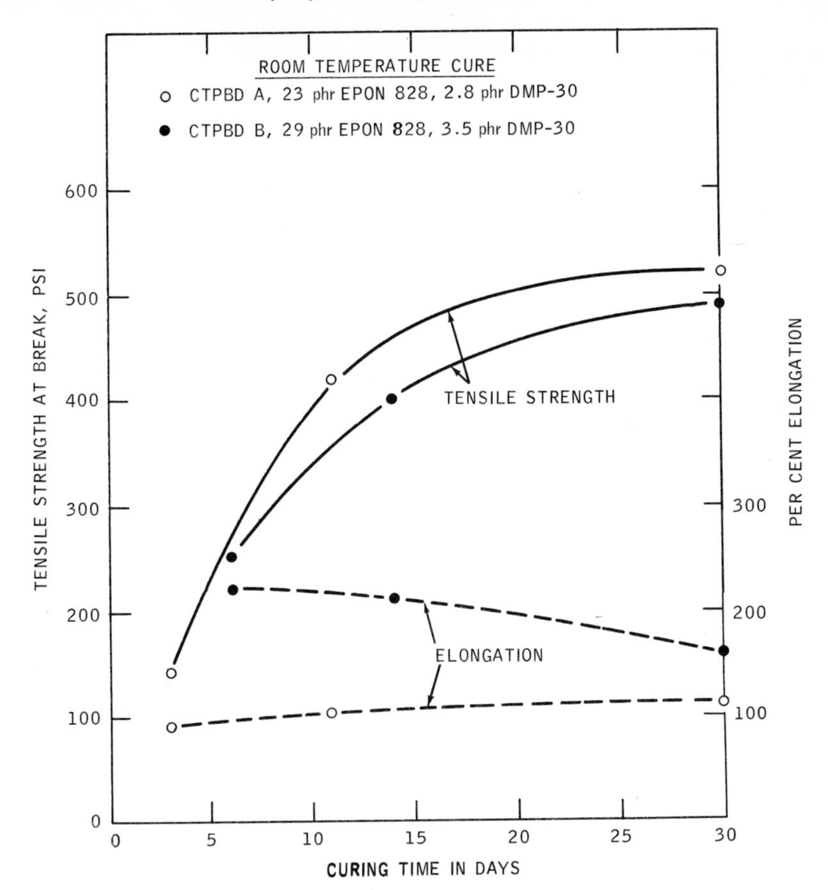

Figure 6. Effect of curing time on stress-strain relationship of carboxy-terminated polybutadiene-epoxy resin systems

pare favorably with the conventional modified epoxies as far as flexibility is concerned. Composition B, in particular, is softer and more flexible than conventional modified epoxies which are fairly tough and of higher modulus.

Stress–strain properties of analogous systems involving commercially available carboxy-terminated polybutadienes (CTPBD) indicate considerably lower tensile strengths than those obtained with CTPIB compositions. The results presented in Figure 6 show that both CTPBD–epoxy systems produce about 500 p.s.i. tensile strength after 30 days of curing at room temperature, compared with about 2200 p.s.i. obtained with similar CTPIB products (Figure 4). [Both systems contain 3.6 equiv. Epon 828 per 1 equiv. CTPBD.] At the same time the elongation of CTPBD structures is higher than that observed with polyisobutylene-based materials. This difference in physical properties is most probably caused by the higher molecular weight of CTPBD, compared with CTPIB. This is expected since it is known that networks with longer chains between crosslinks (M_c) will exhibit lower tensile strength and higher elongation (*16*).

The stress–strain data obtained after curing at 195°F. (1–3 hours) are presented in Figure 7. These results show a steep rise in tensile strength and a sharp decrease in elongation at increased concentrations of epoxy resin. A sharp decrease in tensile strength beyond the 3.6 equiv. epoxide (75 p.h.r.) level is most probably caused by the incompatibility of epoxide with CTPIB in this region. As shown in Figure 7, low epoxide concentration should be used if a highly flexible structure is desired. (An elongation of about 500% can be achieved with 20 p.h.r. Epon 830).

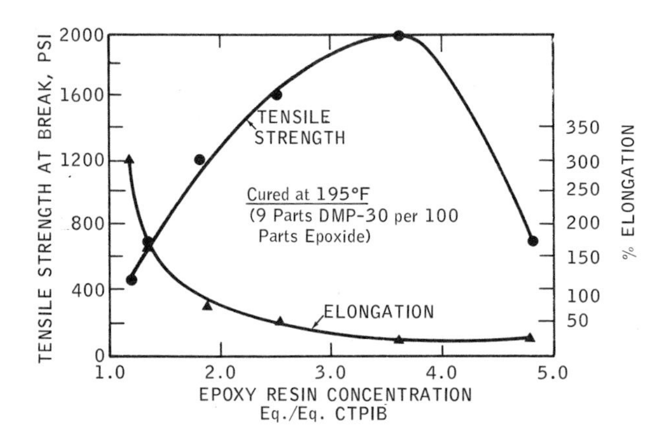

Figure 7. Effect of epoxy resin concentration upon the tensile strength and elongation of CTPIB

Effect of Plasticizers and Fillers on Stress–Strain Relationship of CTPIB–Epoxy Systems. Several plasticizers were added to the CTPIB–Epon 828 (75 p.h.r.) mixture in an effort to improve its elastic properties. A two- to three-fold increase in elongation was achieved in the presence of 25 p.h.r. Chlorowax LV (chlorinated paraffin, Diamond Alkali), Aroclor 1242 (chlorinated polyphenyls, Monsanto), and Flexon 845 (paraffin oil, Humble Oil). At the same time the tensile strength was reduced, as shown in Figures 4 and 8. As indicated, the type of plasticizer has a considerable effect upon the reduction of tensile strength relative to the unplasticized CTPIB–Epon 828 system.

The addition of various fillers to the plasticized CTPIB–epoxy composition does not seem to improve its strength significantly. As presented

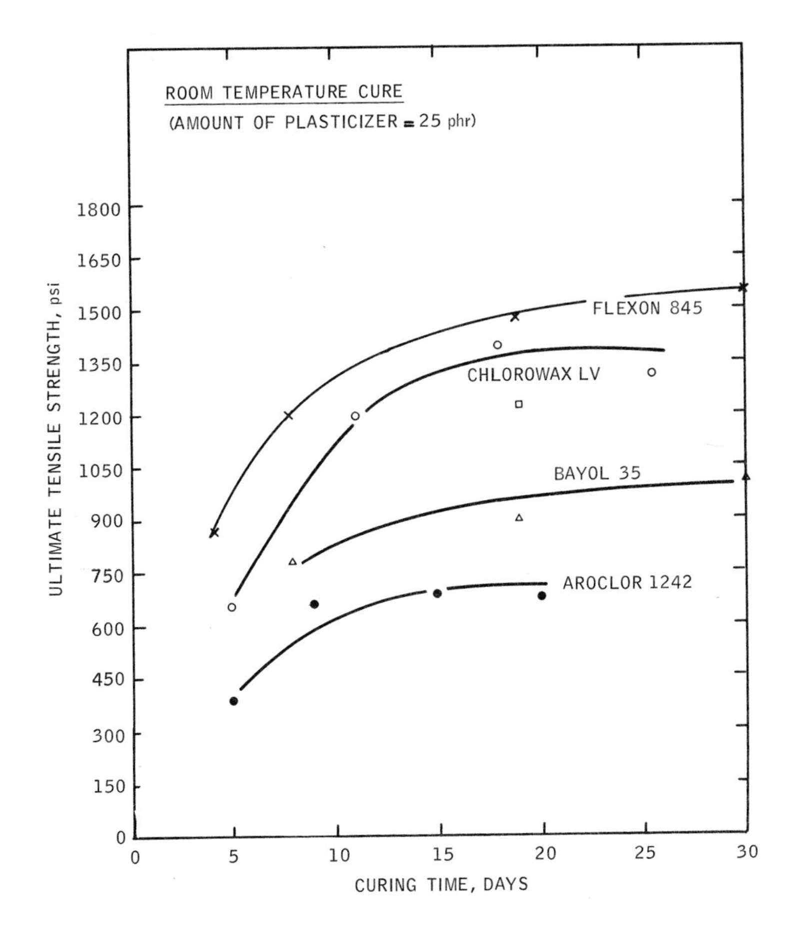

Figure 8. Effect of various plasticizers upon the tensile strength of CTPIB-Epon 828 (75 p.h.r.) composition

in Figure 9, in all cases the tensile strength is reduced. The lack of reinforcement in the presence of fillers is probably caused by poor dispersion of the filler arising from hand mixing. High shear mixing should improve the dispersion of fillers and thus increase the tensile strength.

As expected, the addition of fillers generally lowers the elongation of the plasticized CTPIB–Epon 828 composition (not shown). However, no noticeable stiffening occurred in the presence of 25 p.h.r. Suprex Clay (hydrated aluminum silicate, J. M. Huber Corp.). The CTPIB–epoxy system containing Suprex Clay has good appearance, and its flexibility is about the same as that of the plasticized, unfilled system (Figure 5).

Adhesion. Adhesive strength of various CTPIB compositions to aluminum (2024-T3), stainless steel (304), and aluminum-to-glass was measured by the standard tensile-shear method described in ASTM D-1002. In most cases the metallic surfaces were wiped thoroughly with MEK and were not subjected to the extensive chemical treatment usually employed in adhesion studies. For comparison several aluminum panels were cleaned using the standard chromic–sulfuric acid etch method. The adhesion between aluminum and glass was measured by bonding a small piece of thin glass (1 inch × 3/4 inch) between the aluminum panels. Standard 1/2 inch overlap was maintained between one aluminum panel and the glass. Triplicate samples were tested, and the reproducibility was usually within 15%.

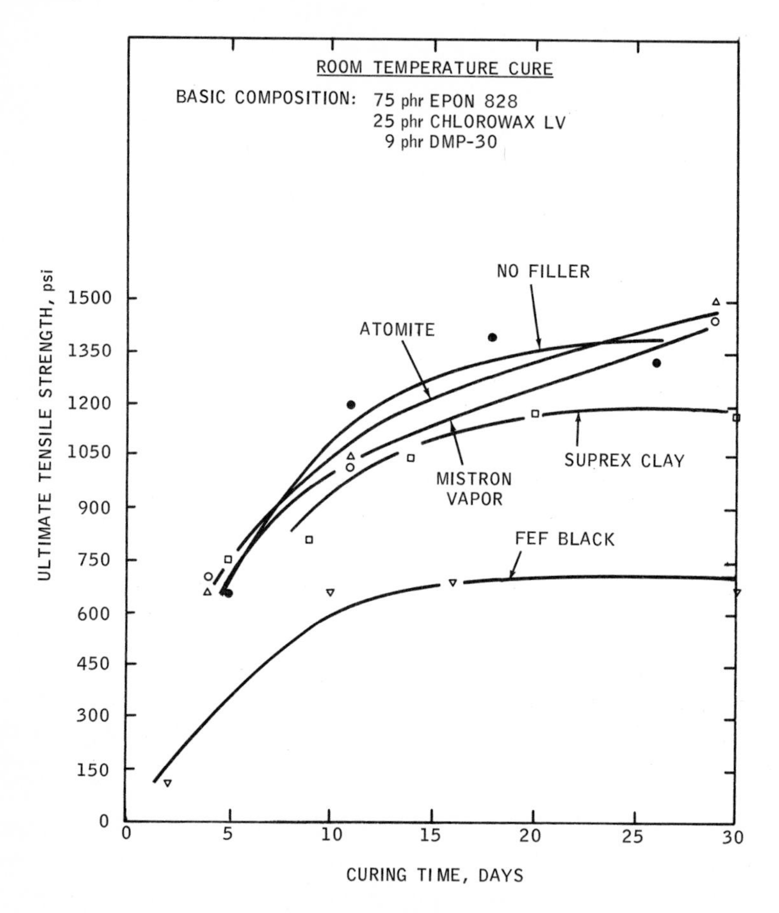

Figure 9. Effect of various fillers (25 p.h.r.) upon the tensile strength of plasticized CTPIB composition

The lap shear adhesion data presented in Table I indicate good adhesion of various CTPIB systems to untreated metallic surfaces. In general, the adhesive strength of CTPIB products compares favorably with that of epoxy–polyamides, epoxy–polysulfide, and a commercial epoxy adhesive. Similar adhesion values were also obtained with systems involving carboxy-terminated polybutadienes. Note that water appears to be detrimental to the adhesion of conventional epoxy compounds, while the strength of CTPIB systems tends to increase in most cases after water submersion. No satisfactory explanation can be given for this interesting observation.

Table I. Adhesive Strength (p.s.i.) of Various Compositions as Measured by the Lap Shear Test (ASTMD-1002)

MEK Treated Surfaces; Room Temperature Cure

Composition	*Aluminum (2024-T3) Dry/Wet*[a]	*Stainless Steel (304) Dry/Wet*[a]	*Aluminum to Glass Dry/Wet*[a]
CTPIB, Epon 830[b]	700/750	850/1000	Not tested
CTPIB, Epon 828[c]	520/760	730/840	420/415
CTPIB, ERLA-0500[d]	390/340	755/820	420/440
CTPBD A, Epon 828[e]	480/430	Not tested	Not tested
CTPBD, Epon 828[f]	620/480	Not tested	Not tested
Epoxy-polysulfide[g]	605/580	1250/1170	460/300
Commercial epoxy adhesive	790/540	930/890	450/250
Epon 828-polyamide[h] (50–50)	430/340	630/710	Not tested
Epon 828-Versamid 140 (50–50)	480/450	Not tested	Not tested

[a] Tested wet after 3 days submersion in water.
[b] 40 p.h.r. Epon 830, 3.5 p.h.r. DMP-30. Cured at 195°F. for 2 hours.
[c] 75 p.h.r. Epon 828, 9 p.h.r. DMP-30.
[d] 51 p.h.r. ERLA-0500, 6p.h.r. DMP-30.
[e] 23 p.h.r. Epon 828, 2.8 p.h.r. DMP-30.
[f] 29 p.h.r. Epon 828, 3.5 p.h.r. DMP-30.
[g] 100 parts Epon 828, 100 parts polysulfide (mol. wt. 1000), 7.5 parts DMP-10, 2.5 parts DMP-30.
[h] Polyamide of very low viscosity (4-7 poises).

The tensile–shear adhesion obtained to chemically treated aluminum is shown in Table II. Higher adhesion than that observed to untreated surfaces was measured in all cases. However, the values obtained with CTPIB compositions did not approach the 2000–3000 p.s.i. level usually desired in structural applications. The cohesive failure observed in all cases indicates that the strength of the material is the limiting factor. All compositions included in Table II (except one) were cured at room temperature, and it is possible that post curing at high temperature will produce higher adhesion values.

The effect of the Chlorowax plasticizer and fillers on tensile–shear strength of a CTPIB–epoxy composition is presented in Table III. The addition of 25 p.h.r. Chlorowax LV to the CTPIB–Epon 828 (75 p.h.r.) composition reduces the adhesion to aluminum. However, the adhesion

Table II. Effect of Surface Preparation on Lap Shear Adhesion to Aluminum (2024-T3), p.s.i. (ASTM D-1002)

Room Temperature Cure

Composition[a]	*MEK Treatment*[b]	*Chromic-Sulfuric Acid Etch*[c]
CTPIB, Epon 830[d]	600	800
CTPIB, Epon 828	520	900
CTPIB, ERLA-0500	450	860
Epoxy-polysulfide	600	2200
Epon 828-Versamid 140 (100–75)	840	1300

[a] Same compositions as those shown in Table I.
[b] Surface wipe with MEK.
[c] Vapor degreasing with trichloroethylene followed by 10 min. immersion in a hot bath (150°–160°F.) containing 30 p.b.w. water, 10 p.b.w. sulfuric acid (95%), and 1 p.b.w. sodium dichromate, followed by thorough rinsing with hot tap water (about 140°F.), followed by drying in a forced air oven at 100°–150°F.
[d] Cured at 195°F. for 2 hours.

Table III. Effect of Chlorowax LV Plasticizer and Fillers on Lap Shear Strength, p.s.i. (ASTM D-1002)

MEK Treated Surfaces; Room Temperature Cure

Composition	*Aluminum (2024-T3) Dry/Wet*[a]	*Stainless Steel (304) Dry/Wet*[a]	*Aluminum to Glass Dry/Wet*[a]
CTPIB, Epon 828[b]	520/760	730/840	420/415
CTPIB, plasticized[c]	360/390	760/820	380/480
CTPIB, filled with clay[d]	580/520	760/700	470/510
CTPIB, filled with black[e]	760/680	720/750	600/670
Commercial epoxy adhesive	790/540	930/890	450/250

[a] Tested wet after 3 days submersion in water.
[b] 75 p.h.r. Epon 828, 9 p.h.r. DMP-30.
[c] Same as Footnote b plus 25 p.h.r. Chlorowax LV.
[d] Same as Footnote c plus 25 p.h.r. Suprex Clay.
[e] Same as Footnote c plus 10 p.h.r. FEF carbon black.

can be restored to the original level by the addition of 25 p.h.r. Suprex Clay. An additional considerable increase in adhesive strength (approaching that of a commercial epoxy resin) occurs by using 10 p.h.r. FEF carbon black as a filler. Similar improvement in strength was observed with joints involving aluminum to glass, while the lap shear strength to stainless steel remained essentially unaffected by the presence of Chlorowax and fillers.

Effect of Surface Treatment on Adhesion. The effect of surface characteristics upon the adhesion of various compositions was tested by applying a thin coating of oil (ASTM No. 3) to the mating surfaces before bonding. Control panels were cleaned with MEK. The results shown in Table IV indicate that the lap shear adhesion of CTPIB systems bonded to oiled aluminum increased slightly while that involving stainless steel remained essentially unchanged. In contrast, the adhesion of the epoxy–polysulfide decreased by about 40–50% in the presence of oil. A smaller decrease was observed with a commercial epoxy adhesive.

Table IV. Effect of Oily Surfaces Upon the Lap Shear Adhesion of Various Compositions, p.s.i. (ASTM D-1002)

	Surface Treatment with	
Composition	*MEK* *Dry/Wet*[a]	*Oil (ASTM Oil No. 3)* *Dry/Wet*[a]
Aluminum (2024-T3)		
CTPIB, Epon 828 (75 p.h.r.)[b]	520/760	620/600
CTPIB, ERLA-0500 (51 p.h.r.)[b]	390/340	500/500
Epoxy-polysulfide[c]	605/580	300/220
Commercial epoxy adhesive	790/540	650/520
Stainless Steel (304)		
CTPIB, Epon 828 (75 p.h.r.)[b]	730/840	800/860
CTPIB, ERLA-0500 (51 p.h.r.)[b]	755/820	700/820
Epoxy-polysulfide[c]	1250/1170	740/400
Commercial epoxy adhesive	930/890	840/580

[a] Tested wet after 3 days submersion in water.
[b] Contain 12 wt. % DMP-30, based on epoxy resin.
[c] 100 parts Epon 828, 100 parts polysulfide (mol. wt. 1000), 7.5 parts DMP-10, 2.5 parts DMP-30.

In another series of experiments (not shown) the adhesion of CTPIB–epoxy systems to aluminum coated with a baked lubricant was considerably higher than that of a commercial epoxy adhesive. Based on these results and those shown in Table IV it appears that the adhesion of CTPIB compositions is not affected by the presence of oil on bonding surfaces. These observations are not entirely unexpected since CTPIB is compatible with various hydrocarbon oils and conventional epoxies are not. These results are of considerable practical significance since careful removal of dust and oil is usually required with commercial products if good adhesion is to be obtained.

Effect of Heat Exposure on Adhesion. The effect of high temperatures upon the adhesion of CTPIB compositions to untreated aluminum and stainless steel was tested after subjecting the bonded panels to two different sets of conditions. In one case, the specimens were tested hot after a relatively short exposure (30–120 min.) to temperatures up to 450°F. Another set of panels was tested at 350°F. after 7 days exposure at this temperature. The performance of two CTPIB systems, one containing Epon 828 (difunctional epoxy) and another cured with ERLA-0500 (trifunctional, tertiary amine-type epoxy) was compared with that of an epoxy–polysulfide (50–50 blend), a commercial epoxy adhesive, and a commercial silicone rubber which is used as an adhesive and sealant in high temperature applications. The effect of heat exposure upon the lap shear adhesion of these materials to stainless steel is shown in Figure 10.

The results obtained indicate that after 7 days of exposure at 350°F. the CTPIB compositions exhibit higher adhesion than epoxy–polysulfide or silicone rubber but are comparable with that of a commercial epoxy adhesive. Because of their higher flexibility, CTPIB products may be advantageous in certain applications over the commercially available epoxy adhesives in bonding systems requiring high resistance to heat. Similar results were obtained with CTPIB compositions bonded to aluminum.

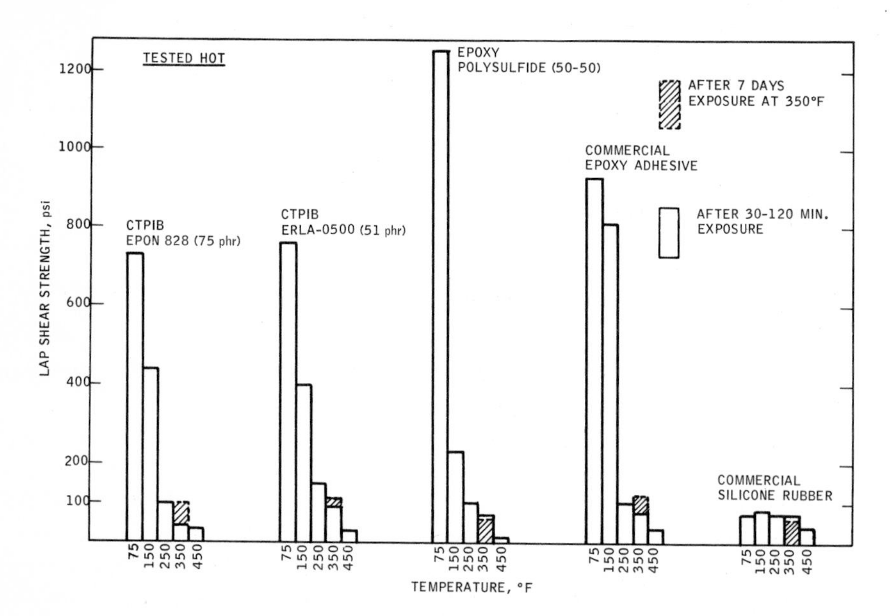

Figure 10. Effect of high temperatures upon the adhesive strength of various compositions to stainless steel (304)

Heat Aging. Because of the absence of unsaturation, CTPIB exhibits high oxidative and thermal stability. This high resistance to oxidation and heat was also observed with various CTPIB–epoxy systems. These properties were tested by measuring (a) the stress–strain relationship after 7 days exposure at temperatures up to 400°F. (ASTM D-573), and (b) the weight loss of rectangular specimens (3 inches × 1-1/2 inches ×

1/4 inch after 7 days exposure up to 500°F. The effect of high temperature exposure upon the stress–strain properties of CTPIB and conventional materials is shown in Figure 11. The results presented were obtained at room temperature, 2–3 days after the termination of heat exposure. The data clearly indicate the superior strength of all CTPIB compositions as compared with conventional flexible epoxies.

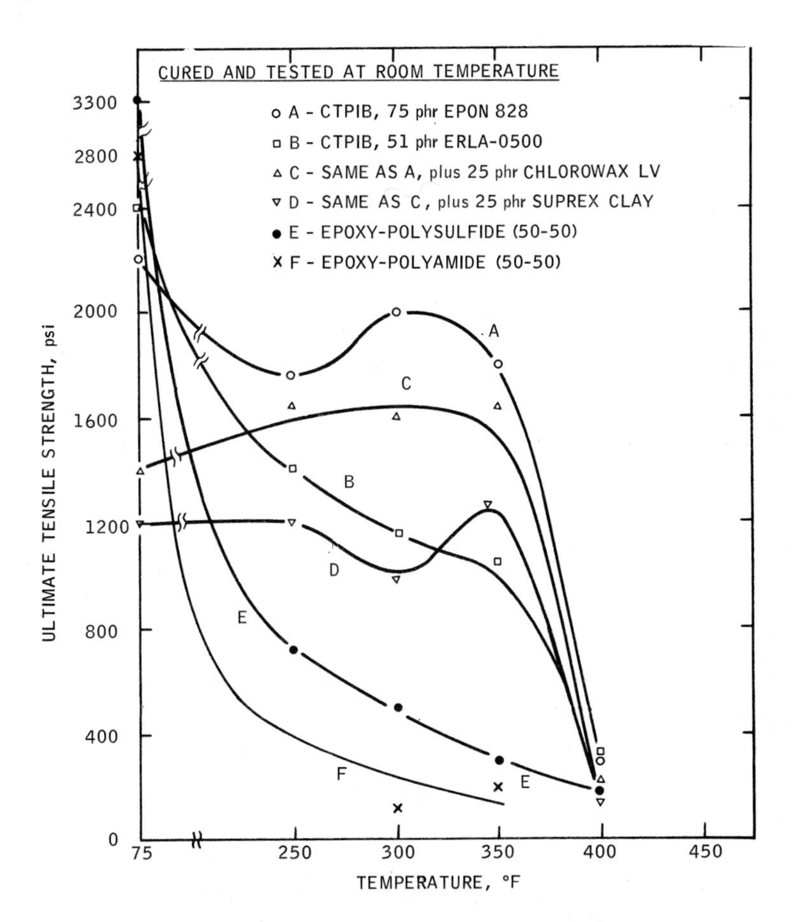

Figure 11. Effect of high temperature exposure (7 days) upon the tensile strength of various compositions

CTPIB products became softer and more flexible after heating up to about 350°F., indicating a reduction in the crosslinking density. Beyond this temperature, the samples turned dark and hard as a result of oxidation. The epoxy–polysulfide and epoxy–polyamide, on the other hand, became very hard and brittle at 250°F.

Weight loss data obtained after 7 days exposure at temperatures above 400°F. provide further evidence for the high heat stability of CTPIB systems. The results presented in Table V and Figure 12 show that the unplasticized CTPIB products are more stable at 450°F. and above than the conventional flexible epoxies or silicone rubber which is recommended for applications in this temperature range.

Table V. Effect of Heat Aging (7 Days) Upon the Weight Loss of Various Compositions

Room Temperature Cure

	Percent Weight Loss	
Composition	*500°F.*	*450°F.*
CTPIB, Epon 830 (40 p.h.r.) [a]	10	8.4
CTPIB, Epon 828 (75 p.h.r.) [b]	14	9.3
CTPIB, ERLA-0500 (51 p.h.r.) [b]	20	7.3
Epoxy-polysulfide [c]	Not tested	21 [d]
Commercial epoxy adhesive	29 [f]	10
Commercial silicone rubber	25	13
Epoxy-polyamide [e]	37 [f]	Not tested
CTPBD A, Epon 828 (23 p.h.r.) [b]	4	Not tested
CTPBD B, Epon 828 (29 p.h.r.) [b]	7 [f]	Not tested
Epon 828-Versamid 140 (50–50)	36 [f]	Not tested

[a] Contains 3.5 p.h.r. DMP-30; cured at 195°F. for 2 hours.
[b] Contains 12 wt. % DMP-30, based on epoxy resin.
[c] 100 parts Epon 828, 100 parts polysulfide (mol. wt. 1000), 7.5 p.h.r. DMP-10, 2.5 p.h.r. DMP-30.
[d] After 2 hours at 450°F. Considerable cracking and expansion of the sample observed during this time.
[e] 100 parts Epon 828, 100 parts polyamide-type curing agent (viscosity 4–7 poises).
[f] Severe cracking and expansion of the sample observed.

Figure 12. Effect of heat aging at 500°F.

After 7 days at 450°F. the visual appearance of CTPIB samples changed only slightly (samples became black), while the commercial epoxy resin bent to an arc-like shape and produced numerous surface cracks and tiny holes. Also, its weight loss was somewhat higher than that of CTPIB specimens (Table V). Under the same conditions the polysulfide–epoxy expanded greatly with a weight loss of 21% after only 2 hours of heating.

The weight loss of CTPIB specimens after 7 days at 500°F. ranged from 10–20%, as compared with 29–37% for conventional epoxies and 4–7% for carboxy-terminated polybutadiene–epoxy systems (Table V). Numerous surface cracks formed during the exposure of CTPIB samples, but their dimensions remained essentially unchanged. The silicone rubber experienced considerable shrinkage (no cracks observed), and the epoxy adhesive expanded considerably and produced large cracks. A drastic change in appearance after 4 days of exposure at 500°F. was also observed with the epoxy–polyamide composition, while little visible change occurred with the CTPIB–epoxy sample (Figure 12). A relatively low weight loss measured with two carboxy-terminated polybutadiene–epoxy compositions is probably caused by the presence of an antioxidant (1–1.5%). It should be pointed out that none of the CTPIB products contained antioxidants, and it is possible that greater heat stability could be achieved in the presence of such additives. The thermal degradation of epoxy resins has been studied by numerous workers, and various degradation mechanisms have been suggested (*11, 12*). Bishop and Smith (*3*) conclude that the mechanism of the thermal degradation of epoxy resins is not well understood.

Resistance to Water. It was mentioned previously that water does not appear to affect the adhesion of CTPIB–epoxy resin compositions. In fact, the adhesive strength of these materials tends to increase after 3 days of water submersion (Table I). An opposite trend, on the other hand, was observed with commercial products (epoxy–polysulfide, commercial epoxy adhesive, epoxy–polyamide, epoxy–CTPBD).

The effect of water submersion upon the weight change and the stress–strain properties of various compositions is discussed now. The resistance to water was tested by submerging the tensile microdumbells in water at room temperature for 7 and 14 days. The results presented in Table VI indicate a significant reduction in tensile strength of all specimens after 7 days exposure to water. All samples became softer and more flexible, indicating effective plasticization by the water. This is not surprising since it is known that epoxy adhesives lose strength in the presence of moisture (*19*). After drying in an oven at 140°F. or in a vacuum desiccator, the original strength of most compositions was restored. The tensile strength of other samples increased to a level of

80–85% of the original value after vacuum drying. [Samples cured at 195°F. were dried in an oven, while those cured at room temperature were dried under vacuum in a desiccator.]

Table VI. Effect of 7 Days Water Submersion Upon the Stress–Strain Properties of Various Compositions

CTPIB Compositions	*Water Absorption, wt. %*	*% Retention of (Tested Wet)*	
		Ultimate Tensile St.	*Elong.*
26 p.h.r. Epon 830, 2.3 p.h.r. DMP-30[a]	1.3	50	105
40 p.h.r. Epon 830, 3.5 p.h.r. DMP-30[b]	1.5	65	120
75 p.h.r. Epon 828, 9 p.h.r. DMP-30[c]	7.0	60	300
75 p.h.r. Epon 828, 9 p.h.r. DMP-30[b]	1.5	75	120
51 p.h.r. ERLA-0500, 6 p.h.r. DMP-30[c]	9.0	35	100
51 p.h.r. ERLA-0500, 6 p.h.r. DMP-30[b]	3.1	74	100
Control Samples[c]			
Epoxy-polysulfide[d]	3.4	45	150
Epoxy-polyamide[e]	7.7	33	200
CTPBD A-Epon 828 (23 p.h.r.)[f]	4.0	40	225
CTPBD B-Epon 828 (29 p.h.r.)[g]	13	10	250

[a] Cured at 195°F. for 3 hours.
[b] Cured at 195°F. for 2 hours.
[c] Cured at room temperature.
[d] 100 parts Epon 828, 100 parts polysulfide (avg. mol. wt. 1000), 7.5 parts DMP-10, 2.5 p.h.r. DMP-30.
[e] 100 parts Epon 828, 100 parts polyamide-type curing agent (viscosity 4–7 poises).
[f] Contains 2.8 p.h.r. DMP-30.
[g] Contains 3.5 p.h.r. DMP-30.

The data shown in Table VI also indicate that CTPIB systems cured at 195°F. exhibit considerably lower water absorption and higher tensile strength retention as compared with compositions cured at room temperature. This is demonstrated particularly clearly with CTPIB products cured with 75 p.h.r. Epon 828, and 51 p.h.r. ERLA-0500. Since both room and high temperature cured systems show similar low swelling and high percent insolubles, the large difference in water sensitivity indicates that their structures must be different. One possibility is that hydrogen bond linkages which are very susceptible to water may convert during the heating process to covalent linkages which are resistant to water. The data presented in Table VI show that this type of transformation may be taking place.

This result is of considerable importance because it shows that the resistance of CTPIB systems to water can be improved beyond the level obtained with conventional flexible epoxies, such as epoxy–polysulfide and epoxy–polyamide. High temperature curing (195°F., 2 hours) of these materials did not indicate an improvement in water resistance similar to that observed with CTPIB–epoxy products. This increased resistance to water of CTPIB–epoxy materials by simple heating may be particularly advantageous in coating applications. (Carboxy-terminated polybutadiene–epoxy compositions were not subjected to high temperature).

The relatively high sensitivity of various compositions to water and the restoration of the original tensile strength upon subsequent drying strongly indicate the presence of hydrogen bonding between the polymeric chains in the crosslinked structure. Since one hydroxyl is formed for every epoxy group in the esterification process during the curing of CTPIB, hydrogen bonds can form intermolecularly between hydroxyl groups or between carbonyl and hydroxyl groups. The hydrogen bond crosslinks obtained in this way would be analogous to those present in polyamides (*23*) (nylon, proteins, polyurethanes), cellulose fibers, and wood (*21*) which are all susceptible to attack by polar substances (such as water) capable of forming hydrogen bonds with these materials. The presence of hydrogen bonding in epoxy–polysulfide, epoxy–polyamide and CTPBD–epoxy structures is probably also responsible for their tensile strength loss under wet conditions.

Table VII. Electrical Properties of Various Compositions

Based on 70 mils Thickness

Composition	*Volume Resistivity (ASTM D-257) ohm-cm.*	*Dielectric Strength (ASTM D-149) volts/mil*
CTPIB, Epon 830 (26 p.h.r.)[a]	10^{14}	400
CTPIB, Epon 830 (40 p.h.r.)[b]	10^{14}	420
Epoxy-polysulfide[c]	10^{14}	560
Epoxy resin[d]	10^{13}	425
Butyl rubber	10^{14}	450[e]

[a] Contains 2.3 p.h.r. DMP-30; cured at 195°F. for 3 hours.
[b] Contains 3.5 p.h.r. DMP-30; cured at 195°F. for 2 hours.
[c] 100 parts Epon 828, 100 parts polysulfide, 7.5 p.h.r. DMP-10, 2.5 p.h.r. DMP-30; cured at room temperature.
[d] Based on 125-mils thick sample (*10*).
[e] Ref. 20.

Electrical Properties of CTPIB–Epoxy Resin Systems. Volume resistivity and dielectric strength of CTPIB systems cured at 195°F. with 26 and 40 p.h.r. Epon 830, respectively, were measured according to standard ASTM procedures to determine their potential in electrical applications. The results shown in Table VII (based on 70 mils thickness) indicate that CTPIB epoxy resin compositions possess very good insulating properties and in this respect compare very favorably with known materials. [Dielectric strength depends strongly upon the thickness of the sample: the thinner the specimen, the higher the dielectric strength per unit thickness.]

Summary and Conclusions

Carboxy-terminated polyisobutylene–epoxy resin compositions are highly flexible products capable of producing good adhesion to metals, glass, wood, and concrete. They are highly resistant to ozone, heat, and water, and for these reasons may be advantageous, compared with the presently available flexible epoxies, such as the epoxy–polysulfide and epoxy–polyamide. Possible disadvantages of CTPIB–epoxy systems include higher viscosity, slower cure rate, lower tensile strength, and low resistance to fuels.

Acknowledgment

The author acknowledges the help of A. Fraga who performed all experimental work discussed in this paper.

Literature Cited

(1) Baldwin, F. P. *et al.*, ADVAN. CHEM. SER. **91,** 448 (1969).
(2) Bertozzi, E. R., *Rubber Chem. Technol.* **41** (1), 114 (1968).
(3) Bishop, D. P., Smith, D. A., *Ind. Eng. Chem.* **59** (8), 32 (1967).
(4) Brown, H. P., Gibbs, C. F., *Ind. Eng. Chem.* **47,** 1006 (1955).
(5) Brown, H. P., *Rubber Chem. Technol.* **30,** 1347 (1957).
(6) Brown, H. P., *Rubber Chem. Technol.* **36,** 931 (1963).
(7) Drake, R. S., McCarthy, W. J., *Rubber World* 51 (Oct. 1968).
(8) French, D. M., *Rubber Chem. Technol.* **42** (1), 71 (1969).
(9) Lee, H., Neville, K., "Handbook of Epoxy Resins," pp. 5–20, McGraw-Hill, New York, 1967.
(10) Lee, H., Neville, K., "Epoxy Resins," p. 60, McGraw-Hill, New York, 1957.
(11) Lee, L. H., *J. Appl. Polymer Sci.* **9,** 1981 (1965).
(12) Lee, L. H., *J. Polymer Sci., Pt. A* **3,** 859 (1965).
(13) Mika, T. F., *J. Appl. Chem.* **6,** 365 (1956).
(14) Narracott, E. S., *British Plastics* **24,** 342 (1951).
(15) Oswald, A. A., Esso Research and Engineering Co., private communication.
(16) Saunders, J. H., Frisch, K. C., "Polyurethanes—Chemistry and Technology," Part I, p. 311, Interscience Publishers, New York, 1962.
(17) Saunders, J. H., Frisch, K. C., "Polyurethanes—Chemistry and Technology," Parts I and II, Interscience, New York, 1962 and 1964.
(18) Schechter, L., Wynstra, J., *Ind. Eng. Chem.* **48** (1), 86 (1956).
(19) S9harpe, L. H., *Appl. Polymer Symp.* (3), 353 (1966).
(20) Smith, W. C., Enjay Polymer Laboratories, private communication.
(21) Stamm, A. J., Tarkow, H., *J. Phys. Colloid Chem.* **54,** 745 (1950).
(22) Uraneck, C. A., Hsieh, H. L., Buck, O. G., *J. Polymer Sci.* **46,** 535 (1960).
(23) Valentine, L. J., *Polymer Sci.* **23,** 297 (1957).

RECEIVED June 4, 1968.

11

Formulation of an Epoxy Compound for Maximum Moisture Resistance

LARRY A. LIEBOWITZ

Nytronics, Inc., Berkeley Heights, N. J. 07922

One of the most important properties of an epoxy formulation, particularly if it is to be used in the electrical/electronics industry, is its moisture resistance. This paper reports on a test program to determine which types of formulations are most likely to have the highest moisture resistance. The experimental procedure consisted of encapsulating metal film resistors with test formulations and monitoring the components' resistance changes during humidity cycling. These changes in electrical resistance are correlated with the encapsulants' moisture resistance by an empirical relationship devised specifically for this study. Glycidyl, cycloaliphatic, and novolac epoxy resins compounded with various hardeners and fillers were evaluated. A mica-filled PMDA cured cycloaliphatic resin and a silica-filled MPDA cured epoxidized novolac turned out best.

One of the most important attributes of an epoxy formulation, if it is to be used in the electrical/electronics industry, is good moisture resistance (MR). Whether or not a given compound possesses this vital characteristic is determined by two of its properties:

1. Resistance to absorption of liquid water.
2. Resistance to transmission of water vapor.

The first of these properties can be readily measured on a sample of the cured compound in terms of weight gain during an immersion in hot water. Epoxy systems with values substantially below 0.10% increase are relatively easily formulated (2).

On the other hand, compounds with very low moisture vapor transmission rates are hard to come by. This can be explained by the relative mobility of a molecule in the gaseous state as compared with one in the

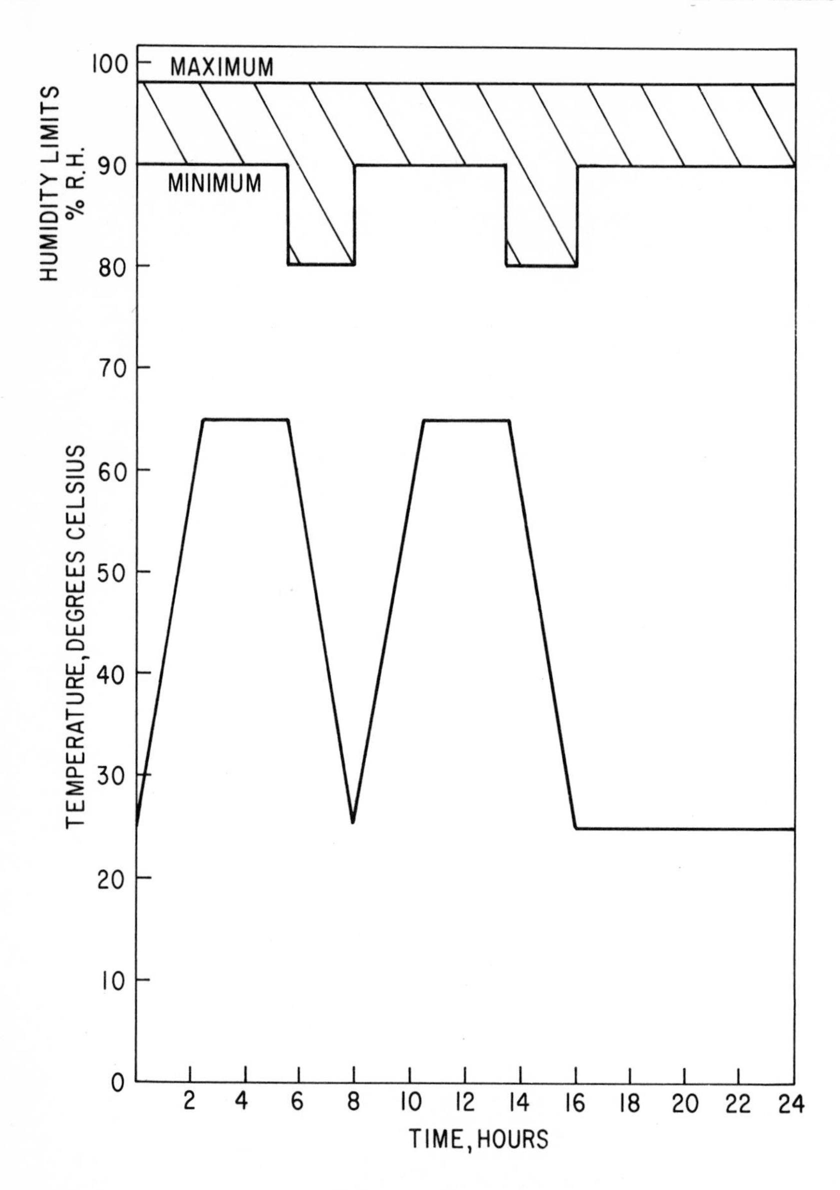

Figure 1. Moisture resistance test cycle

liquid state, compounded by the fact that, for water, the molecule exists as unassociated H_2O in the gaseous phase, whereas, in the liquid hydrogen bridging causes the formation of $(H_2O)_2$ and $(H_2O)_3$. These larger associated molecules have far more difficulty in fitting into the interstices in the epoxy crosslinked network than do the smaller, more mobile gas molecules.

Experimental

Direct testing of a sample of material to determine its resistance to penetration of water vapor is also much more difficult than the test for liquid absorption. Hence, it is common in the electronics industry to measure this property in terms of change during exposure to high humidity in some parameter of the device the material in question is to be used on—*e.g.*, resistance shift of precision resistors, insulation resistance deterioration of capacitors, etc. In the current investigation, said device is an encapsulated metal film resistor, and the material under study is the encapsulant, which is 0.010 to 0.012 inch thick. The measured parameter is the device's resistance change (measured with a Wheatstone Bridge accurate to within 0.02%) during a ten-day exposure to humidity between 95 and 98% at temperatures cycling from 75 to 165°F., per the schedule given in Figure 1 (*6*). The test is made extremely sensitive

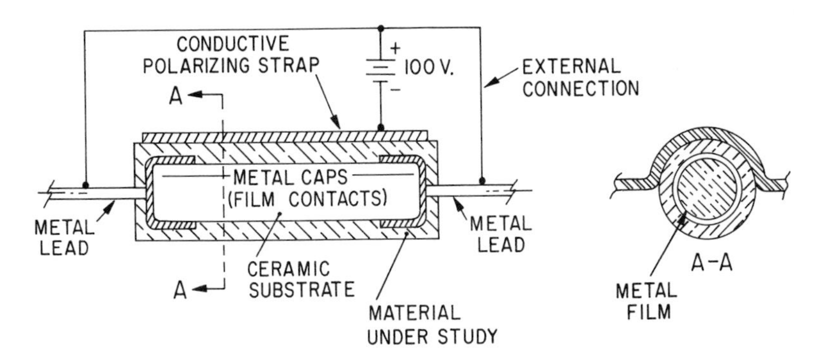

Figure 2. Diagram of resistor undergoing moisture vapor penetration test on encapsulant

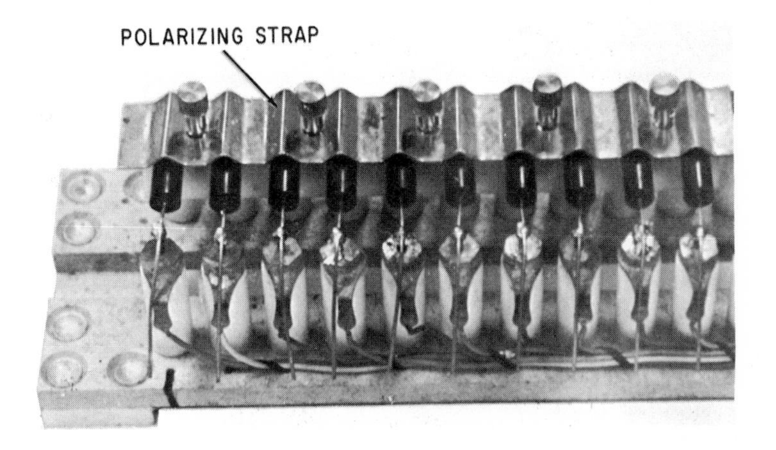

Figure 3. Photograph showing resistors loaded onto MR *test fixture with polarizing strap partially in place*

by mounting a conductive strap in contact with the surface of the encapsulant. This strap is maintained at a negative potential of 100 VDC with respect to the metal film (*see* Figures 2 and 3). This is in effect a polarizing potential directly across the encapsulant. In addition, the voltage acts as a driving force for transfer (by electrophoresis) of metal ions from the metal film (anode) to the external strap (cathode), decreasing the film's thickness and thereby causing an increase in its resistance (as measured between the leads of the test resistor). This transfer will occur to a measurable degree only in the presence of "carrier" molecules, in this case water. The degree to which the transfer occurs, as measured by the degree of resistance shift, is in turn related to the amount of moisture vapor penetrating the encapsulant and condensing on the metal film surface.

A more or less arbitrary industry standard for this test is that a resistance shift of greater than 0.40% constitutes a failure. In practice, shifts of 0.20% and less can be achieved. Quantitative evaluation of results can be expressed in terms of an empirical factor, devised specifically for the purpose of this study and referred to simply as "*H*".

$$H = \frac{100\,(N - \sum_{i=1}^{N} \Delta Ri)}{N + \frac{10}{N} F^2}\ ; \Delta Ri \leqslant 1$$

N = Number of samples in test group
ΔRi = Individual resistance shift of each unit expressed in percent, or 1.00; whichever is less
F = Number of resistors in test group with ΔRi greater than 0.40%

The 1% maximum is placed on ΔR_i because from the standpoint of the *H* formula this represents complete failure, and the use of any higher number would unduly influence the calculated *H*. The F^2 factor in the denominator is meant to penalize severely any test group with more than one "failure" per ten units. The numerical value of *H* will be between 0 and 100, with the better formulations turning out above 90.

Analysis

The foregoing discussion leads directly to one prime requirement of any resin to be used where maximum moisture resistance is essential. This requirement is that the resin itself should contain a minimum of ions or ionizable material. This is one area in which the relatively new cycloaliphatic epoxy resins have excellent potential to offer improved performance over the old glycidyl ether resins, of which the most well-known is diglycidyl ether of bisphenol A (DGEBA). DGEBA is prepared by the reaction of bisphenol A and epichlorohydrin with sodium hydroxide. However, in addition to the DGEBA, sodium chloride is a reaction product (Figure 4) (*4*). The utility of the DGEBA in high moisture resistance applications is therefore dependent upon the degree to which the Na and Cl ions can be extracted.

The cycloaliphatic resins, on the other hand, are prepared by direct epoxidation of cycloaliphatic olefins (*1*), eliminating the objectionable salt formation and yielding a resin with inherently lower ion content. Of the glycidyl type resins, those found to yield formulations with the highest MR are the novolacs. This can be attributed to their relatively high functionality and consequently high crosslinking density.

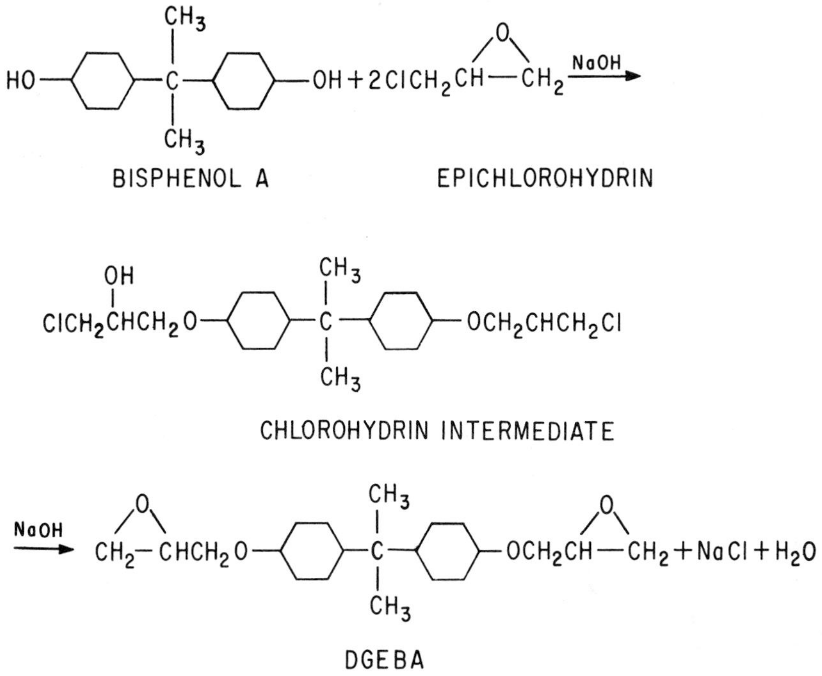

$$HO-C_6H_4-C(CH_3)_2-C_6H_4-OH + 2\,ClCH_2CH(O)CH_2 \xrightarrow{NaOH}$$

BISPHENOL A EPICHLOROHYDRIN

$$ClCH_2CH(OH)CH_2O-C_6H_4-C(CH_3)_2-C_6H_4-OCH_2CH(OH)CH_2Cl$$

CHLOROHYDRIN INTERMEDIATE

$$\xrightarrow{NaOH} CH_2(O)CHCH_2O-C_6H_4-C(CH_3)_2-C_6H_4-OCH_2CH(O)CH_2 + NaCl + H_2O$$

DGEBA

Figure 4. Reaction chemistry for typical DGEBA preparation. (Note that NaCl is also a reaction product)

Crosslinking density is also an important factor when considering the hardener to be used to cure an epoxy resin. Generally speaking, a highly functional curing agent will yield a highly crosslinked structure, but other factors such as resultant architectural symmetry and residual reaction products must also be given serious consideration. Curing agents can be categorized by their gross reaction mechanism as being either "true" catalysts if they are not depleted during the cure but serve to initiate or promote reaction, or as hardeners if they enter into the curing reaction and become part of the crosslinked structure. The true catalyst types are chemically either ionic or ion (or free radical) generators and since they tend to remain entrapped in the cured resin, they are not too useful in high MR formulations for reasons previously discussed.

Of the reactive type hardeners, two chemical species are most widely used:

1. Nitrogen bearing compounds, particularly amines and amides.
2. Organic acid anhydrides.

Within each of these groups there are hundreds of compounds and combinations from which to choose. Obviously all of these could not be tested. The prime factor considered in determining which of these would be evaluated with each resin type was rate of cure reaction.

The utility of amines with cycloaliphatic resins is severely limited, due to very slow reaction rates (*3*). Hence the anhydrides, which are useful with all epoxy resins, were the only curing agents considered for use with the cycloaliphatics. However, aromatic amines are for the most part more reactive with glycidyl and novolac type resins. In addition, the aromatic amines can be used to form "B-stage" compounds. One of these, *m*-phenylenediamine is widely used in commercial molding compounds. Polyamides generally have better moisture vapor resistances than amines. However, this must be weighed against their lower reaction rates.

Because of the size to which epoxy molecules grow during polymerization, reaction rate is also somewhat dependent upon quantity and type of filler in a formulation. Chain termination can occur by reaction with a filler particle. If this occurs after the growing molecule has attained a high degree of polymerization (*DP*), or if polymerization can continue through other active sites on the molecule (as would be the case so long as filler content is not excessively high), this reaction with filler particles is desirable from a moisture resistance standpoint because potential capillary leakage paths are eliminated. The problem of moisture "wicking" along resin-filler interfaces is a serious one, particularly when glass in any form other than micro-mesh (milled) particles is used as filler. To eliminate wicking, complete wetting of all filler particles by resin is required. Various treatments for glass flakes and fibers as well as addition of wetting agents, such as silanes, to the resin have been previously tried without much success. At this time it still appears that their use in high MR formulations should be limited to those applications where it is absolutely required to attain desired mechanical properties, and even in these applications as little glass as possible should be used. Combinations of glass plus another filler such as silica or mica could be considered as a means of reducing glass content.

Silica and mica are more readily wetted by epoxy resins, but, even with these, care must be exercised in selection of particle size and processing to assure proper wetting. It appears that up to about 50 microns the MR of silica-filled formulations increases with increasing particle

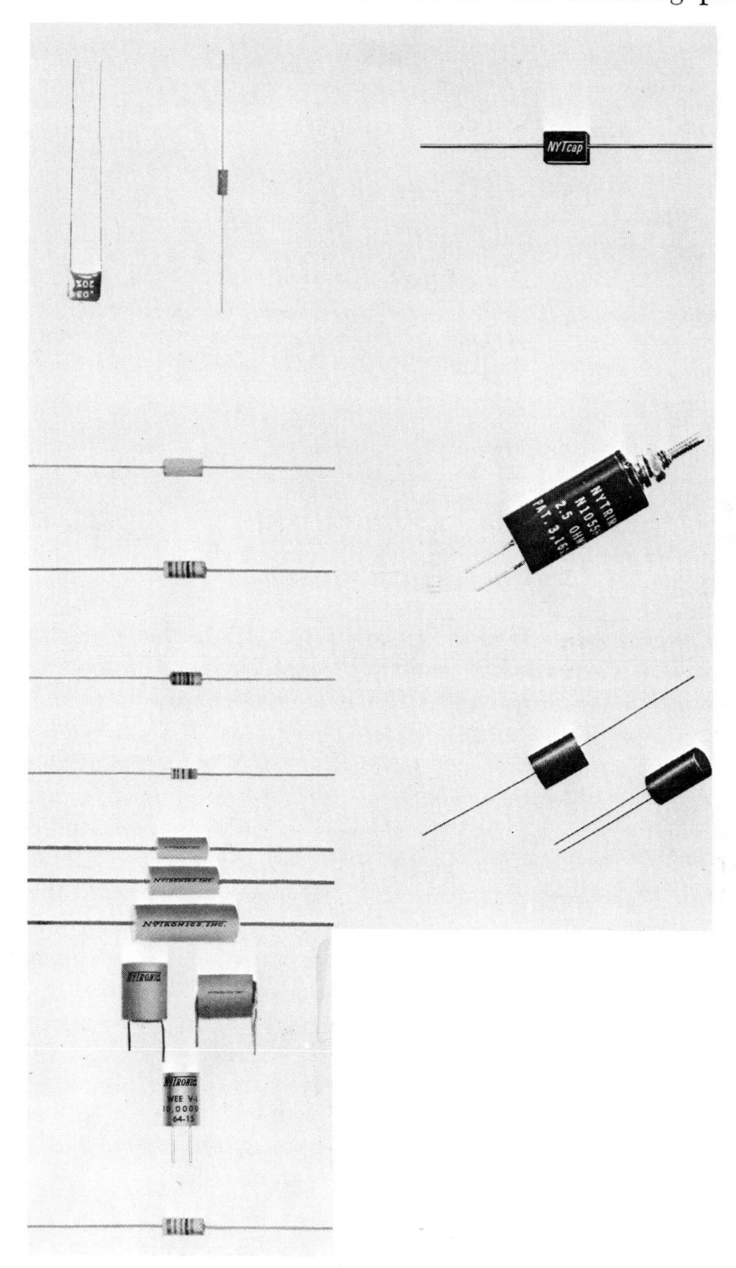

Figure 5. Some typical electronic components, encapsulated with various epoxy formulations

Table I. Results of This Study

Resin Type	*Hardener*	*Filler*	*Liquid Immersion Weight Gain*	H
Cycloaliphatic	PMDA	Mica	0.06%	98
Cycloaliphatic	PMDA	Silica	.07	92
Cycloaliphatic	PMDA	Zirconia	.07	82
Cycloaliphatic	Phthalic Anhydride	Mica	.09	83
Cycloaliphatic	Methyl Nadic Anhydride	Mica	.10	77
Novolac	MPDA	Silica	.09	97
Novolac	MPDA	Silica & glass	.23	58
Novolac	PMDA	Silica	.05	97
Novolac	MPDA	Mica	.08	88
Novolac	MDA	Silica	.11	79
DGEBA	MPDA	Silica	.14	44
DGEBA	MPDA	Mica	.14	32
DGEBA	PMDA	Silica	.12	55
Epoxidized phenolic	Dicyandiamide	Mineral	.10	Cracks
Epoxidized phenolic	Dicyandiamide	Mineral & glass	.10	90
Epoxidized phenolic	Dicyandiamide	Glass fibers	.18	14

size. It also appears from the current series of tests that mica filler yields higher MR when used in anhydride cured systems, whereas, silica is better with amine cures. Work is in progress to verify this.

Other properties of an encapsulant can also have secondary effects on its moisture resistance. For example, if it is to retain its moisture resistance, an encapsulant must not develop even micro-cracks owing to thermal stress (induced by changes in ambient temperature and/or self-heating of the component). This characteristic is a function of thermal expansion coefficient, thermal conductivity and mechanical strength. All of these properties are largely dependent on the filler content (both type and amount) in a formulation, and they can be varied over a wide range by a relatively small change in filler (5).

Test Results

Table I presents the significant results of the current study. It should be noted that in each case H is based on a test group of 20 samples.

Conclusions

In order to formulate an epoxy encapsulant with high moisture resistance it is important that resistance to transmission of water in both liquid and vapor states be taken into account. Of those compounds tested for this study, a cycloaliphatic coating resin filled with 325-mesh mica, cured with pyromellitic dianhydride and a *m*-phenylenediamine cured epoxidized novolac filled with 40-micron silica yielded best results.

Literature Cited

(1) Dorman, E. N., *Soc. Plastics Eng. Ann. Tech. Confr.*, 1965.
Electrical Insulation," *Soc. Plastics Eng. Ann. Tech. Confr.*, 1965.
(2) Epoxy Products Division, Allied Products Corp., technical literature.
(3) Hersch, P., *Plastics Tech.* (December 1966).
(4) Lee, H., Neville, K., "Epoxy Resins," McGraw-Hill, New York, 1957.
(5) Liebowitz, L. A., *SPE J.* (May 1968).
(6) MIL-STD-202C, Method 106B, "Military Standard Test Methods for Electronic and Electrical Component Parts; Moisture Resistance," U. S. Defense Supply Agency, September, 1963.

RECEIVED October 18, 1968.

12

Electrodeposition of Surface Coatings
I. Electrochemical Reactions

G. SMITH and C. A. MAY

Shell Development Co., Emeryville, Calif. 94608

During the anodic deposition of a surface coating cyclic voltammetry studies show that a number of organic and inorganic reactions can occur. The method soon loses its value as an analytical tool, however, since a resistive film forms on the electrode masking the true working potential. Combining these findings with chemical analysis of the electrodeposited film and the anolyte gases reveals three possible anodic reactions: dissolution of the anode metal, the Kolbe oxidation of the carboxylate ions on the polymer, and oxidation of hydroxyl ions. The latter reaction is, in part at least, responsible for precipitation and coagulation of the polymer since a large pH drop is expected at or near the anode surface.

The electrodeposition of surface coatings is not a new process. As far back as 1936 a patent was issued to Cross and Blackwell Limited on a process and apparatus for the internal coating of metal containers (*6*). At that time suitable polymers were not available, and the process received little further acceptance.

The literature indicates that more recent interest could have commenced in the early 1950's (*11*). The automotive industry began the use of unitized body construction, and this proved quite troublesome. Severe corrosion problems were encountered in the bottoms of doors and rocker panels because these areas could not be protected adequately by conventional coating techniques. Studies by a major automobile manufacturer (*5*) indicated that electrodeposition could supply an answer. Coatings deposited in this manner developed high electrical resistivity, thus forcing the polymer to seek out uncoated areas. In addition the process had other attractive features—low fire hazard because of the essentially aqueous system, cost saving because of minimized needs for organic solvents, low vehicle solids in the bath meaning reduced inventories, simplicity of operation over manual application by spray, uniform coating thickness, etc.

The process is highly complex. This was pointed out in a series of early articles by Berry (*2, 3, 4*). It involves not only the physical movement and dehydration of the polymer but numerous organic and inorganic electrochemical reactions. More recently the theoretical aspects of the process have been discussed by Tawn and Berry (*12*), and a somewhat different view was presented by Beck (*1*). The latter article discusses a portion of the authors' efforts to understand better the fundamentals of the process.

The work reported herein was conducted using two carboxy terminated, epoxy based coating systems. Both of the base polymers had carboxylic acid contents of 0.09 equivalent per 100 grams. One vehicle was made by complete esterification of a bisphenol A epoxy resin with linseed fatty acids followed by subsequent reaction between the double bonds of the fatty acid and maleic anhydride. The other was an epoxy resin 40% esterified by linseed fatty acids, and the carboxy functionality was introduced by half-ester formation with phthalic anhydride. Thus, one resin system contained an aliphatic carboxylic acid function while the other was aromatic. The water solubilizing bases used were ammonia and triethylamine, respectively. A more precise description of these products is reported elsewhere (*13*).

Voltammetric Studies

The electrodeposition of a coating is generally carried out at high voltages wherein a low molecular weight polymeric material containing organofunctional groups is deposited on a metal electrode. Because of production requirements industrial processes are rarely run below 40 volts. Most electrocoating resins currently employed are carboxy containing polymers dissolved in aqueous bases; hence depositions occur on anodic surfaces. All of the known electrochemical reactions occurring at an anode require working potentials of less than +3.5 volts (*vs.* a standard calomel electrode). A broad spectrum of electrochemical reactions would thus appear possible. Our initial efforts were consequently directed to a study of the voltammetric aspects of the process, that is the voltage-amperage relationships on anodic surfaces.

Shown in Figure 1 are the voltammetric traces of the phthalated epoxy ester. The scan rate was one volt per minute. Three different anodic surfaces were used: platinum, mild steel, and a bonderized steel with a zinc phosphate surface (Bonderite 37). For clarity the curves obtained on the three substrates have been offset by 100 milliamperes.

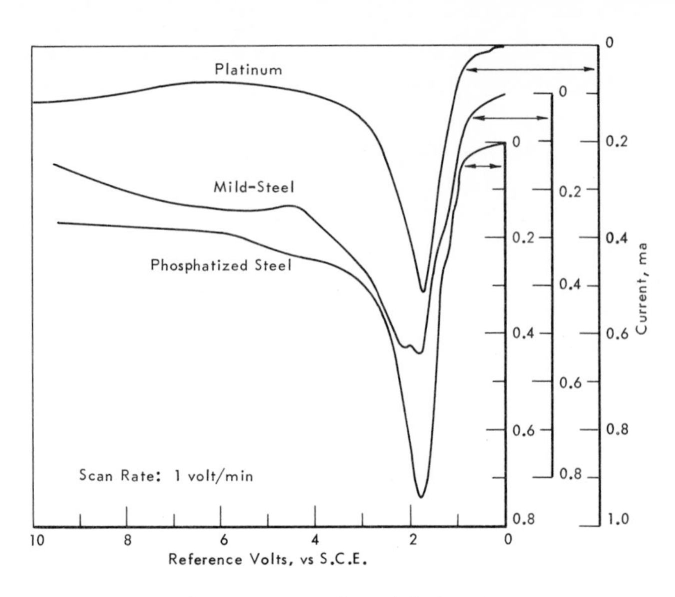

Figure 1. Voltammetry of the phthalated epoxy ester at different anodes

In the region of zero to one volt several shoulders are visible, indicative of oxygen evolution and/or metal dissolution. As will be shown later, oxygen is present in the anolyte gases. A major peak also appears at around 1.9–2.1 volts in each case. This is a region where many electroorganic reactions occur. It should be noted that the bonderized surface gave the highest peak indicating a greater degree of reaction. Interestingly, it has been found that bonderized metal surfaces coated by electrodeposition give generally better corrosion protection than mild steel. The mild steel anode shows a double peak; the significance of which at the moment, however, is not fully understood.

The results shown in Figure 2 were obtained using a commercial electrodeposition resin. The product is a combination of a phenol-formaldehyde resin and a carboxy terminated alkyd. The curves are much more complex. This is not entirely unexpected since a mixture of materials is involved. As in the first figure, major peaks are observed at around 1.9–2.1 volts. In addition, on all three metal surfaces, a third peak appears around 2.5 to 3.0 volts. The occurrence of the peaks in the 1.9–2.1 volt range for both this resin and the aforementioned phthalated epoxy ester indicates that both resins have some similarity of their organo-functional groups, probably carboxyl. The 2.5–3.0 volt peak indicates another type of electrochemical reaction. This could arise from reactions such as the oxidation of a different type of carboxyl group, the phenolic hydroxyl group, or oxidation of the aromatic nucleus itself (*10*). Reactions of the latter type are more likely to occur with aromatic rings containing substituents which make the nucleus more subject to electrophilic attack, such as the phenolic hydroxyl (*14*). The peak heights, that is the degree of reaction, follow the same general pattern as observed in Figure 1 with the bonderized metal surface showing the greatest reactivity.

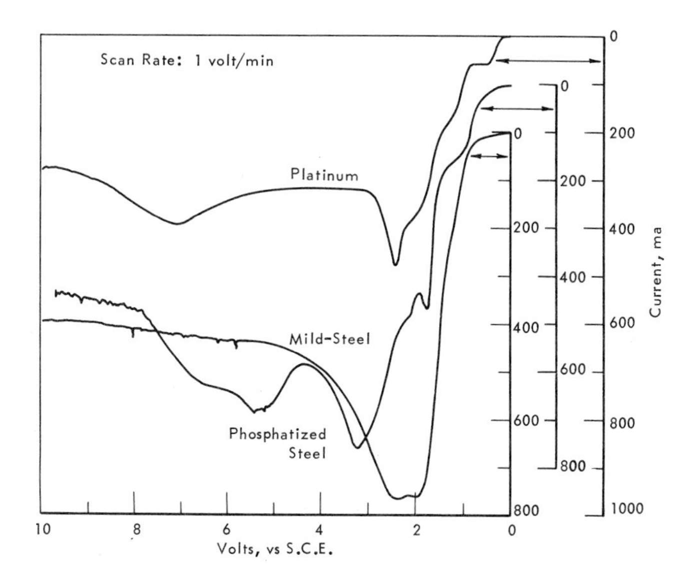

Figure 2. Voltammetry of a commercial alkyd-phenolic system at different anodes

In both figures, at potentials greater than about 3.0 volts, the waves become quite erratic and do not lend themselves to simple interpretation in terms of electrochemical reactions. This latter effect is probably caused by the electrodeposition of a highly resistant polymer film on the anode surface disguising the true current-voltage relationship.

The external voltage (E) applied to the electrodeposition cell can be considered to be composed of the voltage required to overcome resistances in the cell (IR) and the voltage required to set up the working potentials at both the anode (V_A) and the cathode (V_B).

$$E = IR + V_A + V_B$$

When a film is formed on the anode, the resistance of the film (R_F) increases the internal resistance of the cell circuit. Thus, a higher applied voltage must be supplied to maintain the initial working potentials at the electrodes.

$$E_1 = IR + V_A + V_B + IR_F$$

During the initial stages of the voltammetric investigation the anodic working potential measured by the reference probe (V_M) was indeed the actual working potential of the anode ($V_M = V_A$). However, as the voltammetric scan time increased, an anode film was being deposited which continually increased the resistance between the reference probe and the electrode. Thus, shortly after the onset of the scanning the measured anodic working potential differed from the true working potential to the extent of the potential drop across the film ($V_M = V_A + IR_F$).

The effect of the films' resistance on the measurement of working potential can be seen when the voltammetry is carried out in a series of repeating cycles using the same anode. The size of the anodic peak heights decreases with each cycle, indicating that the extent of the reaction is continually decreasing. The anodic reactions can thus only proceed at those points on the anode surface which have not been coated during the previous scanning operation. Microscopic examination of freshly deposited coatings reveal bare spots on the metal surface, supporting this hypothesis.

Because of the interference of the film in the voltammetric scanning it was felt that voltammetric investigations on an electrodeposition system had only limited applicability in the fundamental interpretation of the electrochemical reactions involved. The early portions of the scans (before film formation becomes significant) indicate that both inorganic and organic reactions occur, but a true evaluation of their relative magnitude in the overall process cannot be readily ascertained.

Voltammetric analysis may be used in a diagnostic sense, to determine the relative activity, the potential coating efficiency and the potential coating quality of a resin system. However, it cannot be considered as affording a quantitative analytical interpretation of the reactions occurring at the anode.

Electrode Reactions During the Deposition of Coatings

In view of the quality of coatings deposited on anodic surfaces, it would appear that other reactions occur in addition to the simple precipitation of the polymer in its acid form with subsequent coalescence. If organic electrochemical reactions take place, two benefits may arise; chemical interaction, allowing better adhesion of the deposited polymer to the substrate, and chemical reactions which cause an increase in molecular weight and enhance the deposition process. The latter would also permit thicker film build-up with less sagging during the subsequent baking. At times gel particles have been observed on attempted redissolution after deposition. Considering the voltammograms discussed previously three reactions appear possible at an anode:

1. Dissolution of iron from the anode could, under these conditions of high potential, produce some, if not all, of the iron species, ferrous to ferric or ferrite to ferrate.

$$Fe^{\circ} \xrightarrow{-2e^-} Fe^{2+} \xrightarrow{-e^-} Fe^{3+} \xrightarrow{-ne^-} Fe^{n+}$$

2. The Kolbe reaction involving carboxylate ions of the polymer. This could give rise to carboxylate radicals or to their decomposition products, a hydrocarbon radical and carbon dioxide.

$$RCOO^- \xrightarrow{-e^-} RCOO\cdot \rightarrow R\cdot + CO_2$$

3. The oxidation of hydroxyl ion, which has been postulated as proceeding *via* an active hydroxyl species, then hydrogen peroxide, before giving water and oxygen (7). This reaction is probably responsible for a part of the polymer precipitation and coagulation since a large pH drop would obviously occur at or near the anode surface.

$$4OH^- \xrightarrow{-4e^-} 4HO\cdot \rightarrow 2H_2O_2 \rightarrow H_2O + O_2$$

Iron Content of Films

Determination of the electrodissolved iron was made by laying down a series of coatings from the resin in question and subsequently measuring iron contents of both the films and the electrodeposition bath. The results are shown in Table I, all depositions being carried out at 60 volts for two minutes. As noted, almost all of the iron is in the deposited film; very little passed into the solution. Because of the small amount of material obtained from a single coating operation it was necessary to prepare 12 panels for each analysis. The same electrocoating bath was used to prepare the 12 coated panels in each batch. It should, therefore, be considered that, if both bath and film had an equal amount of iron from each deposition the quantity of iron found in the bath would be 12 times that found in the combined deposit, using resin solids content as a base. The fact that some iron is found in the bath is not too surprising

Table I. Iron Content of Films Deposited from Various Resin Systems (P.p.m. Iron on a Basis of Resin Solids)

Resin System	*Film*	*Solution*[a]
Maleinized epoxy ester	1240	13
Phthalated epoxy ester	830	<0.25
Alkyd-phenolic mixture	3120	66

[a] The values given are those resulting from coating 12 panels in the deposition bath.

in that metal substrates were always placed in the bath before switching on the current which allowed a short period for iron to dissolve directly into the bath.

In the case of the phthalated epoxy ester the electrodeposited film was also subjected to chemical analysis. In order to find out more about oxidation products which may have been present in the unbaked film a peroxide determination was made by the ferrithiocyanate method. The results proved negative. This indicated that the iron found in the film must be present as Fe^{2+}. Any trivalent iron would show up as peroxide by this technique. The electrode reaction involving iron should thus be:

$$Fe^{\circ} \xrightarrow{-2e^{-}} Fe^{2+}$$

Visual evidence also supports this conclusion. On removal of the panel from the electrodeposition bath the fresh coating is clear and colorless. However, after baking the film darkens to a yellow or light brown color. These observations are in agreement with others which indicate that the ferrous salts of carboxylic acids are usually colorless, whereas the ferric salts have a yellow or brown color.

Anolyte Gases

During the electrodeposition process large quantities of gas are evolved from the anode surface. In light of the potentials involved, as discussed above, it is not unreasonable to assume that a number of organic and inorganic electrochemical reactions occur. The system contains an aqueous solution of a carboxylic acid polymer and hence in addition to oxygen, carbon dioxide may be present as a result of the Kolbe electrolysis. The previously discussed voltammograms also indicate this possibility. Accordingly, an analysis of the anolyte gases was obtained using mild steel anodes.

For the purpose of conducting the analysis modifications of the anolyte area were made as shown in Figure 3. In carrying out the measurements the gas bell and the gas sampling tube were completely freed from any traces of oxygen by purging with pure nitrogen. Following this a slight vacuum was applied to draw some of the bath liquid into the gas collection bell. A slow stream of nitrogen was then introduced at the bottom of the anode so that it flowed up the anode surface simultaneously with the start of current passage. The current and voltage were adjusted, within the limits used for practical electrodepositions, to give the maximum volume of anolyte gas in the minimum time thus minimizing the nitrogen content of the gas sample as far as possible. This caused a lowering of the liquid in the gas sampling bell. When the liquid level in the bell reached that of the original bath level the current and gas flow were stopped. At 60 volts this operation required 0.25 to 0.5 of a minute. The anolyte gases and nitrogen sweep gas were subsequently drawn into the previously evacuated gas sampling tube. Analysis was conducted by means of a mass spectrometer. Some typical results appear in Table II.

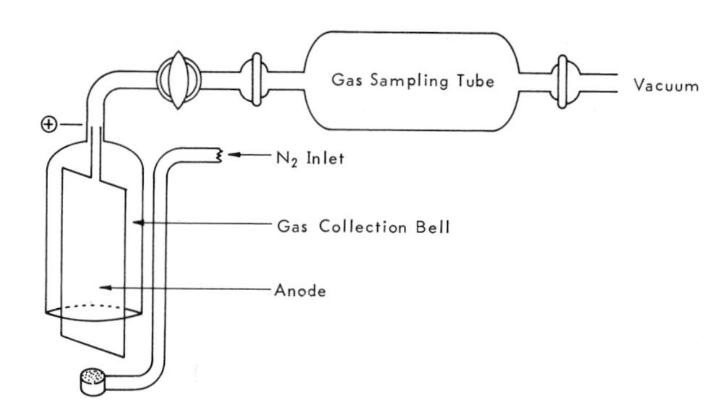

Figure 3. Anode modifications for anolyte gas collection

Table II. Typical Analysis of Anolyte Gases (Mole %)[a]

Resin System	*Phthalated Epoxy Ester*	*Alkyd-Phenolic*	*Maleinized Epoxy Ester*
Voltage	60	60	60
Time, min.	0.5	0.25	0.5
Hydrogen	—	0.4	0.6
Water	1.7	1.4	5.7
Nitrogen (sweep gas)	100.0	92	82
Oxygen	—	5.7	12.0
Carbon dioxide	—	0.0-0.1	0.2
sec-Butyl alcohol	—	0.2	—

[a] Uncorrected for proper closure.

Although the conditions used for these experiments were not optimum for analysis of the gaseous products, it was believed that a valuable and qualitative indication of the reactions occurring at the anode would be obtained. Inaccuracies could arise from the fact that carbon dioxide is slightly water soluble and could be lost if present in only small amounts. Further, different voltages caused variations in the gas analysis. Under this particular set of experimental conditions two of the resins evolved substantial quantities of oxygen. Oxygen evolution was also observed with the phthalated epoxy ester when this deposition was carried out at 10 volts. Perhaps the short reaction time employed in the gas analysis experiments is the reason that oxygen was not found in those reactions at higher voltage. The water found in the anolyte gases undoubtedly arose from the sweeping out of water vapor by the gaseous purge. The secondary butyl alcohol detected most probably comes from the auxiliary solvent used for the alkyd-phenolic system.

The detection of carbon dioxide can be taken as strong evidence that the Kolbe reaction occurs in both the alkyd-phenolic and maleinized epoxy ester systems. Its absence does not, however, preclude the possibility for the Kolbe reaction in the case of the phthalated epoxy ester. It has been established that aromatic carboxylic acids do not necessarily lose carbon dioxide following the one-electron transfer which forms the carboxylate radical of the Kolbe oxidation. It thus might be expected that this resin system will give products of the benzyloxy type—*e.g.*, esters. Ester formation has been observed as the principle route to the Kolbe reaction products derived from aromatic carboxylic acids (*8*, *9*), whereas alkylation is its usual result from aliphatic acids.

Formation of ester linkages in the case of the aromatic acid-based system was further supported by chemical analysis of the electrodeposited film. A substantial increase in ester value was found. In addition, some decrease in the acidity and virtually no change in the iodine number of the deposited resin offer the tentative explanation that a reaction of the carboxyl radicals with the fatty acid unsaturation has occurred. Gel particles were also found at times in the deposited films suggesting crosslinking.

$$RCOO\cdot + \text{—}CH_2\text{—}CH = CH\text{—} \rightarrow RCOOH + \text{—}CH\text{—}CH = CH\text{—}$$

$$\text{—}\dot{C}H\text{—}CH = CH\text{—} + RCOO\cdot \rightarrow RCOO\text{—}{'}CHCH = CH\text{—}$$

Conclusions

Based on the evidence presented it would appear that three main types of electrochemical reactions occur at an anode during the electrodeposition of surface coatings. These reactions result in iron dissolution from steel anodes, oxidation of hydroxyl ions to oxygen, and oxidation (Kolbe) of the carboxylate ions of resin. Large amounts of iron were found in the films, but only insignificant quantities were found in the bath, using three different resin systems. Anolyte gas analysis definitely indicated the possibility of hydroxyl ions and carboxylate ions' taking part in the electrochemical process. The latter oxidation was further indicated by increase in ester value of the electrodeposited film obtained from the phthalated epoxy ester, a reaction known to occur as a result of the Kolbe oxidation of aromatic acids in presence of olefins. Voltammetric studies indicate the existence of all three reaction types.

It can be calculated from the experimental results that iron dissolution accounts for 5% of the total current. The remainder of the current consumed must therefore be involved in reactions such as those concerning hydroxyl ions, carboxyl ions, and the electrophoretic discharge of the resin. Unfortunately, the experimental findings do not permit a quantitative separation of the organic and inorganic electrochemical reactions. Voltammetry fails to be of assistance here owing to the build-up of a resistant film on the anode, and gas analyses, besides the inaccuracies from solubility in the bath, vary with voltage.

The rates of the reactions involved during the course of electrodeposition of a coating are no doubt voltage dependent. The event probably most dependent on voltage is that of electrophoretic deposition. The data described also show that different resin systems react quite differently, producing different coatings. These factors tend to make accurate, quantitative estimates of the various reactions quite difficult.

Acknowledgments

The authors wish to acknowledge the most valuable assistance of D. B. Bruss in obtaining and interpreting voltammetric data for assistance in other experimental works thanks are due to C. M. Walkup and P. R. Schreiner.

Literature Cited

(1) Beck, J., *Farbe Lack* **72** (3), 218 (1966).
(2) Berry, J. R., *Paint Tech.* **27** (12), 13 (December 1963).
(3) *Ibid.*, **28** (1), 24 (January 1964).
(4) *Ibid.*, **29** (3), 53 (March 1964).
(5) Bogart, H. N., Burnside, R. L., Brewer, G. E. F., *SAE paper* **650270** **(988A)** (January 1965).
(6) Cross and Blackwell Ltd., *British Patent* **455,811,** October 28, 1936.
(7) Glasstone, S., Hickling, A., *J. Chem. Soc. (London)* **1934,** 1772.
(8) Rand, L., Mohar, A. F., *J. Org. Chem.* **30,** 3885 (1965).
(9) Rawlings, F. F., Thiessan, G. W., Peterson, P., *Electrochem. Tech.* **3,** 154 (May-June 1965).
(10) Ross, S. D., Finkelstein, M., Peterson, R. C., *J. Am. Chem. Soc.* **86,** 4139 (1964).
(11) Reeves, H. F., *Metal Finishing* **63,** 59 (February 1965).
(12) Tawn, A. R. H., Berry, J. R., *J. Oil and Colour Chemists' Assoc.* **48,** 790 (1965).
(13) v. Westrenen, W. J., Weber, J. R., Smith, G., May, C. A., VIIIth FATIPEC Congress, 126, Scheveningen, The Netherlands (June 1966).
(14) Vermillion, F. J., Pearl, I. A., *J. Electrochem. Soc.* **111,** 1392 (December 1964).

RECEIVED June 14, 1968.

13

Diafoams—New Lightweight Epoxy Foams

WARREN R. BECK, MARVIN W. SAGE, and DONALD L. O'BRIEN

Minnesota Mining & Manufacturing Co., St. Paul, Minn.

New lightweight epoxy foams have been prepared by introducing a second bubble phase into syntactic foams. These diafoams extend the useful range of syntactic foams to lower density ranges. They are stronger than air-blown foam at the same density. Resin-starved syntactic foams have also been prepared and tested. Using the diafoams the density can be calculated very accurately. By adding the secondary void phases to syntactic foams, the composite density can be reduced from 36 to 28 pcf. In all cases, the use of glass bubbles as the microvoid in the media gives maximum properties. Tests of laminate structures made with syntactic foams show that those made with glass bubbles retain more strength after exposure to moisture than foams made with sodium silicate bubbles.

This paper describes glass-bubble reinforced foams of densities lower than achieved previously, and some applications for these strong, light foams are noted. These reinforced foams are called syntactic foams, and they consist of a dispersion of small hollow glass spheres in a continuous phase or matrix.

Properties of Syntactic Foams

Resnick (*13*) compared the syntactic foams with other buoyant materials, and he found that the syntactics have a higher crush strength at any given density. Johnson *et al.* (*9*) showed the relative crush strengths of several types of hollow microspheres. The glass microbubbles have 50% volume collapse at hydrostatic pressures of 5000 p.s.i.g. and greater, while the sodium silicate and phenolic bubbles have 50% volume collapse at pressures of 600–1800 p.s.i.g.

Table I gives the hydrostatic crush strengths of a series of syntactic foams and shows that stronger bubbles permit a stronger foam, and that

Table I. Syntactic Foams Made with Different Bubbles
Matrix of Room Temperature Cured Epon 828—Versamid 125

Bubbles	*Vol. % Fill (best attainable)*	*Density, lbs./ft.^{3}*	*Uniaxial Compressive, p.s.i.g.*	*50% Crush of Bubbles*
Phenolic	42 (poorly wet)	47	About 5000	700
Stabilized sodium silicate glass	55	40	7700	1800
High strength glass B-22A	60	36	8100	4500
High strength glass B-35D	60	38	9000	7700

the foam strength exceeds the bubble strength. The superior strength of the syntactic foams over natural cellular materials like wood and expanded plastics like Styrofoam or foamed polyurethane makes them the material of choice for applications where hydrostatic and uniaxial compressive strengths are important. For some applications, the desired density is lower than that presently available in a syntactic foam. The density of a syntactic foam arises from two separate factors—the density of the resin matrix and the density and packing factor of the bubbles (in our case glass bubbles).

The range of sizes in any commonly available glass bubble sample is a skewed normal distribution below a given maximum. The best possible packing available with such a size range randomly distributed would be less than the theoretical maximum packing factor for uniform spheres of 60.5–62% (*16*). A continuous distribution of sizes over a restricted range will permit internal structures to form and enclose voids, resulting in a lower than theoretical packing factor (*7*).

If the lowest density available in a glass bubble sample is 0.20 gram/cc. and the densities of available thermosetting resins vary from 1.1 to 1.3 gram/cc., this results in a calculated density of:

$$0.20 \times 0.60 + 1.2 \times 0.40 = 0.60 \text{ gram/cc.}$$
$$(d_B) \times (\% \ V_B) + (d_M) \times (\% \ V_M) = (d_{foam})$$

As long as the geometry of the syntactic foam limits the lower density phase to 60% of the total volume, very little reduction in final foam density to below 0.6 can be expected.

The 60% packing factor for uniform spheres doesn't represent the most efficient arrangement for filling space. Extended vibration can increase the packing factor to 62.5% (*10*), and so can other methods of agitating the bubble bed. The explanation of this improved packing involves two mechanisms. The first supposes that the number of larger voids is reduced when the surrounding structural members receive a small kinetic energy to overcome friction and then rearrange into a higher packing by void collapse. The second predicts that the orthorhombic or usual packing obtained with initial compaction—not the most efficient space filling—is supplemented on extended vibration by some 20% of all possible double nesting (*2, 5, 6, 7, 10*).

Improved packing has also been noted when a liquid phase is introduced to prepare a slurry. Surface roughness prevents efficient statistical packing (*3, 12, 14*), and the introduced liquid can reduce surface friction resulting from roughness to almost zero.

When the particles are in intimate contact and the packing fraction is a maximum, the system is rigid. Since we desire a semiplastic or dilatant system, we lower the volume percent of bubbles slightly below that for the maximum packing fraction attainable. Since our goal is to extend the densities of syntactic foams below the density limitation of 0.60 gram/cc. mentioned, the packing factor must be increased if densities of bubbles and resins remain fixed.

Improved packing involves blending two or more sets of spheres whose diameter are in the ratio of at least 6 to 1 (*10*). No glass bubbles were available in the larger size range(s) desired (0.5–5 mm.), so other lightweight spheres were sought to increase the volume percent of low density material. Our goal was a non-rigid precured material that can be cast, troweled, or molded. The most natural matrix for the larger spheres is our precured syntactic foam described above.

Problems in Manufacturing Syntactic Foams

Slurries prepared from glass bubbles and epoxy resin are quite different from other dilatant slurries because the dispersed phase has a low density. The tendency toward settling causes the resin phase to go down and the glass bubbles to float out of the continuous phase upon standing. Even with the chosen resin system of 100 parts of Epon 828 (Shell Chemical Co.) to 100 parts of Versamid 125 (General Mills) the glass bubbles will migrate upward.

To prevent phase separation, the matrix should be made thixotropic or dilatant until the thermosetting resin can gel. Polymers which can make this resin system thixotropic have all been found to be somewhat incompatible with this matrix, and the resultant materials have low uniaxial compressive strengths. Soaps that make the resin phase thixotropic lower the compressive modulus and greatly increase the brittleness. Submicron inorganic thickening powders such as Cab-O-Sil have been used in syntactic foams, but at the levels necessary to prevent bubble migration there is tremendous air entrapment in non-spherical geometrical shapes, and the uncured syntactic foam becomes hard to work, even crumbly. It is impossible to mix the blend until it has almost gelled because the shear necessary to move such a viscous dilatant mixture will break the glass bubbles.

When glass microbubbles are added to saturate almost completely our viscous resin system, a dilatant mixture results. There is adequate pot life to this system for our purposes, but the dilatancy prevents separation of glass bubbles.

Comparison of Air Blown with Syntactic Foams

The advantages of a matrix of syntactic foam rather than air-blown or expanded foam are apparent when one compares the physical properties of these two types. Air-blown or expanded epoxy and urethane foams are usually made to have densities from about 2 to 18 pcf (lbs./cu. ft.) (*1*), although such foams are known with densities as high as 30 pcf.

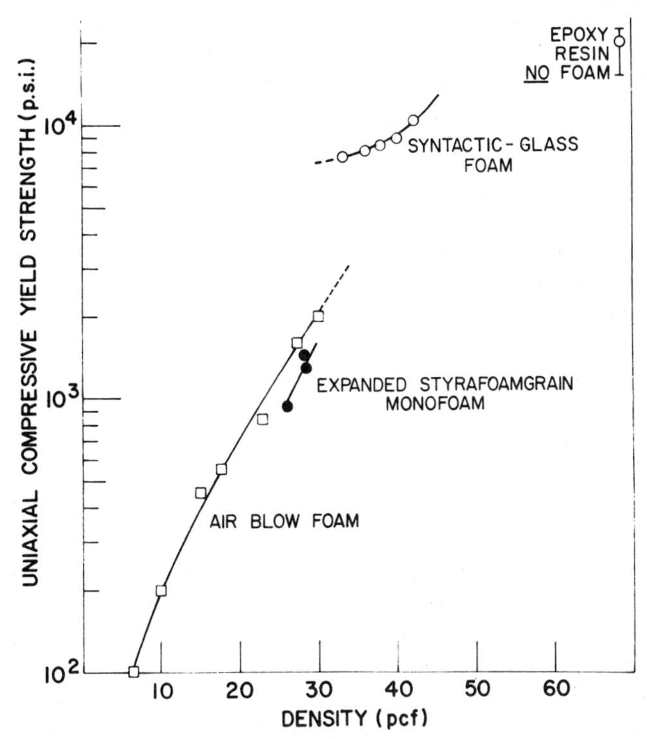

Figure 1. Strength–density ratios for air-blown and syntactic foams

At higher densities the air bubbles tend to rise, causing a stratification unless the matrix has a very high viscosity and a fairly short gel time. Inorganic thickeners add density to the composite and make the precured mass crumbly and subject to poor cohesion.

Syntactic foams commonly have densities of 34–44 pcf (*1, 9, 13*), although higher density foams have been prepared. Some very low density glass bubbles have produced 30-pcf syntactic foam, and denser glass bubbles are available to produce syntactic foams of higher density. Strength–density ratios for air-blown foams are compared with those for syntactic foams in Figure 1. At the point where the same density exists, the uniaxial compressive yield strength of the syntactic foam is much higher than that of the air-blown foam, but additional comparison is difficult because the density ranges don't overlap except in this case. These two types of foam are prepared for different end uses, and the expanded foam is used as a support member (where strength is critical) without reinforcement.

Resin-Starved Foams

Resin-starved foams are those in which the voids between packed glass bubbles are incompletely filled by the resin. They can be prepared by any method that will disperse uniformly a smaller volume of resin than that necessary to saturate the final composite. These resin-starved composites are open cell rather than closed cell; hence, they cannot be called diafoams.

A series of resin-starved composites was prepared and tested. Densities were 13–40 pcf. The density–compressive strength relation of a series of starved composites is recorded in Figure 2. The upper limit for density of the resin-starved composite is that of the syntactic foam. Since these foams are porous and have a lower strength than other available foams of the same density, there is no application requirement for them at the present time.

Diafoams

Syntactic monofoams require a volume fill of glass bubbles close to saturation. This gives a restricted density range with any given glass bubble and limits the practical available densities to 30–45 pcf, with a theoretical lower density limit at 25 pcf for resin alone. To overcome this, diafoams were contrived. A diafoam is a stable, predominantly closed cell foam of closely predetermined density comprising the three phases: (1) binder, (2) microcells, (3) macrocells. The binder is a polymer, the microcells are hollow spheres of 10–100μ average diameter,

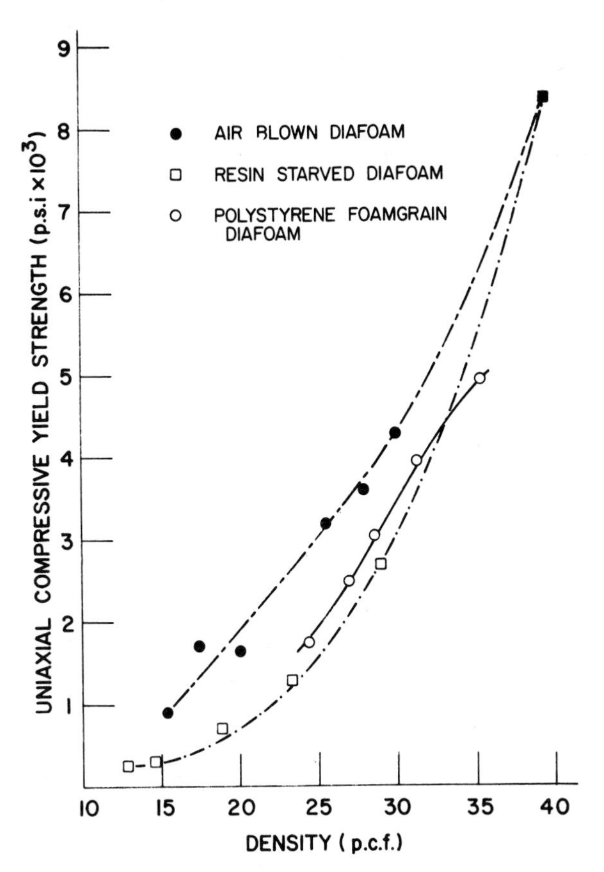

Figure 2. Density vs. *compressive strength for starved foams*

and the macrocells are spheres or spheroids averaging 10–100 times the diameter of the microcells.

Two basic types of macrocells are recognized—those prepared *in situ* by any of the standard expansion techniques for producing a gas bubble during the gel or cure cycle of the matrix, and those prepared as a separate spherical entity in advance and added to the syntactic foam matrix. The increased crush strength of a syntactic foam over that of the component bubbles (Table I) was expected to apply also to the foam made with macrobubbles.

Syntactic–Air Diafoams (blown)

Blown syntactic air diafoams are prepared by first including blowing agent ingredients with the epoxy resin in the matrix of a syntactic foam. At the appropriate designated temperature the blowing occurs in conjunction with gel formation, resulting in a composite of glass bubbles in a matrix of foamed epoxy, or air macrocells in a syntactic foam. The air bubbles must be small to have any strength advantage over air-blown monofoams. This is achieved by the standard technique of nucleation and blowing, careful control of times and temperatures, and use of foam control additives.

The density-*vs.*-compressive strength relation of a series of blown diafoams without large or connected voids is given in Figure 2. Densities of the gas blown diafoams are 15–40 pcf. The graph of this system shows that at a given density the blown diafoam has a higher strength than the starved diafoam.

Syntactic–Foamgrain Diafoams (mixed)

Foamgrains are also called macrospheres. They represent a second foam phase which is 10–100 times the diameter of the average glass bubble of which the syntactic foam is formed. These second foam phase particles are not formed *in situ* as the diafoam is prepared, but they are pre-formed, classified, treated, and then incorporated into the composite.

This second foamed or macrosphere phase is incorporated into the composite to reduce the density below that obtainable with syntactics at a minimal loss of strength. The second foam phase chosen has a very low density and can float out of its matrix unless that matrix has a very high visocity or unless there is some mechanism for agitating the reaction system until it gels (not a feasible solution when the matrix is a syntactic foam).

The chosen method of preparation is to mix the syntactic foam by first adding the bubbles to the resin mix and blending thoroughly. The foamgrains are then added and incorporated by kneading, as raisins are incorporated into a thick cake dough. Some small air bubble entrainment occurs and is acceptable as long as no large voids are produced. For example, 54 grams of Epon 828 (Shell) are blended thoroughly with 54 grams of Versamid 125 (General Mills) to give 100 cc. of resin. As soon as blending is considered complete, 51 grams (150 cc.) of glass bubbles (Type B-34D, density = 0.34) are added slowly and blended into the mix; 5.3 grams (107 cc.) of expanded "Styrofoam" granules, 10–18 mesh (density = 0.049), are worked into the mass by kneading. The composite is shaped by trowelling into molds, hardened at room temperature overnight, then cured at 180°F. for one hour. Samples made this way had a density of 24.3 pcf and a uniaxial compressive yield strength of 1700 p.s.i.g.

Most of these premixes are very thick and pasty and are filled almost to the point of becoming crumbly. These are trowellable diafoams.

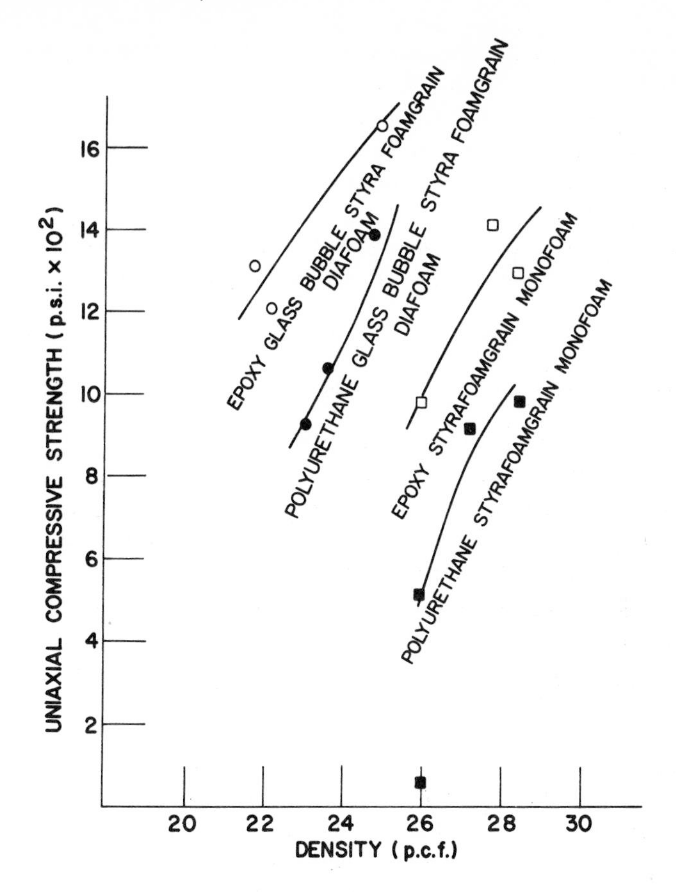

Figure 3. Comparison of media for diafoams and monofoams

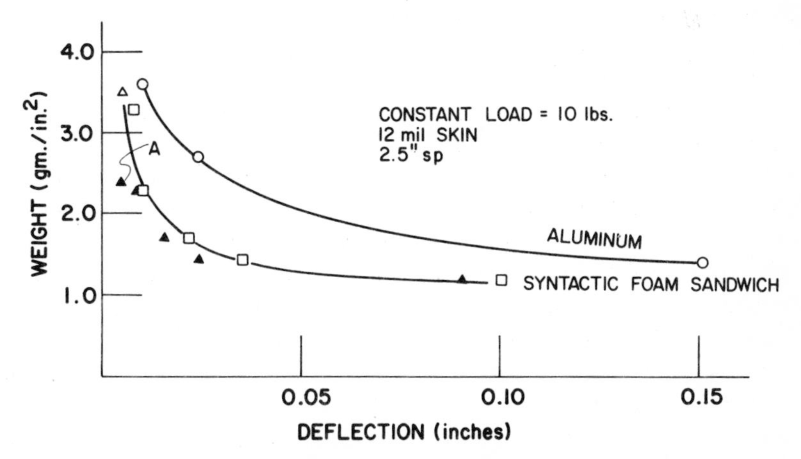

Figure 4. Deflection vs. *weight at constant load*

Where the total percent resin is decreased, a difficultly extrudable premix is obtained, which can only be pressure cast.

Diafoams are prepared from expanded polystyrene foamgrains (Sinclair Koppers Co.) dispersed in a syntactic epoxy foam matrix. The high viscosity of the syntactic foam prevents the foamgrains from floating up out of the matrix. Densities for representative diafoam samples range from 20 to 36 pcf. The plots of uniaxial compressive strength *vs.* density for some resin-starved foams and diafoams are presented in Figure 2.

Polyurethane vs. *Epoxy Media for Foams*

A series of foams was prepared by substituting for the epoxy matrix a rigid polyurethane matrix containing expanded polystyrene foamgrains with and without glass bubbles. This series was compared with a similar series using the epoxy matrix. The results of the tests of density and uniaxial compressive strength are plotted in Figure 3. Diafoams are stronger than monofoams here, and epoxy is stronger than polyurethane.

Uses of Epoxy Syntactic Foams and Diafoams

Syntactic foams have been suggested for use as a core material for structural laminates. Recently, this application has been expanded to include the use of both syntactic foams and diafoams as sandwich layers between aluminum skins. Under optimum conditions weight reductions of up to 50% can be obtained with sandwich constructions compared with aluminum sheets of equal flexural modulus (*see* Figure 4).

A laminate density of 0.858 gram/cc. was obtained using a syntactic foam and 12-mil aluminum skins at total thickness of 1/4 inch. Laminates of syntactic foam-air diafoams were made to lower the composite densities to the range 0.6–0.7 gram/cc. The physical properties of these laminates were compared with those of similar density foam where weight was removed by coring portions of the foam in an ordered pattern. Figure 5 shows that the strongest composites resulted when the heavier foams were cored. This suggests that honeycomb structures of syntactic foam can yield a higher strength per unit weight and permit even lower densities than presently available diafoams. Point A in Figure 4 represents such a structure, and the strength of this material surpasses that of an aluminum honeycomb or of balsa wood at a similar density.

The type of glass bubble used for core construction is a critical determinant of physical property retention under adverse exposure conditions. Figure 6 shows the results of strength tests made on syntactic foam cores before and after a 2-hour exposure to boiling water. The

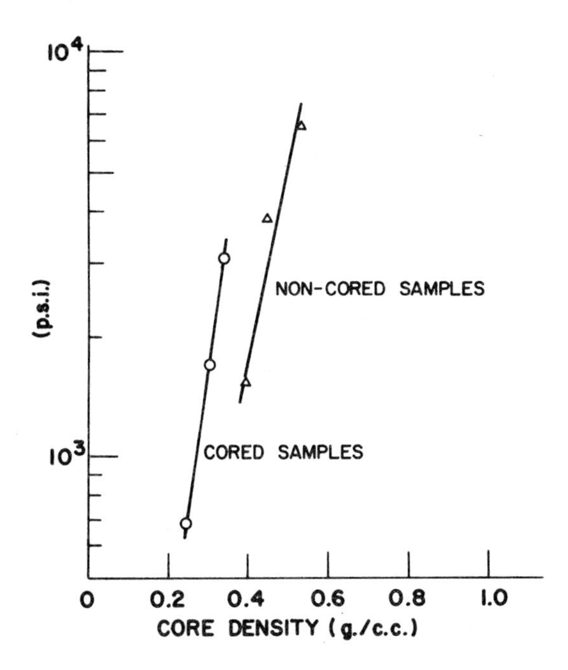

Figure 5. Cored and non-cored samples

glass spheres are stable towards water, and the foam retains its strength. The stabilized sodium silicate spheres are weakened by water, and the foam acts like an air foam with its characteristically lower strength.

The use of syntactic foams as buoyancy media for deep-diving undersea craft is well documented (*9, 13*). Syntactic foams have also gained wide usage for unmanned apparatus such as instrument capsules, cable buoys, seismic gear, etc. The ease of fabrication, reliability, and control of density (within certain limits) are attractive features for the use of syntactic foam in underseas applications.

Two-phase foams have also been suggested for buoyancy use (*4, 8*). Because of their lower crush strengths, these foams have been suitable only for shallow depths, such as in submarine appendage fillers

Syntactic foams and diafoams can be cast in place in a variety of shapes. The art object shown in Figure 7 was cast with syntactic foam. One key design requirement is the control of resin exotherms during cure. Thicknesses, cure temperature, and time must be arranged so that interior portions of the casting do not overheat. Female molds have been made by casting around the original object.

Syntactic foams handle much like soft metals or woods, and they are easily shaped, sanded, or worked into complex, intricate models. This property, coupled with the ease of casting, makes syntactic foams

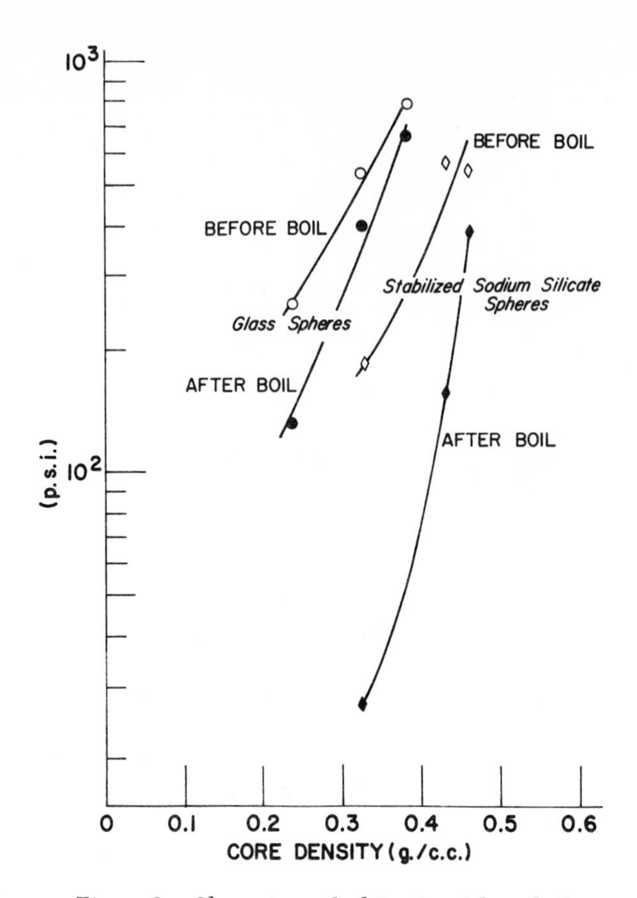

Figure 6. Shear strength shift after 2-hour boil

and diafoams useful for various modeling purposes. The ease with which syntactic foam is machined makes it ideal for models such as that in Figure 8.

The strength of glass bubbles has permitted the development of a commercial lightweight compression molding compound (*11*). With this material the lightweight pressings can be made by standard techniques. The glass bubble-filled objects are lighter in weight than the common mineral-filled materials (ratios of strength to weight being essentially equal), and they have lower thermal conductivity and better electrical properties. The lower thermal conductivity, for example, can be utilized in a baking dish handle which is gripped for removal from the oven, whereas mineral filled pressings cannot be held in the hand.

The newer diafoams have thus far found less utility as molding media, partly because of lower strengths and the absence of need for lower density. They can, however, be cast or trowelled into place easily,

Figure 7. Art object cast with syntactic foam

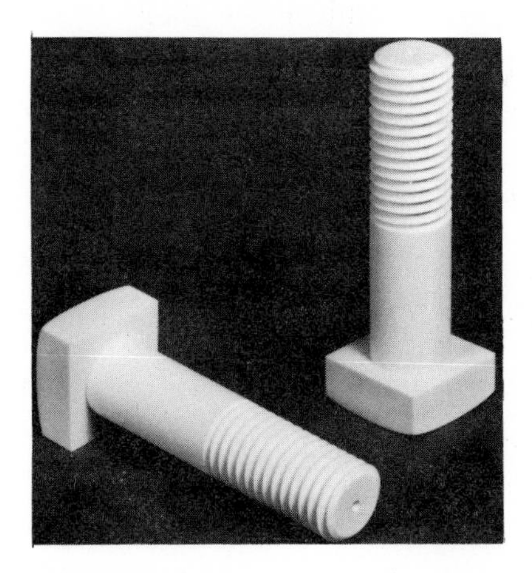

Figure 8. Machinability of syntactic foam permits the fabrication of pieces such as these bolts (4 inches long with seven threads per inch)

and they may be useful for applications where balsa wood is used but greater moisture resistance is desired. Further investigation of diafoam properties should indicate other application areas.

A summary of the applications of these new foams shows that secondary void phases have been added to syntactic foams to reduce composite densities from 36 to 28 pfc. Properties of these new lightweight foams have been measured, and in all cases the use of glass bubbles as the primary void media results in higher strengths. Exposure tests of laminate structures made from syntactic foams show that those made with glass bubbles retain more of their original properties than do other foams which have been made with sodium silicate bubbles.

Conclusions

The diafoams extend the useful range of bubble-filled syntactic foams down to lower densities. Their strength is greater than that of an air-blown foam at the same density. The resin-starved foams also extend the useful range of densities to lower values at greater strength than expanded foams, but these are open-cell foams. The diafoam density is lowered below that of syntactic foam by obtaining a higher packing fraction by using a wider range of sizes of packed spheres of low density and by incorporating a macrosphere of very low density. The final density achieved with an air-blown foam is often uncertain. With a mixed diafoam it is possible to calculate the final density of the composite from the densities and volume percentages of the ingredients. Practice in the manufacture of diafoams should result in the ability to predict final densities as accurately as those of syntactic foam.

Literature Cited

(1) Bender, R. J., "Handbook of Foamed Plastics," Lake, Libertyville, 1965.
(2) Chessick, J. J., Zettelmoyer, A. C., Christian, J. B., *Can. J. Chem.* **41,** 1619 (1963).
(3) Crosby, E. J., *Am. Perfumer Aromat.* **75,** 43 (Sept. 1960).
(4) Gross, S., *Undersea Technol.* **7** (3), 23 (1966).
(5) Heckel, R. W., *Trans. Am. Soc. Metals* **221,** 671 (1961).
(6) *Ibid.,* p. 1001.
(7) Heywood, H., *Powder Met.* **7,** 1 (1961).
(8) *Ind. Equipment News* **34** (9), 12 (1966).
(9) Johnson, R. W., Montgomery, P. W., O'Brien, D. L., *Mater. Eng.* **66** (3), 75 (1967).
(10) McGeary, R. K., *J. Am. Ceram. Soc.* **44,** 513 (1961).
(11) "Molding Compounds X4586 and FM-4555," Fiberite Corp., Winona, Minn.
(12) Orr Jr., C., DallaValle, J. M., "Fine Particle Measurement," MacMillan, New York, 1959.

(13) Resnick, Israel, *Mod. Plastics* **43** (1), 144 (1965).
(14) Robertson, R. H. S., Emodi, B. S., *Nature* **152,** 539 (1943).
(15) Seelig, R. P., Wulff, J., *Trans. AIME* **166,** 492 (1946).
(16) White, H. E., Walton, S. F., *J. Am. Ceram. Soc.* **20,** 155 (1937).

RECEIVED October 7, 1968.

14

Extracoodinate Siliconate Salts as Latent Epoxy Resin Curing Agents

HAROLD L. VINCENT, CECIL L. FRYE, and PAUL E. OPPLIGER

Dow Corning Corp., Midland, Mich. 48640

The thermal instability of penta- and hexacoordinate siliconate derivatives of catechol suggested their possible utility as latent heat activated epoxy resin curing agents. Although numerous methods have been described for attenuating the activity of amines in epoxy systems, the siliconates possess unique opportunities for structural modification and consequent tailoring of their latency. Illustrative examples of siliconates containing crosslinking agents—i.e., *primary and secondary aliphatic amines and aromatic amines—and catalytic amines*—i.e., *tertiary amines—are discussed.*

Wide interest in latent epoxy curing agents coupled with the development of a little known branch of organosilicon chemistry has led to a new family of heat activated, amine type, epoxy curing agents. In **1931**, Rosenheim (5) reported the preparation of crystalline salts containing the dibasic hexacoordinate siliconate anion $[Si(C_6H_4O_2)_3]^{2-}$ from the reaction of silica with aqueous ammoniacal catechol:

$$SiO_2 + 3\ C_6H_4(OH)_2 + 2\ NH_4OH \rightarrow [Si(C_6H_4O_2)_3]^{2-}(NH_4^+)_2(H_2O)_x$$

He noted that other bases such as guanidine, pyridine, dimethylaniline, potassium hydroxide, or barium hydroxide could be employed. These studies were complicated by the presence of hydrated products arising from the use of aqueous media. It was recently found (2) that anhydrous, but otherwise analogous products could be readily prepared starting from ethyl silicate rather than silica. Furthermore, this type of reaction was extended to include organosilicon derivatives (3) such as $ZSi(OMe)_3$ where Z can be alkyl or aryl. In contrast to the hexacoordinate siliconates, these organosilicon derivatives were found to be pentacoordinate silicon species (I and II, where R can be hydrogen, alkyl or aryl).

I. $(R_4N^+)_2$ Si^{2-} $\left(C_6H_4O_2 \right)_3$ II. R_4N^+ ZSi^- $\left(C_6H_4O_2 \right)_2$

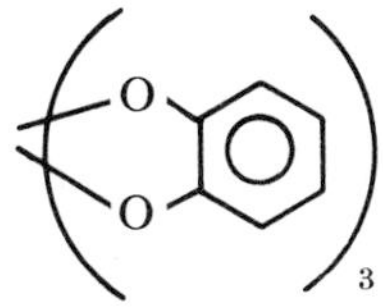

Hexacoordinate Pentacoordinate

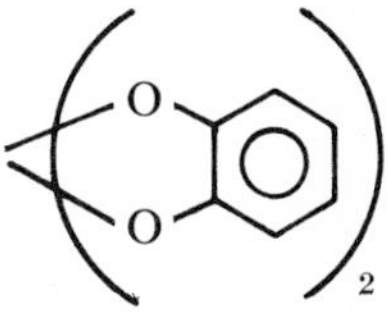

Bases ranging in strength from pyridine to quaternary ammonium hydroxides have been used in preparing these extra-coordinate siliconate salts. Extracoordinate siliconates of increased amine content have also been prepared in which some of the amine remains unprotonated (*4*). These amine-enriched penta- or hexacoordinate salts retain thermal stability comparable with that of the salts in which all of the amine is protonated. The stability of these materials at ambient temperature, the variety of amines that can be incorporated into their structure, coupled with their relative instability at higher temperatures suggested their evaluation as latent, heat activated epoxy curing agents.

It should be noted that related borate structures (*6*) have been used for many years as vulcanizing agents for chloroprene polymers (*1*). The siliconates are more versatile than the borates, however, since one may vary the substituent on the silicon and thereby alter the stability of the pentacoordinate siliconate salt. Furthermore, their marked tendency to incorporate additional amine molecules affords increased efficiency. Their epoxy curing action is believed to depend on thermal transformation of the salt to a free base and a tetracoordinate silicon species—*e.g.*,

$$PhCH_2\overset{+}{N}HMe_2\ Ph\ \overset{-}{Si}(C_6H_4O_2)_2 \xrightarrow{\Delta} PhCH_2NMe_2 + PhSi(C_6H_4O_2)(OC_6H_4OH)$$

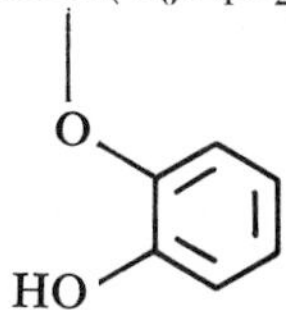

The above is supported by mass spectral studies which showed cation derived parent ions corresponding to the loss of one hydrogen—*i.e.*, benzyldimethylammonium salts gave $PhCH_2NMe_2$ parent ion peak) and anion derived parent ions corresponding to the acquisition of a hydrogen. In the case of quaternary ammonium salts, a small alkyl was transferred instead of a hydrogen. The hexacoordinate species are believed to undergo decomposition by analogous processes.

Experimental

Preparation of Amine Salts. These materials were readily prepared by simply warming the appropriate reactants in a suitable solvent.

BENZYLDIMETHYLAMINE SALT. Benzyldimethylammonium bis(*o*-phenylenedioxy)phenylsiliconate was prepared in 74% yield from a methanol solution of $PhSi(OMe)_3$, catechol and benzyldimethylamine. The reactants were boiled on a hot plate for 10–15 minutes during which time a crystalline solid deposited. This material was filtered out, washed with cold methanol, and evacuated to constant weight: m.p. 196°–198°C. *Anal.* Calc'd. for $SiC_{27}H_{27}O_4N$: C, 70.9; H, 5.91; Si, 6.14; N, 3.06; neut. equiv., 457. Found: C, 70.9; H, 6.08; Si, 5.98; N, 3.00; neut. equiv., 462.

***m*-Phenylenediamine Salt.** Catechol (0.030 mole), *m*-phenylenediamine (0.030 mole), and ethyl silicate (0.067 mole) were placed in a 125 ml. Erlenmeyer flask and heated on a hot plate for 45 minutes at 120°–140°C. The resulting crystalline material was diluted with benzene, heated to 75°C., filtered and washed with warm benzene. A yield of 89% (m.p. 190°–200°C.) was obtained after evacuating to constant weight. Larger scale preparation of this material was readily carried out in 98–100% yields without difficulty; furthermore, it was not necessary to use greater than the stoichiometric amount of *m*-phenylenediamine. The above example employed a 50% excess of *m*-phenylenediamine. *Anal.* Calc'd. for $Si_{30}H_{30}N_4O_6$: C, 63.2; H, 5.26; N, 9.82; Si, 4.92; neut. equiv., 142.5. Found: C, 64.3; H, 5.47; N, 8.66; Si, 4.85; neut. equiv., 151.

Benzyltrimethylammonium Hydroxide Salt. A 30% by weight methanol solution (1.00 mole of contained base) was added to a solution of catechol (2.00 mole) in 200 ml. of methanol. Combination of the two materials resulted in a considerable exotherm and after cooling to room temperature, $PhSi(OMe)_3$ (1.00 mole) was added. A crystalline product precipitated shortly thereafter. This product was collected by filtration, washed with methanol, and evacuated to constant weight. A 92% yield of a product melting with decomposition at 211°–213°C. was obtained. *Anal.* Calc'd. for $SiC_{28}H_{26}NO_4$: C, 71.4; N, 2.97; Si, 5.96; neut. equiv., 471. Found, C, 71.3; N, 2.74; Si, 6.29; neut. equiv., 481.

Recrystallization from methanol lowered the neutralization equivalent to 474.

Evaluation Procedure. These materials were evaluated as potential latent curing agents using both liquid DER 331 (The Dow Chemical Company) (EEW 190) and solid DER 664 (The Dow Chemical Company) (EEW 925) bisphenol A/epichlorohydrin epoxy resins. The salts were mixed in near stoichiometric amounts with the liquid epoxy resins using either hand stirring or a mechanical device such as a three-roll mill or a Baker-Perkins Mixer. The solid epoxy resins were mixed with the siliconate salts by either dry blending and passing the mixture through a hammer mill or by milling the ingredients on a warm two-roll mill. The gel time of these systems was obtained at some elevated temperature, generally 147°–200°C., and the system was aged at or near room temperature to determine the degree of latency.

The most promising candidates were further evaluated by more realistic testing as adhesives. Lap shear adhesive specimens were prepared from individual 1 inch × 3 inch × 0.090 inch aluminum panels with a 3/8 inch hole drilled 1 inch from an end. A standard 1/2 inch overlap was used for the bonded area. While an attempt was made to keep the bond line at a constant thickness by using a uniform technique, no rigorous method, such as the use of shims, was employed.

The surface preparation for the aluminum test panel was:

1. Liquid hone the surface to a uniform smoothness.
2. Wash with water and acetone; further cleanse in perchloroethylene vapor bath.
3. Etch panels 15 minutes in at bath of 30 parts distilled water, 10 parts sulfuric acid, and 1 part sodium dichromate at 65°C.
4. Rinse with distilled water and dry at 150°C.

The lap shear specimens were pulled at a speed of 0.05 inch/minute. All tests were conducted at room temperature.

Results and Discussion

Degree of Latency. The effect of the silicon substituent in a series of benzyldimethylammonium salts was measured by obtaining T.G.A. weight loss data on the salts. These data were then compared with the 200°C. gel time and the shelf life at ambient temperatures of a solid epoxy resin formulated with 14 p.h.r. trimellitic anhydride and 2 p.h.r. of the amine-containing salt. The salt in this case was used as an accelerator for the anhydride cure system (Table I).

Table I. Stability Effects of Silicon Substituent Group (Benzyldimethylammonium Salts)

Substituent Group (Z)	*T.G.A. Wt. Loss (Temperature at 10% Wt. Loss)*	*200°C. Gel Time (seconds)*	*Shelf Life (months)*
Vinyl (Pentacoordinate)	—	Gelled	0
methyl (Pentacoordinate)	125°C.	Gelled	0
phenyl (Pentacoordinate)	220°C.	8.5	5
none (Hexacoordinate)	185°C.	5.0	1

Electron-donor groups on the silicon produce increased reactivity as evidenced by gelation when the vinyl and methyl substituted salts were hot-milled into the solid epoxy resin-anhydride system. Apparently, the aryl pentacoordinate species are more latent than related hexacoordinate analogs since the aryl species show more thermal stability and longer shelf life. The effect of the substituent group on the reactivity or thermal stability of these materials has been observed with other amine salts and can be a useful tool in regulating the shelf life and cure schedule of epoxy resins.

The effect of the level of phenyl substituted benzyldimethylammonium salt on the gel time of the above resin is shown in Table II. The shelf life of these epoxy resin-anhydride systems using this salt as an accelerator was always in excess of three months and often exceeded one year.

Table II. Dependence of Gel Time on Accelerator[a] Concentration

Amount in p.h.r.	*200°C. Gel Time (seconds)*
0.5	15
1.0	11
1.5	9
2.0	8

Formulation: 100 pts. solid epoxy resin EEW of 925
8 pts. trimellitic anhydride

[a] Benzyldimethylammonium bis(*o*-phenylenedioxy)phenylsiliconate.

Epoxy resins containing a crosslinking type of siliconate curing agent—*i.e.*,

$$(H_2NCH_2CH_2N^+H_3)_2\, Si^{2-}(C_6H_4O_2)_3,$$

were aged at temperatures of 43°, 56°, and 70°C. as well as room temperature. The shelf life of these materials, as measured by the loss of tack when warmed on a hot plate, at the various temperatures was plotted on an Arrhenius graph. Extrapolation of these points proved to be a useful indicator of the shelf life of these systems at ambient conditions. The data on two formulations is given in Figure 1. It appears that the systems represented will have an extrapolated shelf life in the range of 400–600 days. Actual long term aging at ambient temperatures has resulted in shelf life measurements of greater than 300 days. This application of the Arrhenius theory has proven to be extremely useful in determining the degree of latency of these extracoordinate siliconate salts.

Speed of Cure. The ability of the extracoordinate siliconate amine salts to cure epoxy resins was determined by evaluating the elevated temperature gel time and the measurement of adhesive strengths using various cure schedules. Figure 2 illustrates the effect of temperature on the gel time of the solid epoxy resin cured with 8 p.h.r. trimellitic anhydride and using 2 p.h.r. benzyldimethylammonium phenylsiliconate as

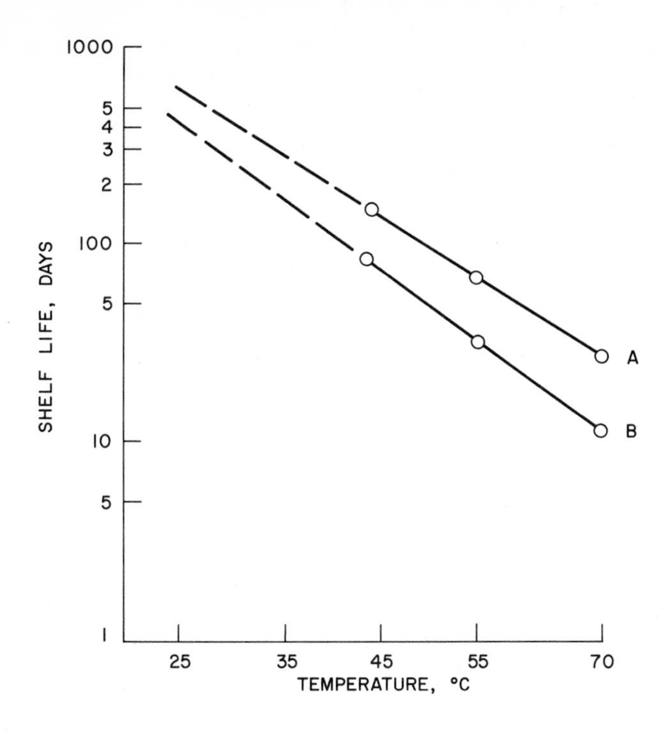

Figure 1. Shelf life of epoxy-ethylene diammonium siliconate systems

Formulation A: 100 pts. EEW 190 and 35 pts. siliconate
Formulation B: 55 pts. EEW 190, 45 pts. EEW 925, and 40 pts. siliconate

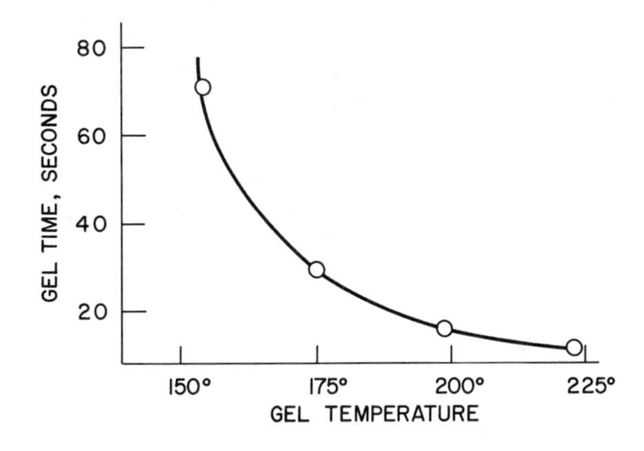

Figure 2. Dependence of gel time on temperature

Formulation: 100 pts. EEW 925, 8 pts. Trimellitic anhydride, and 2 pts. $BzMe_2N$ siliconate

an accelerator. The gel time of this system is about 25 seconds at 175°C., while the gel time of an analogous system without the accelerator was about 100 seconds when measured at 175°C. This tertiary amine accelerator does not appear to function with anhydride cured epoxy systems at temperatures much below 150°C. Siliconates which utilized benzyltrimethylammonium hydroxide as the base were readily prepared and were observed to have about the same effect as the corresponding benzyldimethylammonium siliconate. However, these quaternary ammonium salts did exhibit shorter shelf lives when used in similar epoxy systems.

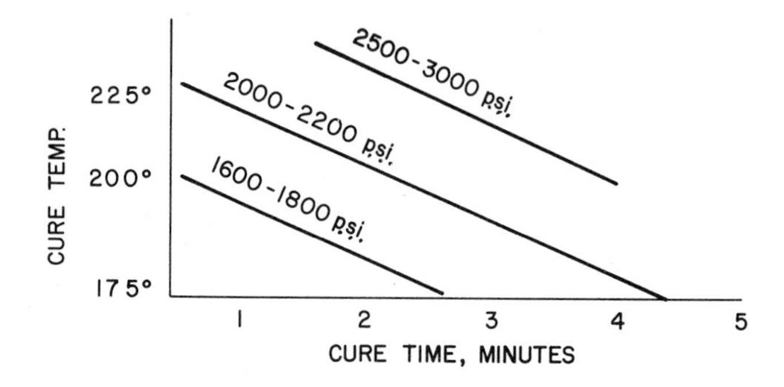

Figure 3. Typical adhesive properties (lap shear strength)

Formulation: 100 pts. EEW 190 and 35 pts. Ethylenediamine siliconate

Figure 3 illustrates the strength parameters achieved by the liquid epoxy resin cured with 35 p.h.r. of the above ethylenediamine derivative. Lap shear strengths of 2500–3000 p.s.i. were obtained with the use of a short cure cycle. Although 35 p.h.r. of this siliconate would be considered a stoichiometric amount, adequate adhesive strengths could be obtained with lesser amounts (Table III).

Table III. Dependence of Adhesive Strength on Curing Agent[a] Concentration

Curing Agent Concentration Parts Per Hundred Resin	*Adhesive Strength Lap Shear—p.s.i.*
10	600- 700
15	2000-2100
20	2000-2100
25	2100-2200
35	2300-2500

Cure cycle of 60 minutes at 150°C.

[a] $(H_2NCH_2CH_2N^+H_3)_2\,Si^{2-}(C_6H_4O_2)_3$.

Increasing the cure temperature to 175°C. resulted in lap shear values of 2500–3000 p.s.i. with the 25 p.h.r. hardener concentration. Cure temperatures above 175°C. appear to result in some void formation in the glue line. This could be caused by the rapid release of volatile products such as ethylenediamine at these temperatures. The effect of using less volatile analogs such as triethylenetetraamine has not been examined in this application, but might permit void-free cures at even higher temperatures.

Aromatic amines such as *m*-phenylenediamine and 4,4′-methylenedianiline have been incorporated into the siliconate structure. However, the adhesive strengths of a system containing 100 parts of the liquid epoxy resin and 31 parts of the analogous bis(metaphenylenediamine) derivative were in the 980–1100 p.s.i. range after a cure cycle of 20 to 180 minutes at 175°C.

Films, Prepregs, and Laminates. Mixtures of the liquid and solid epoxy resin were combined with the above bis(ethylenediamine) siliconate. The resulting putty could be pressed into unsupported films or dissolved in toluene and applied to glass and nylon cloth to form supported films. Adhesive lap shear strengths comparable with the paste system were obtained.

Table IV. Typical Laminate Properties

Formulation 1 — 100 parts epoxy resin EEW 825; 9 parts curing agent[a]

Formulation 2 — 100 parts epoxy resin EEW 190; 35 parts curing agent[a]

Formulation 3 — 100 parts epoxy resin EEW 825; 10 parts trimellitic anhydride; 2 parts curing agent[a]

Formulation	Flexural Strength: *As Received*	Flexural Strength: *After 2 Hr. Water Boil*
1	77,700	70,300
2	74,000	55,700
3	70,100	57,800

[a] $(H_2NCH_2CH_2N^+H_3)_2\ Si^{2-}(C_6H_4O_2)_3$.
[b] $PhCH_2N^+H(CH_3)_2\ PhSi^-(C_6H_4O_2)_3$.

Laminates were prepared by applying the epoxy resin-curing agent to Dow Corning Z-6040 treated 181 style glass cloth. Fourteen plys of prepreg were laminated for 30 minutes at 150°C., and 30 p.s.i. The results are shown in Table IV.

Summary

Penta- and hexacoordinate catechol siliconate derivatives of amines have been shown to be effective epoxy curing agents. Excellent shelf life along with fast cure were obtained on many epoxy systems. Several of these siliconate salts were evaluated in adhesive formulations and good strengths were obtained. These new latent epoxy curing agents should prove useful in such epoxy formulations as adhesives, encapsulants, castings, coatings, laminates, molding compounds, sealants, and tooling compounds.

Literature Cited

(1) Baum, A. A., *U. S. Patent* **2,544,746** (1949).
(2) Frye, C. L., *J. Am. Chem. Soc.* **86,** 3170 (1964).
(3) Frye, C. L., *U. S. Patent* **3,355,477** (1967).
(4) Frye, C. L., *Canadian Patent* **751,461** (1967).
(5) Rosenheim, A., Raibmann, B., Schendel, G., *Z. Anorg. Allgem. Chem.* **196,** 160 (1931).
(6) Williams, I., Neal, A. M., *U. S. Patent* **1,975,890** (1932).

RECEIVED August 5, 1968.

15

The Design and Synthesis of Epoxy Resins for Rapid Room Temperature Cures with Primary Amines in Small Masses

ARTHUR L. CUPPLES, HENRY LEE, and DONALD G. STOFFEY

Research & Development Center, The Epoxylite Corporation, South El Monte, Calif.

Very little has been reported in the epoxy resin literature on epoxy resins designed to cure in small masses of 1–10 grams at room temperature in less than 10 minutes. As a result, over 40 resins of eight classes, the mononuclear aromatic glycidyl ether, di- and polynuclear aromatic glycidyl ether, other mono- and dinuclear epoxy resins including alicyclic glycidyl and peracetic acid route, triazine based glycidyl and glycidyl ether, fluorinated glycidyl ether, cyano glycidyl ether, glycidyl amine, and glycidyl sulfonamides were either synthesized or purified. They were evaluated for reactivity using the primary amines, triethylene tetramine and 1,4-cyclohexane bis(methylamine). The triglycidyl ether of phloroglucinol and the triglycidyl ether of resorcinol were found to be the most reactive of the epoxy resins evaluated even though none of them meet the design criteria.

An extensive study of the epoxy resin literature (*2, 3, 4, 6, 7, 8, 10*) leads to the observation that very little has been reported on epoxy resins designed to cure in small masses at room temperature in less than 10 minutes. The commercial applications for this type of system are varied and can range from tube adhesives for rapid bonding of small electrical components to dental restoratives and adhesives which must cure in very thin sections in a short time (*5*).

In an effort to design and prepare epoxy resins and curing agents for fast, room temperature cures in small masses, a synthesis and study program was undertaken. The targeted requirements, as shown in Figure 1, are for a sample of 1–10 grams which would cure in less than 10

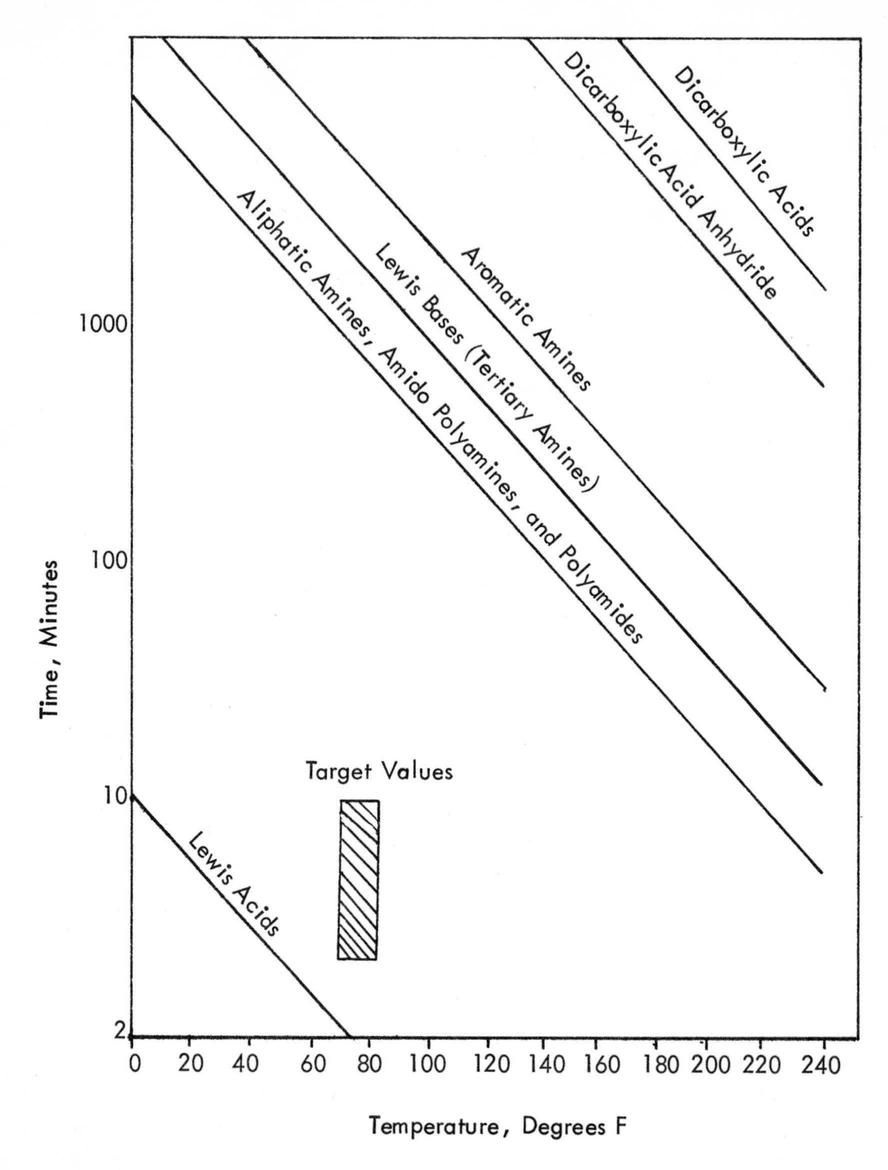

Figure 1. Typical Arrhenius plot showing reaction rates of small masses of diglycidyl ether of bisphenol A epoxy resins with six typical curing agents compared with time and temperature requirements of the target material

minutes at room temperature (20°–25°C.). Figure 1 is also a typical Arrhenius plot showing the reaction rates of small masses of epoxy resins of the general commercial epichlorohydrin bisphenol type—*i.e.,* diglycidyl ether of bisphenol A—with six typical epoxy curing agents compared with the time and temperature requirements of the target specification. It can be seen that the Lewis acid cured systems, while being extremely reactive, are too reactive, with the reactions going to substantial completion in just a few seconds to several minutes at room temperature. Attempts to lengthen the cure time of Lewis acid catalyzed systems to the target requirements involved the study of over 50 Lewis acids and combinations of these with polyglycols and six reactive epoxy resins. They exhibited "go or no go" characteristics. Either the reactions were too rapid and caused charring within a few seconds to two minutes, or no cure at all would take place (5).

As a consequence, subsequent studies involved the primary aliphatic amine curing agents, which, while less reactive than the Lewis acids, did offer the advantages of ease of handling and good over-all physical properties. The selection of amines as the curing agents also narrowed the choice of epoxy resins because the reactivity of the epoxide ring is determined by the accessibility of the epoxy groups as well as by the electronic nature of the epoxy oxygen. Studies have shown that the glycidyl epoxide group is the most reactive toward the amine or basic type of curing agents since the principal mode of attack by the amines is on the terminal carbon of the epoxide group—*i.e.*, nucleophilic attack (6). As a result the diglycidyl ether of bisphenol A (DGEBA), a liquid epoxy resin,

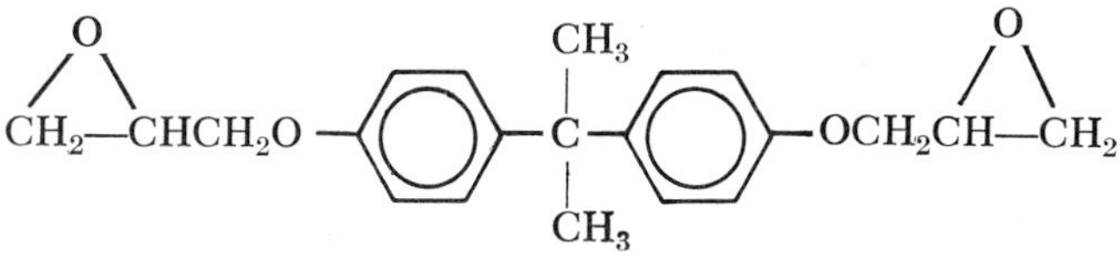

$$CH_2(O)CHCH_2O-C_6H_4-C(CH_3)_2-C_6H_4-OCH_2CH(O)CH_2$$

Diglycidyl Ether of Bisphenol A (DGEBA)

having terminal glycidyl ether epoxide groups, was chosen as a standard reference resin.

The basic problem of reactivity of this and other epoxy resins may be separated into three aspects: (1) the influence of mass, (2) the effect of temperature, and (3) the effect of chemical structure.

The influence of mass on setting time is illustrated in Figure 2. Here the effect of exothermic heat is illustrated. When curing large masses, the exothermic heat released as the resin cures is trapped within the bulk of the resin. This heats the resin and accelerates the cure. If the size of the reacting mass is decreased, the exothermic heat has more chance of being conducted away, and the gel time and cure time of the resin are significantly lengthened as shown. Thus, a resin which is used in industrial size masses of 1–10 pounds may set in 10 minutes with a certain amine curing agent; when the mass is reduced to 1–10 grams, it may require hours to set.

The effect of temperature on the reactivity is roughly illustrated by the Arrhenius equation in which a 10°C. temperature rise is said to double the rate of reaction. In the present studies, however, the curing temperature was held constant, and the mass influence was negligible because of the small mass, leaving the chemical structure as the only factor influencing reactivity.

On the basis of these concepts, a series of resins of varying structure were tested. These resins were of the following types: mononuclear aromatic glycidyl and glycidyl ether epoxy resins; polynuclear aromatic glycidyl ether epoxy resins; aromatic glycidyl epoxy resins; hydrogenated glycidyl ether, glycidyl, and peracetic acid route epoxy resins; triazine

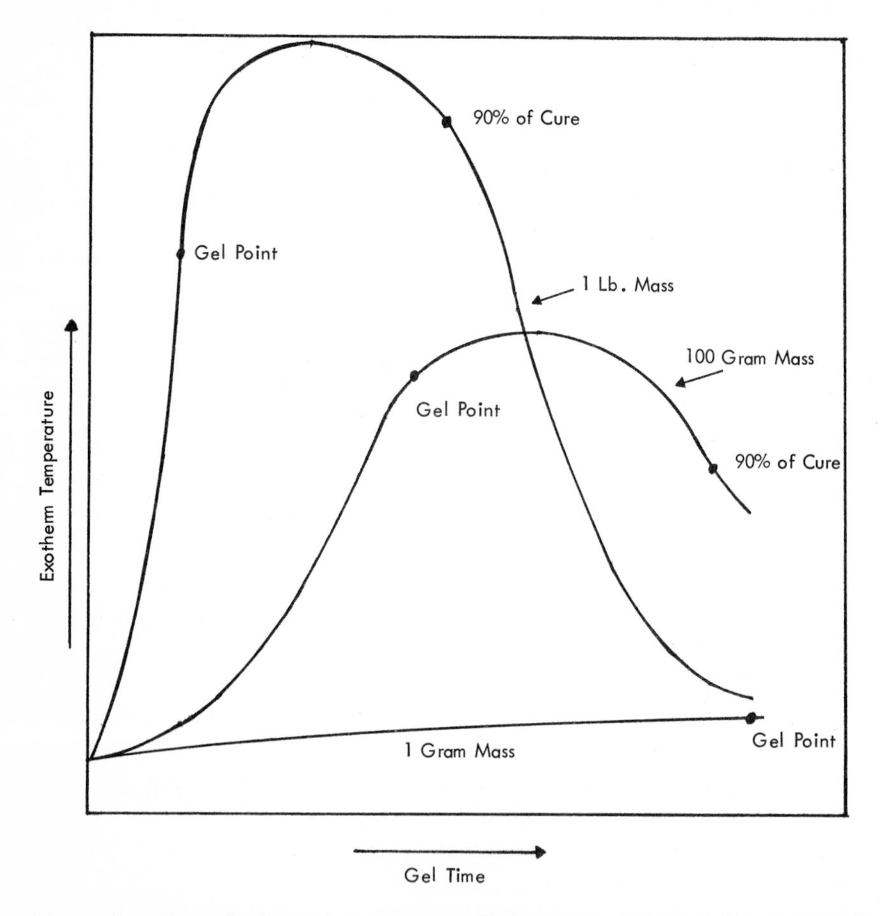

Figure 2. General effect of mass on exothermic temperature and gel time of epoxy resin

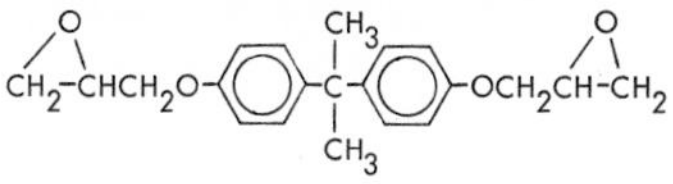

Diglycidyl Ether of Bisphenol A (DGEBA)

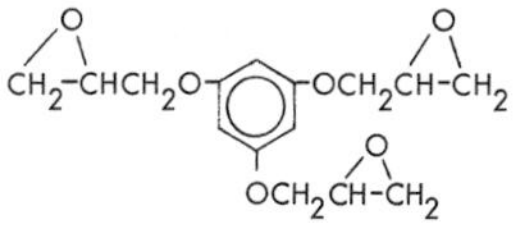

Triglycidyl Ether of Phloroglucinol (TGEP)

Diglycidyl Ether of Resorcinol (DGER)

Figure 3. Mononuclear aromatic glycidyl ether epoxy resins compared with DGEBA

based glycidyl and glycidyl ether epoxy resins; fluorinated glycidyl ether epoxy resins; cyano glycidyl ether epoxy resins; and glycidyl amine and glycidyl sulfonamide epoxy resins. These resins were either obtained from commercial sources or synthesized and purified for testing *vs.* the standard DGEBA resin. In all, over 40 resins were evaluated.

Mononuclear Aromatic Glycidyl Ether Epoxy Resins

The structures of some aromatic mononuclear epoxy resins in comparison with that of DGEBA are presented in Figure 3. This class of resins was selected for evaluation in order to determine the effects of meta substitutions on the aromatic ring. It was felt that the resonance and inductive effects resulting from this type of substitution should make these epoxy groups more reactive than para substituted epoxy groups, such as found on the DGEBA resins, by changing the electron density on the epoxy oxygen and alpha carbon. They are also characterized by having only one benzene ring per molecule (instead of two as in DGEBA), and by having two or more epoxy groups per molecule. The higher epoxy content per unit weight implies faster reactivity with primary amine curatives.

The diglycidyl ether of bisphenol A was obtained from commercial sources as an amber viscous liquid having a viscosity of 14,000 centipoises at 25°C. and an epoxy equivalent weight (WPE) of 189. The triglycidyl ether of phloroglucinol was obtained in 69% yield by the reaction of recrystallized phloroglucinol with epichlorohydrin in the presence of benzyl trimethylammonium chloride catalyst (BTC). After removal of the excess epichlorohydrin by distillation, a sodium methoxide methanol solution was added to dehydrohalogenate the chlorohydrin intermediate to the triglycidyl ether of phloroglucinol. The resultant resin had a WPE of 115 (Theory 98),

OH
HO OH
$+ \; CH_2\!-\!CH\!-\!CH_2Cl$ (epoxide O bridging CH_2 and CH) $\xrightarrow{BTC}$

Phloroglucinol Epichlorohydrin

OH OH OH
$ClCH_2CHCH_2O$ OCH_2CHCH_2Cl OCH_2CHCH_2Cl $\xrightarrow{NaOMe/MeOH}$

Chlorohydrin Intermediate

O O O
$CH_2\!-\!CHCH_2O$ $OCH_2CH\!-\!CH_2$ $OCH_2CH\!-\!CH_2$ + NaCl

Triglycidyl Ether of Phloroglucinol

and had a boiling point at 20 microns of 220°–250°C.

The diglycidyl ether of resorcinol (DGER) was obtained from commercial sources and was purified by molecular distillation to a low viscosity, colorless resin having a WPE of 108 (Theory 103), m.p., 30°–34°C.

Infrared spectroscopy was the first method used to determine the effects of structure on reactivity. The triglycidyl ether of phloroglucinol

(TGEP) and the diglycidyl ether of resorcinol (DGER) were studied *vs.* DGEBA. Stoichiometric amounts of the resins catalyzed with triethylenetetramine were sandwiched between sodium chloride cells, and the infrared spectra of catalyzed samples were determined at various periods of time after mixing at $t = 0, 2, 30, 60, 240$, and 1440 minutes at 23°C. The cure of the epoxies was measured by following the disappearance of the epoxy groups which absorb at 910 and 870 wavenumbers. The results, shown graphically in Figure 4 as a plot of percent change in absorbance at 910 wavenumber *vs.* time, demonstrate the relative reactivities of these resins. The lower the absorbance with time, the faster the reactivity.

The data were analyzed in terms of viscosities and functionalities of the coreactants. The DGER resin, being very fluid, as was its fluid curing agent, attained high molecular weights only after a substantial amount of the total possible reaction had been completed. The more viscous DGEBA, on the other hand, reached a correspondingly higher molecular weight at a lower percent of the reaction. This too must be modified by the tendency of the system to crosslink. Thus, as shown by Carrothers, the more highly functional species gel at a lower percent of the total reaction than do the less functional species. Thus, TGEP would be expected to gel at lower percentage of the reaction than DGEBA, for example, because of the increased functionality of the TGEP. Thus, at

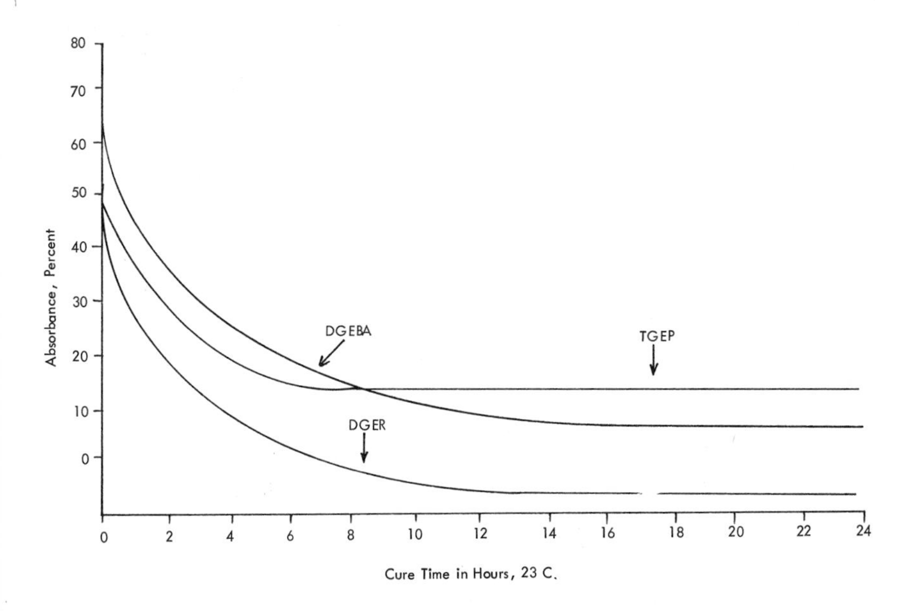

Figure 4. Relative reactivities of DGEBA, DGER, and TGEP by infrared spectroscopy

constant temperature, the gel point of the mixture is a function of both the initial molecular weights of the intermediates and of the functionality of the intermediates.

In these infrared studies, it would appear that the experimental data more nearly represent the inherent reactivity of the species. It should be noted that DGER apparently reacts more rapidly than TGEP. In this case it might be reasoned that steric factors interfere with complete reaction of the third epoxy group and that this group only reacts after many of the other reactions have been concluded. The presence of this unreacted epoxy, visible in infrared, would tend to indicate the faster inherent reaction of the DGER, but in terms of the gel time studies, this conclusion regarding inherent reactivities would not be justified. It would be expected that two of the three epoxy groups on the TGEP would go as quickly as the two on DGER, and in view of the higher functionality of the TGEP, it would be expected that gel time figures would be shorter to the extent that the third epoxy groups enters the reaction. It should be noted that each reaction of the third epoxy group will approximately double the molecular weight of the growing species.

Indeed, actual gel time studies show that the TGEP is more reactive than DGER which is more reactive than DGEBA, which completely contradicts the results observed using infrared spectroscopy.

As a result, all subsequent tests for reactivity were made on the basis of gel time, using 10 gram masses of epoxy resins catalyzed with stoichiometric amounts of primary aliphatic and alicyclic amines, specifically, triethylenetetramine and 1,4-cyclohexane bis(methylamine).

$$H_2NCH_2CH_2NHCH_2CH_2NHCH_2CH_2NH_2$$

Triethylene Tetramine

$$H_2NCH_2-\langle\ \ \rangle-CH_2NH_2$$

1,4-Cyclohexane-bis (Methylamine)

The gel time of an epoxy resin-hardener system is that time required for it to undergo the change in phase from a liquid to a solid. The resin and hardener were agitated separately and brought to 25° ± 0.5°C. They were then combined in a stoichiometric ratio and mixed thoroughly for three minutes, avoiding air entrapment. Exactly 10 grams of the mix were then poured into an aluminum foil dish, and this was noted as the starting time. The samples were then placed in a still air, constant tem-

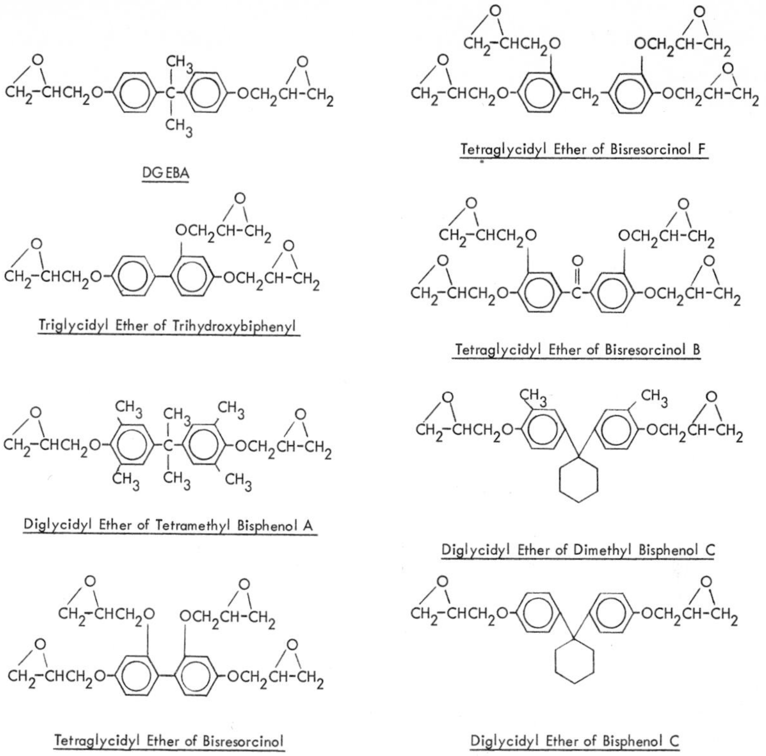

DGEBA

Tetraglycidyl Ether of Bisresorcinol F

Triglycidyl Ether of Trihydroxybiphenyl

Tetraglycidyl Ether of Bisresorcinol B

Diglycidyl Ether of Tetramethyl Bisphenol A

Diglycidyl Ether of Dimethyl Bisphenol C

Tetraglycidyl Ether of Bisresorcinol

Diglycidyl Ether of Bisphenol C

Figure 5. Polynuclear glycidyl ether-type epoxy resins compared with DGEBA

perature environment of 25° ± 0.5°C. on an insulated cardboard surface. The specimens were probed periodically with a wooden applicator stick, holding the stick perpendicular to the material surface. The gel time was the point at which the sample material no longer adhered to the end of a clean probe and it was recorded as the minutes elapsed from starting time (9).

Di- and Polynuclear Aromatic Glycidyl Ether Epoxy Resins

The next class of resins evaluated was that containing the di- and polynuclear glycidyl ether epoxy resins (Figure 5). The triglycidyl ether of trihydroxybiphenyl is an epoxy resin made from resorcinol still-pot residue, the main component of which is the triglycidyl ether of 2,4,4′-trihydroxybiphenyl. This material was obtained commercially and was distilled, decolorized, and redistilled using a two-stage molecular still to give a pale green-colored resin (Gardner 1.5) having a WPE of 128 (Theory 123).

The diglycidyl ether of tetramethyl bisphenol A was prepared by refluxing 2,2-bis(3,5-dimethyl-4-hydroxyphenyl)propane (tetramethyl bisphenol A) with excess epichlorohydrin in the presence of sodium hydroxide.

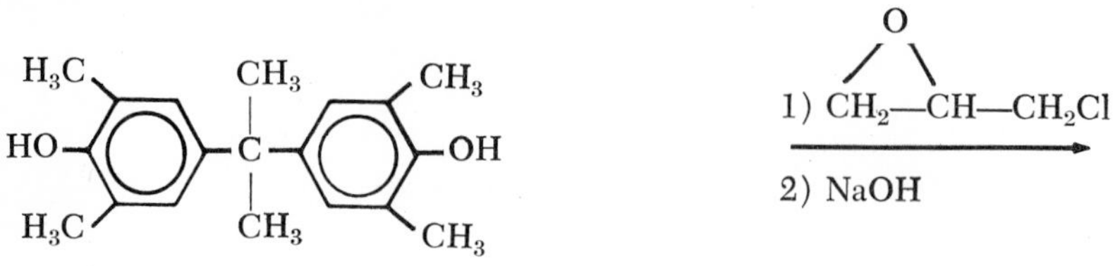

1) CH_2—CH—CH_2Cl (epoxide O bridging CH_2—CH)
2) NaOH

Tetramethyl Bisphenol A

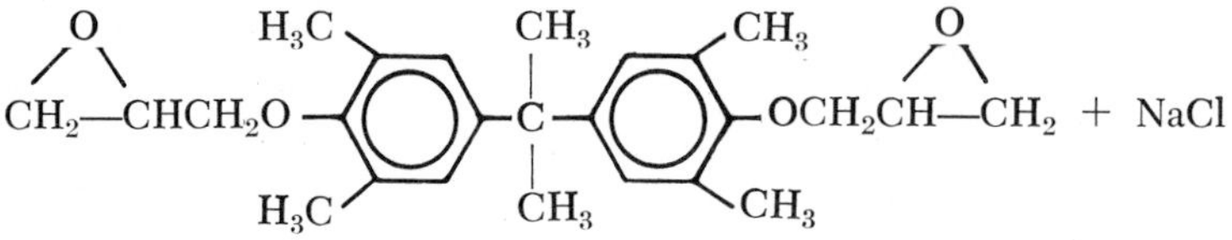

+ NaCl

Diglycidyl Ether of Tetramethyl Bisphenol A

The resin was obtained in 102 percent yield as a pale amber resin, index of refraction 1.5547, with WPE 208 (Theory 198).

The tetraglycidyl ether of bisresorcinol was prepared by the reaction of 2,2′,4,4′-tetrahydroxybiphenyl with excess epichlorohydrin in the presence of sodium hydroxide.

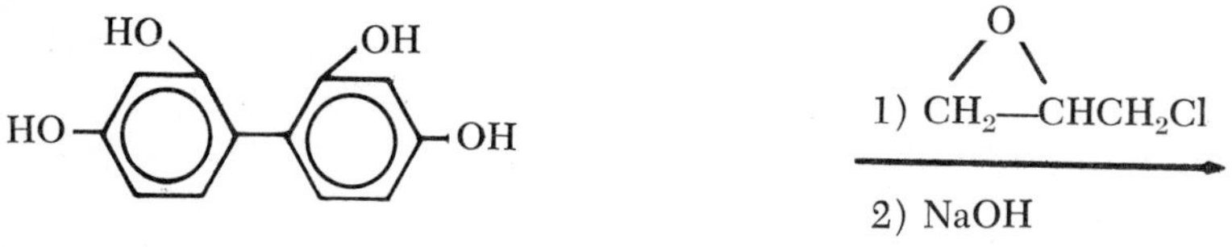

1) CH_2—$CHCH_2Cl$ (epoxide O bridging CH_2—CH)
2) NaOH

2,2′,4,4′-Tetrahydroxybiphenol

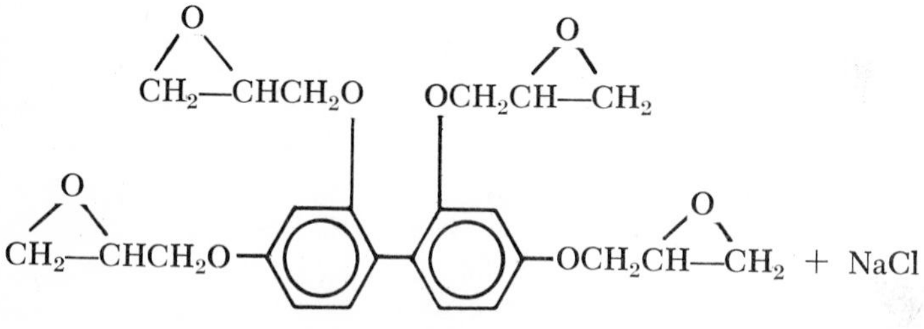

+ NaCl

Tetraglycidyl Ether of Bisresorcinol

A brown, viscous resin was obtained in 95% yield, WPE 149 (Theory 108), index of refraction 1.5750.

The tetraglycidyl ether of bisresorcinol F was used as obtained from commercial sources.

The tetraglycidyl ether of bisresorcinol B was prepared by the reaction of 2,2′,4,4′-tetrahydroxybenzophenone with excess epichlorohydrin in the presence of BTC catalyst.

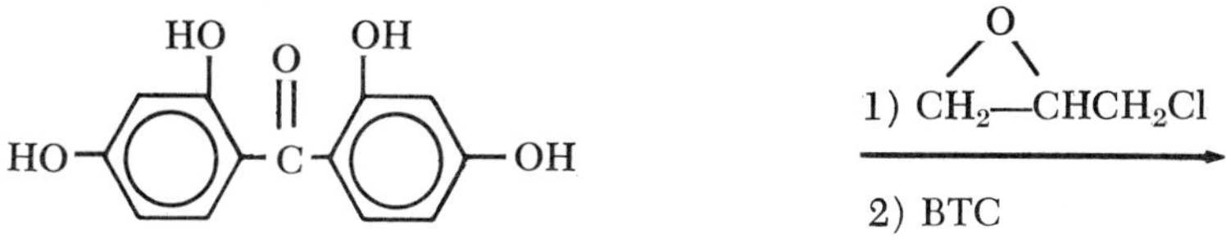

HO O OH
HO — C — OH

O
1) CH_2—$CHCH_2Cl$
2) BTC

2,2′,4,4′-Tetrahydroxybenzophenone

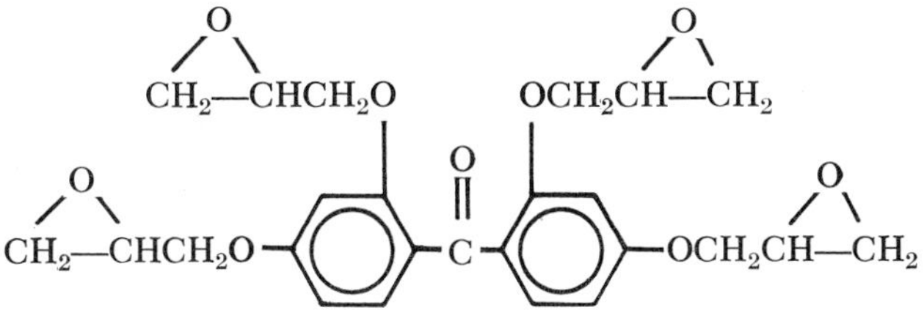

O O
CH_2—$CHCH_2O$ OCH_2CH—CH_2
O O O
CH_2—$CHCH_2O$ — C — OCH_2CH—CH_2

Tetraglycidyl Ether of Tetrahydroxybenzophenone

The result was 96% yield of a semisolid, amber resin having two phases; the oily phase was acetone soluble, while the solid was not. By use of acetone, a white solid, WPE 187, and a yellow, viscous resin, WPE 226 (Theory 118) were obtained.

The diglycidyl ether of dimethyl bisphenol C and the diglycidyl ether of bisphenol C were prepared by reaction of the corresponding bisphenols with excess epichlorohydrin in the presence of sodium hydroxide.

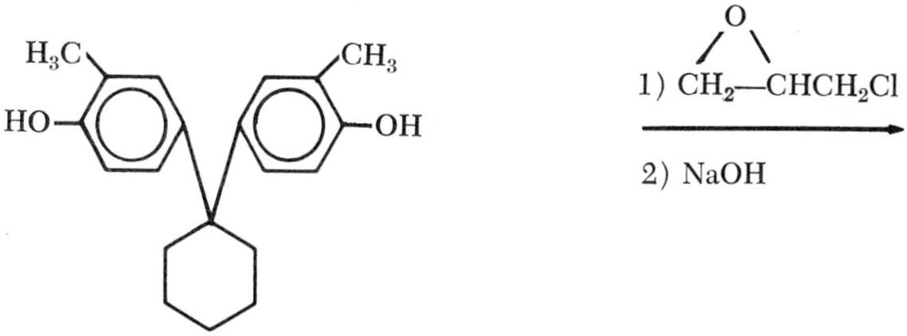

H_3C CH_3
HO — OH

O
1) CH_2—$CHCH_2Cl$
2) NaOH

1,1′-Bis (4-hydroxy-3-methylphenyl cyclohexane)

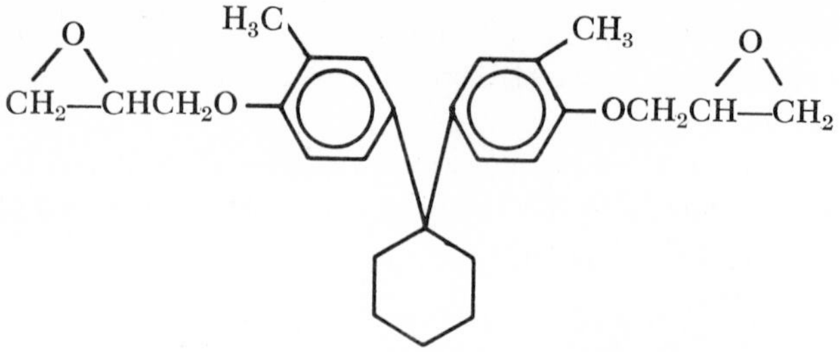

Diglycidyl Ether of Dimethyl Bisphenol C

This product was obtained in 56% yield, having a WPE of 215 (Theory 204), with mechanical losses resulting in the low yield.

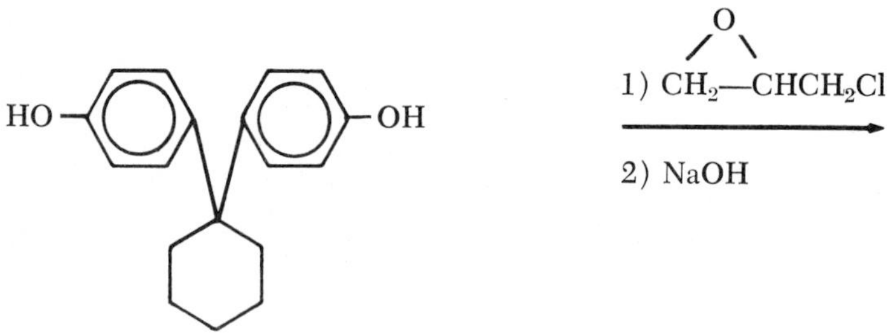

1) CH_2—$CHCH_2Cl$ (epoxide)

2) NaOH

1,1'-Bis (4-hydroxyphenyl) cyclohexane

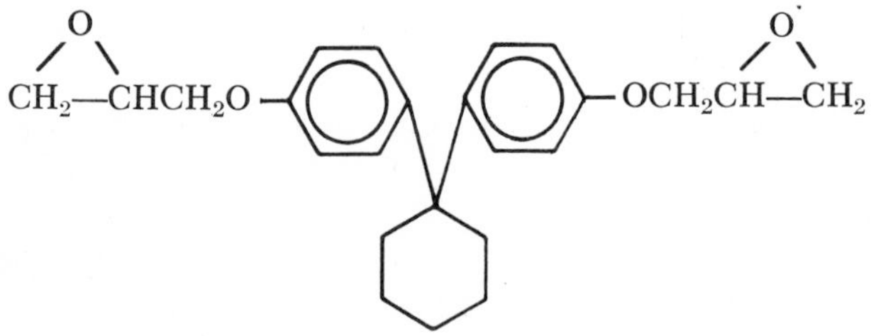

Diglycidyl Ether of Bisphenol C

The WPE of this product of 298 (Theory 190) was extremely high, and no further purification was attempted because of synthesis difficulties.

The resins were mixed with stoichiometric amounts of 1,4-cyclohexane bis(methylamine) and gel time measured. The triglycidyl ether of trihydroxybiphenyl

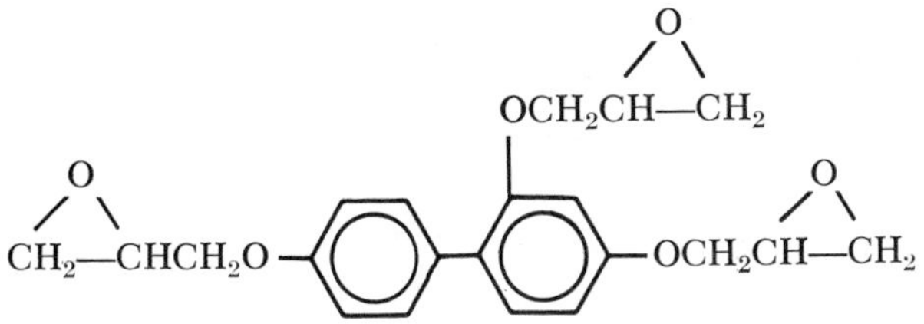

Triglycidyl Ether of Trihydroxy Biphenyl

was found to be the most amine reactive resin of this class, presumably because of the presence of meta substituted glycidyl ether groups and high functionality; however, it was not as reactive as the TGEP and DGER mononuclear resins described earlier.

The diglycidyl ether of tetramethyl bisphenol A had extremely low reactivity, which was attributed to steric hindrance of the methyl groups on the aromatic ring ortho to the glycidyl ether, which prevented the amine groups from reacting with the epoxy groups.

The higher functionality resins such as the tetraglycidyl ether of bisresorcinol, the tetraglycidyl ether of bisresorcinol F, and the tetraglycidyl ether of bisresorcinol B, were slightly more reactive than DGEBA, owing to their higher functionalities; however, they were viscous or semisolid at room temperature even after being mixed with fluid amine catalysts and their relatively slow reactivities at room temperatures were attributed to their low mobilities.

The effort was then shifted from the high functionality aromatics to difunctional resins with much lower viscosities. The two resins in this category included the diglycidyl ether of dimethyl bisphenol C and the diglycidyl ether of bisphenol C.

The low purity of the diglycidyl ether of bisphenol C negated its use in this study, while the diglycidyl ether of dimethyl bisphenol C was found to be less reactive than even DGEBA.

It was concluded that the mononuclear aromatic glycidyl ether resins are more amine reactive than the di- and polynuclear glycidyl ethers because of their higher epoxy content per unit weight and the presence of meta substituted glycidyl ether groups.

Other Mono- and Dinuclear Epoxy Resins

Alicyclic glycidyl and peracetic acid-route epoxy resins, such as

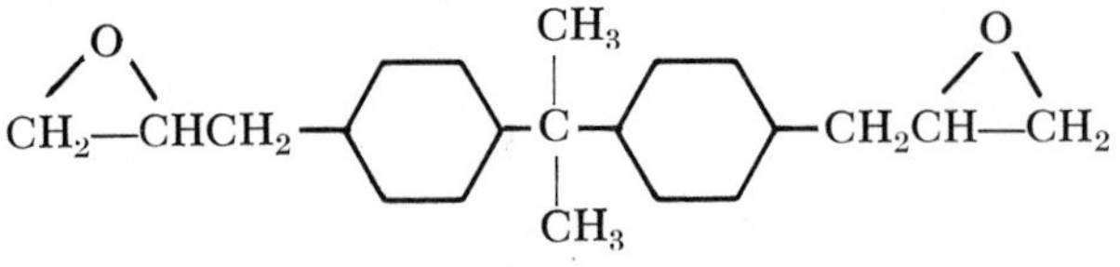

2,2′-Bis[4-(2,3-epoxypropyl)cyclohexyl] propane (BGCHP) and

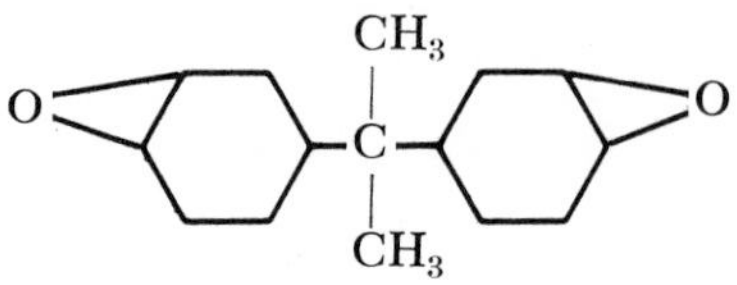

2,2′-Bis (3,4-epoxycyclohexyl) propane (BECHP)

in which there are no ether oxygen atoms, are acid rather than amine reactive and as such were not included in this study. The epoxy-ethyl resins also have a tendency to rearrange to the aldehyde,

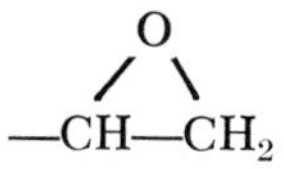

Epoxyethyl Radical

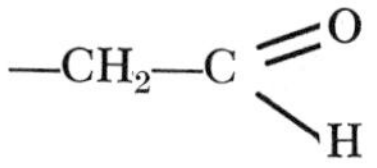

Aldehyde

making them difficult to store and use.

Another resin considered was the hydrogenated analog of DGEBA.

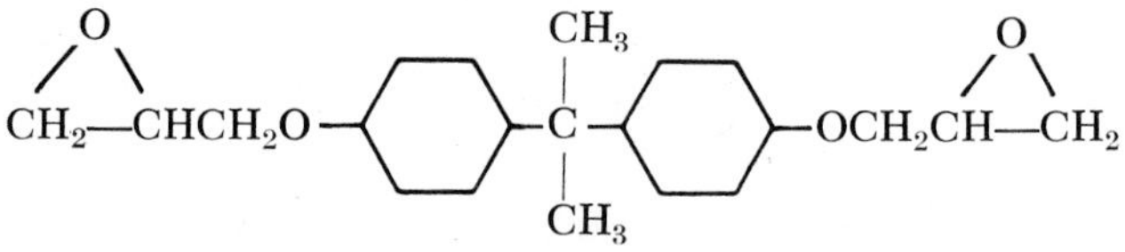

Hydrogenated Diglycidyl Ether of Bisphenol A

A small developmental sample of this resin was received for evaluation, and it was found to be as amine reactive as DGEBA, and as such offered no advantage over the commercial aromatic analogs.

Fluorinated Epoxy Resins

One of the most promising and interesting ways of modifying an epoxy resin is to replace some of the hydrogen atoms with fluorine. Fluorine is the most electronegative atom known. It shifts electron patterns in a molecule very radically and can change the reactivity of the epoxy group as well as markedly improving other properties. There are some limitations to replacing hydrogen atoms with fluorine, however. For example, fluorine atoms substituted on a carbon atom adjacent to a hydrogen substituted carbon, can combine with the hydrogen atom to split out hydrofluoric acid. Similarly, a few fluorine atoms in the molecule tend to lower the melting point of the uncured resin, while making the cured resin somewhat brittle because of reduced intramolecular forces. Higher percentages of fluorine can convert the uncured resin to a very low viscosity which, when cured, is a flexible, rubber-like elastomer owing to lowered cohesive energy density. These effects are not fully predictable. Consequently, a series of fluorinated epoxy resins (*see* Figure 6) was prepared for study.

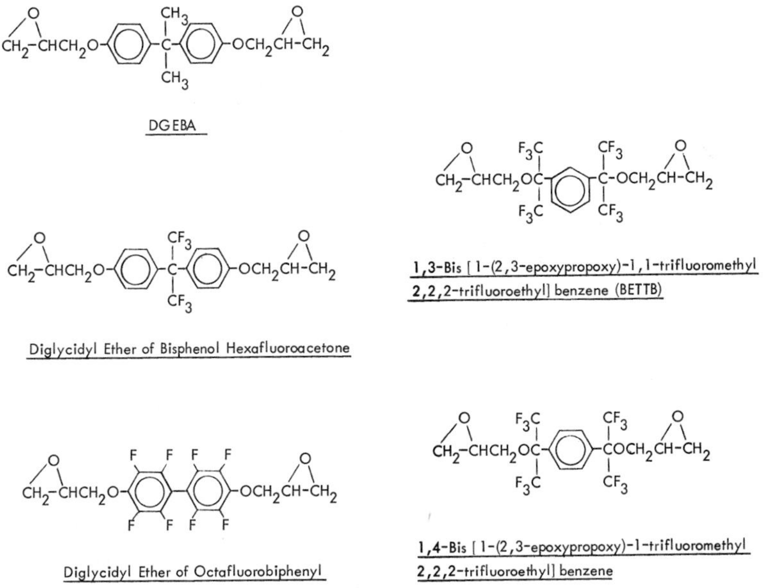

DGEBA

1,3-Bis [1-(2,3-epoxypropoxy)-1,1-trifluoromethyl 2,2,2-trifluoroethyl] benzene (BETTB)

Diglycidyl Ether of Bisphenol Hexafluoroacetone

Diglycidyl Ether of Octafluorobiphenyl

1,4-Bis [1-(2,3-epoxypropoxy)-1-trifluoromethyl 2,2,2-trifluoroethyl] benzene

Figure 6. Epoxy resins containing fluorine compared with DGEBA

The diglycidyl ether of bisphenol hexafluoroacetone was prepared by reaction of bisphenol hexafluoroacetone with excess epichlorohydrin and sodium hydroxide.

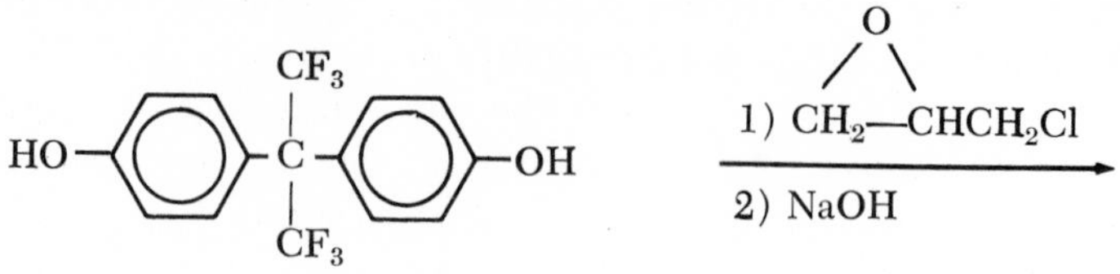

$$HO-C_6H_4-C(CF_3)_2-C_6H_4-OH \xrightarrow[\text{2) NaOH}]{\text{1) } \overset{O}{CH_2-CH}CH_2Cl}$$

Bisphenol Hexafluoroacetone

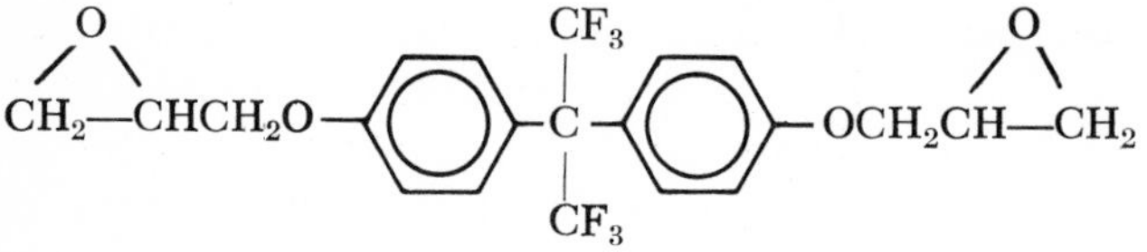

$$\overset{O}{CH_2-CH}CH_2O-C_6H_4-C(CF_3)_2-C_6H_4-OCH_2\overset{O}{CH-CH_2}$$

Diglycidyl Ether of Bisphenol Hexafluoroacetone

It was obtained in 75.5 percent yield and had a WPE of 277 (Theory 234).

The diglycidyl ether of octafluorobiphenyl presented some synthesis problems, but impure material was prepared by the reaction of epichlorohydrin with octafluorobiphenol with BTC as a catalyst.

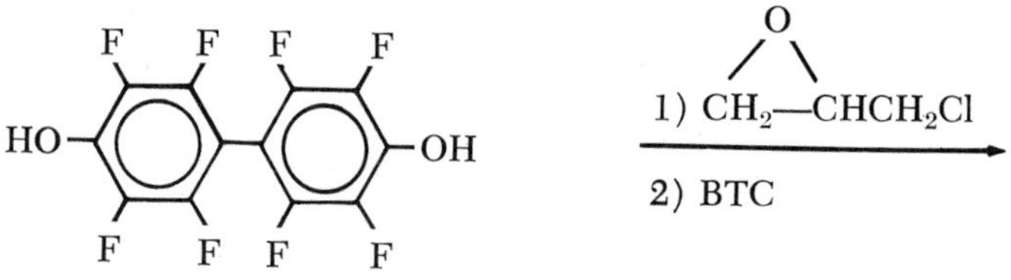

$$HO-C_6F_4-C_6F_4-OH \xrightarrow[\text{2) BTC}]{\text{1) } \overset{O}{CH_2-CH}CH_2Cl}$$

Octafluorobiphenyl

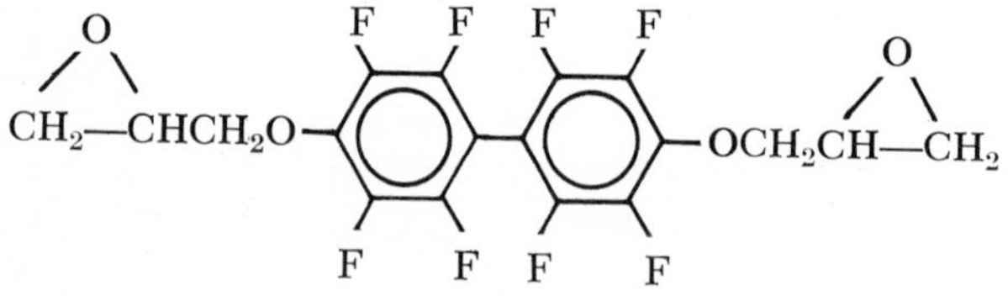

$$\overset{O}{CH_2-CH}CH_2O-C_6F_4-C_6F_4-OCH_2\overset{O}{CH-CH_2}$$

Diglycidyl Ether of Octafluorobiphenyl

The yield of this synthesis was 75% of theory; however, the resin had a WPE of 340 which was well above the theoretical value of 221. Work on this was discontinued when it was found that other researchers at the Naval Research Laboratories in Washington, D. C. (*see* Chapter 2, pp. 8–15) described the low reactivity of this resin.

Based on amine reactivity studies with these two resins, in which they were both determined to be less reactive toward 1,4-cyclohexane bis-(methylamine) than DGEBA resin, another approach toward increased reactivity was considered.

It seems that fluorine has no effect on epoxy reactivity when it is substituted on an aromatic ring or when it is on a benzhydryl carbon as are the trifluoromethyl groups in DGEB-HFA. In order to increase reactivity, resins such as 1,3-bis[1-(2,3-epoxypropoxy)-1,1,1-trifluoromethyl-2,2,2-trifluoroethyl]benzene (BETTB) and the 1,4 isomer, in which the fluorine groups are closer to the epoxy groups were synthesized. It was expected that the electronegativity of the fluorines would increase amine reactivity.

The bis-alcohol precursors for these resins were obtained by reaction of hexafluoroacetone and benzene together, forming a mixture of the 1,3 and 1,4 isomers which were separated chemically. The alcohols then reacted with excess epichlorohydrin in the presence of BTC catalyst, and the resultant resins were evaluated with 1,4-cyclohexane-bis(methylamine).

The amine reactivities of these resins were found to be no greater than DGEBA. It was concluded that either the trifluoromethyl groups were still situated too far from the epoxy group to have any effect on amine reactivity, or that the presence of two bulky trifluoromethyl groups adjacent to each glycidyl ether group sterically prevent the necessary approach of amine curing agents. Hence, it was decided to put the fluorine on the glycidyl ether portion of the epoxy resin itself where it was theorized that it should be the most effective in enhancing reactivity.

β-Trifluoromethyl Glycidyl Ether Resins. Since a β-trifluoromethyl glycidyl ether radical,

```
                 O
                / \
—O—CH2—C—CH2
              |
             CF3
```

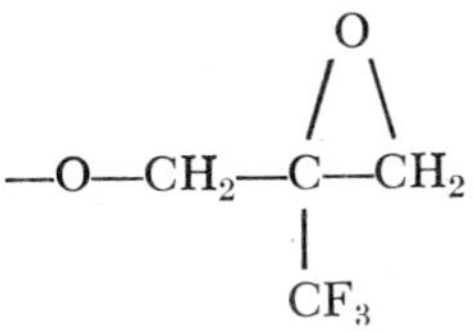

Beta-Trifluoromethyl glycidyl ether radical

if made, could be synthesized into a variety of resins, this was the next

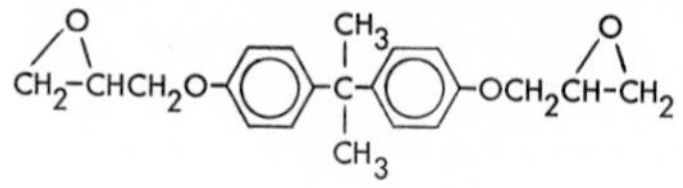

Figure 7. β-trifluoromethyl glycidyl resins compared with DGEBA

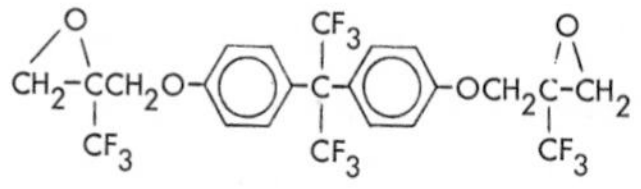

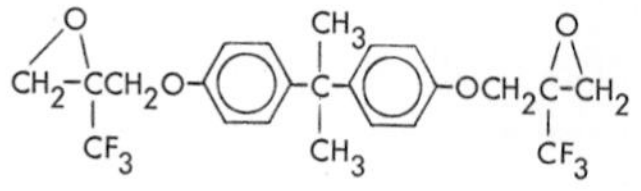

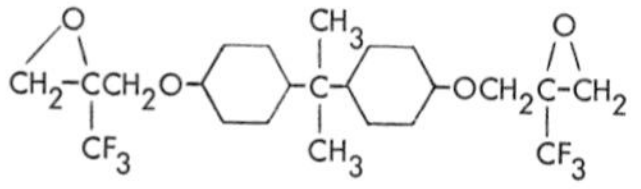

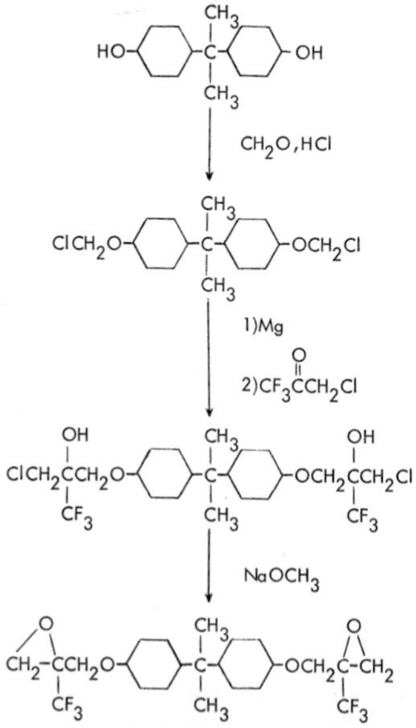

Figure 8. Initial synthesis route for epoxy resin containing fluorine to increase reactivity

approach to the reactivity problem. The three resins which were considered to be most representative of the desired molecular structure are shown in Figure 7.

Initial attempts to synthesize these through the chlorohydrin route (Figure 8) were unsuccessful because of the high reactivity of the fluorinated intermediates which led to other products. However, a new route, based on a recently disclosed route for the synthesis of β-trifluoromethylepibromohydrin (*10*) was used to produce a sample for evaluation (Figure 9). When tested for reactivity with an acetic acid solution of HBr at 50°C., the infrared absorption spectrum showed no reaction. With 1,4-cyclohexane bis(methylamine) no cure at all was obtained at room temperature. It was then concluded that the fluorine atoms inhibit the reaction leading to the opening of the epoxide ring owing to the steric requirements of the bulky trifluoromethyl group.

β-Cyano Glycidyl Ether Resins. From a theoretical standpoint, an attempt was then made to prepare a β-cyanoglycidyl ether resin

$$CH_2\overset{O}{—}C(CN)—CH_2O—C_6H_4—C(CH_3)_2—C_6H_4—OCH_2—C(CN)\overset{O}{—}CH_2$$

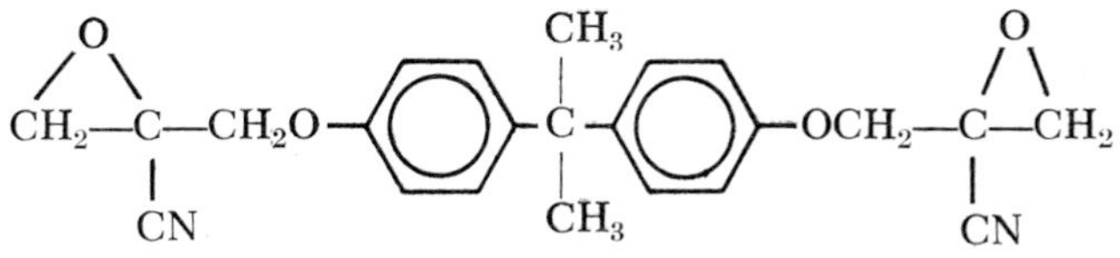

with the feeling that the strong inductive effect of the cyano group on the β-carbon would weaken the C–O bond of the epoxy ring, thereby increasing reactivity toward nucleophiles. Also, the cyano group should

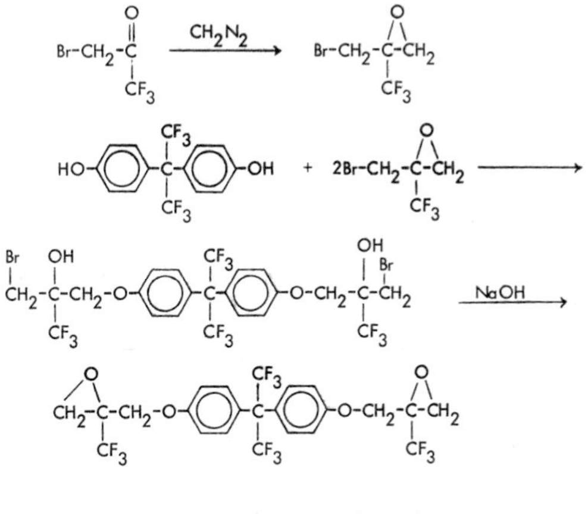

$$Br-CH_2-C(=O)-CF_3 \xrightarrow{CH_2N_2} Br-CH_2-C(CF_3)\overset{O}{-}CH_2$$

$$HO-C_6H_4-C(CF_3)_2-C_6H_4-OH + 2Br-CH_2-C(CF_3)\overset{O}{-}CH_2 \longrightarrow$$

$$BrCH_2-C(OH)(CF_3)-CH_2-O-C_6H_4-C(CF_3)_2-C_6H_4-O-CH_2-C(OH)(CF_3)-CH_2Br \xrightarrow{NaOH}$$

$$CH_2\overset{O}{-}C(CF_3)-CH_2-O-C_6H_4-C(CF_3)_2-C_6H_4-O-CH_2-C(CF_3)\overset{O}{-}CH_2$$

2,2-Bis [4-(2,3-epoxy-2-trifluoromethyl)phenyl] hexafluoroacetone

Figure 9. ***Revised synthesis route for epoxy resin containing fluorine for increased reactivity***

not be as much a steric factor as the bulky trifluoromethyl groups. However, the cyanohydrin intermediates proved impossible to make within the allocated time, and thus no resins of this type were synthesized.

Nitrogen-Containing Epoxy Resins

To this point, the program had been devoted primarily to the preparation of glycidyl ether resins which have been found, in past work, to be the most reactive species primarily because of the inductive effect of the ether oxygen on the epoxide group and the fact that the ether oxygen is able to hydrogen bond with amine curatives thereby holding the amine in a favorable position for reaction with the epoxy ring.

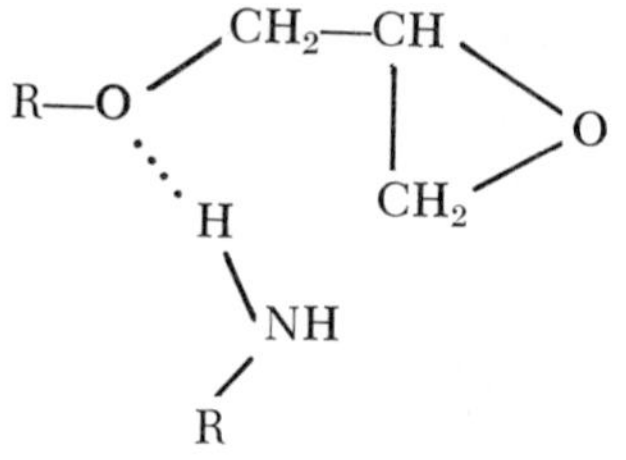

CH_2—CH

R—O O Epoxy ring

Ether oxygen H CH_2

NH

R

Amine

Effect of glycidyl-ether ether oxygen on amine cure

Aromatic Glycidyl Amine Resins. By further expanding the previous reasoning, nitrogen should have a greater inductive effect and should form a stronger hydrogen bond to amines than oxygen since it is more electronegative. Several glycidyl amine resins (Figure 10) were obtained from commercial sources and were tested with 1,4-cyclohexane bis-(methylamine). They were found to be more reactive than the DGEBA resin when tested under similar conditions and were similar in reactivity to the triglycidyl ether of phloroglucinol and the triglycidyl ether of trihydroxybiphenyl.

Glycidyl Amides and Sulfonamides. Another class of resins, the glycidyl amides are theoretically not reactive, as a class, since the carbonyl group adjacent to the amide nitrogen detracts from its electronegativity. One subclass, however, the glycidyl sulfonamides, theoretically showed some promise of increased reactivity. One member of this class is shown in Figure 11 with the possible synthetic route. However, synthesis yields were low, and the products were of questionable purity and composition.

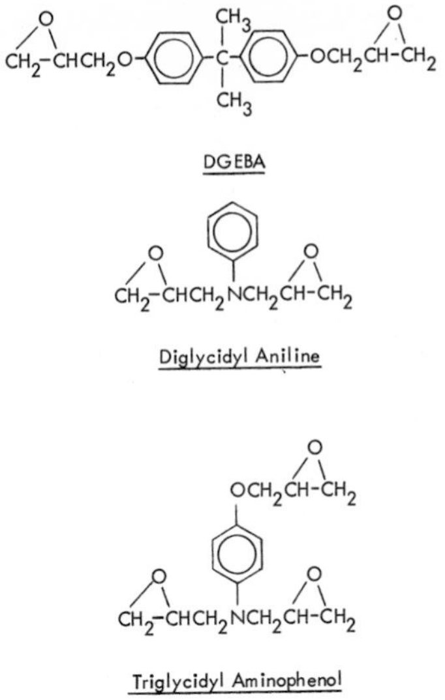

DGEBA

Diglycidyl Aniline

Triglycidyl Aminophenol

Figure 10. Commercially available aromatic glycidyl amines compared with DGEBA

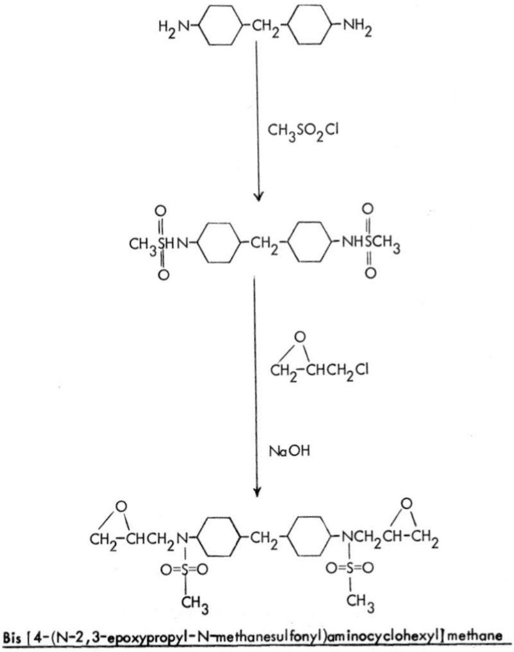

CH_3SO_2Cl

NaOH

Bis [4-(N-2,3-epoxypropyl-N-methanesulfonyl)aminocyclohexyl] methane

Figure 11. Synthesis route for difunctional glycidyl sulfonamide

Triazine-Based Epoxy Resins. As another approach to the problem, the fact that mononuclear trifunctional glycidyl ether epoxy resins and glycidyl amine epoxy resins were found to be more reactive toward 1,4-cyclohexane bis(methylamine) than DGEBA, led to the attempt to prepare epoxy resins which might combine the advantages of both classes. This led to the evaluation of the triazine based epoxy resins (Figure 12). In particular, several attempts were made to prepare 1,3,5-triglycidyl isocyanurate using different synthesis routes. In the first, triallyl isocyanurate was epoxidized with 3-chloroperbenzoic acid in chloroform.

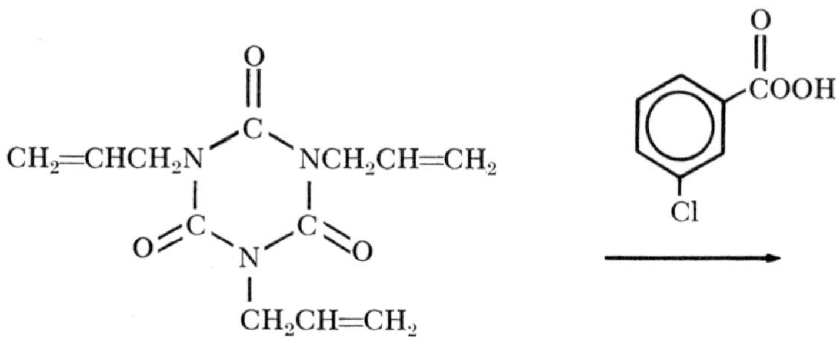

$CH_2{=}CHCH_2N$ $NCH_2CH{=}CH_2$ $CH_2CH{=}CH_2$ (C=O ring, N) → 3-chloroperbenzoic acid (COOH, Cl)

Triallyl Isocyanurate

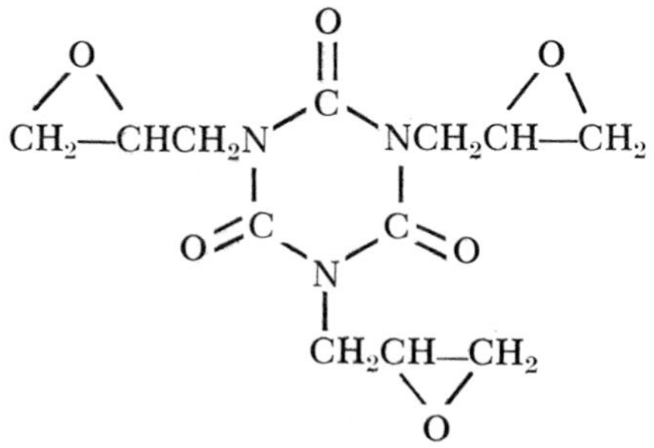

$CH_2{-}CHCH_2N$ (epoxide) $NCH_2CH{-}CH_2$ (epoxide) $CH_2CH{-}CH_2$ (epoxide)

Triglycidyl Isocyanurate

The yield was 72.8% of a crude product with a WPE of 147 (Theory 99). Repeated results were similarly unsuccessful.

Another route, using calcium hypochlorite as a source of hypochlorous acid to form the trichlorohydrin intermediate, was similarly unsuccessful (WPE $>$ 300) (shown opposite).

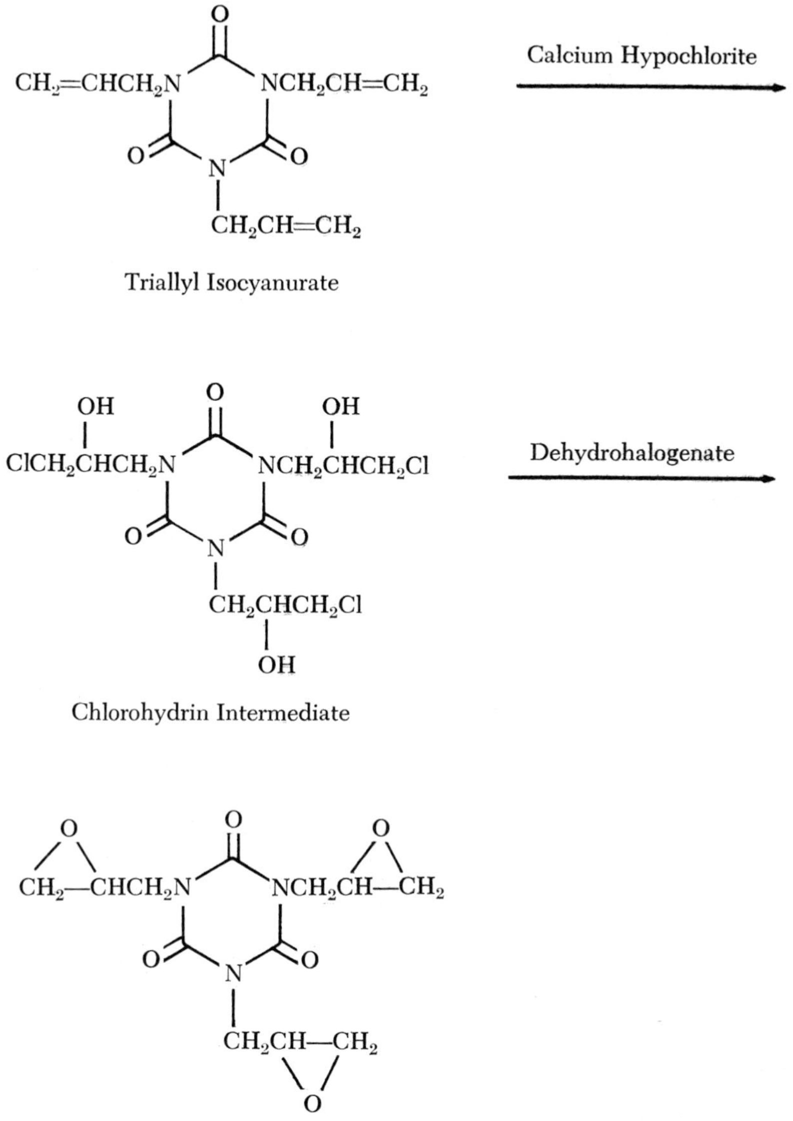

$CH_2{=}CHCH_2N$ $NCH_2CH{=}CH_2$ O O O N $CH_2CH{=}CH_2$

Calcium Hypochlorite →

Triallyl Isocyanurate

OH O OH $ClCH_2CHCH_2N$ NCH_2CHCH_2Cl O O N CH_2CHCH_2Cl OH

Dehydrohalogenate →

Chlorohydrin Intermediate

O O O CH_2—$CHCH_2N$ NCH_2CH—CH_2 O O N CH_2CH—CH_2 O

Triglycidyl Isocyanurate

The 2,4,6-triglycidoxy-*s*-triazine was prepared by the reaction of cyanuric chloride with glycidol using aqueous sodium hydroxide.

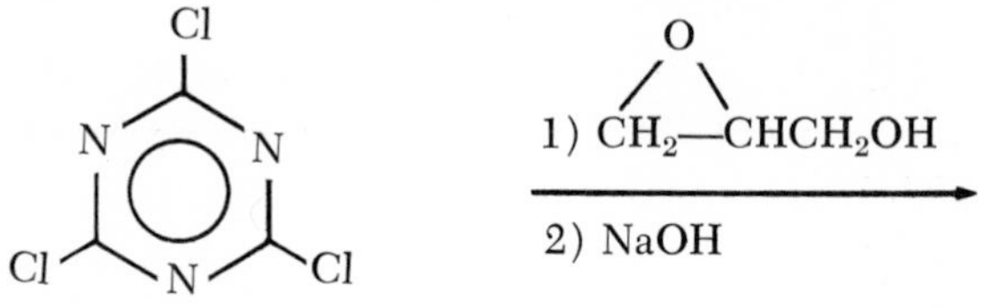

Cyanuric Chloride

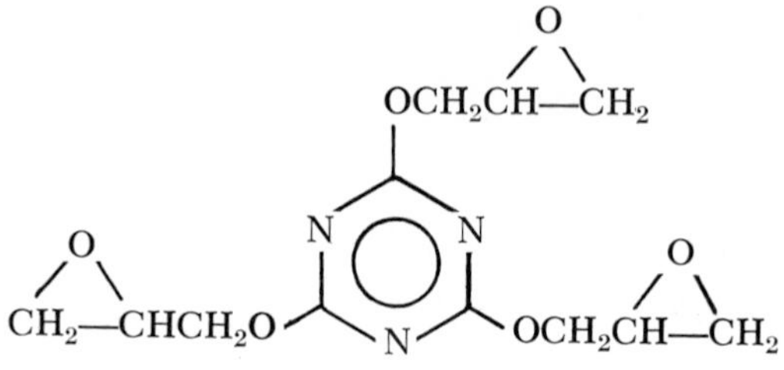

1) $CH_2—CHCH_2OH$ (epoxide O)

2) NaOH

2,4,6-Triglycidoxy-s-triazine

A 76% yield of a solid material of WPE 133 (Theory 99) was obtained.

No attempts were made to synthesize 2,4,6-triglycidyl-*s*-triazine owing to the difficult synthesis procedures involved.

The triazine resins thus prepared were solid and were immiscible with 1,4-cyclohexane bis(methylamine). They were, however, workable at temperatures above 70°C., which was wholly unsuitable for the purpose of this study.

In order to determine the direction for future synthesis efforts, the data were analyzed at this point. The relative order of reactivities of the resins are given in Table I in decreasing order of typical reactivity with 1,4-cyclohexane bis(methylamine) as curing agent.

Conclusions

None of the epoxy resins evaluated met the design criteria of a cure in small masses at room temperature in less than 10 minutes. However, numerous conclusions can be drawn about the effects of structure on epoxy resin reactivity:

1. Trifunctional mononuclear aromatic epoxy resins in which the glycidyl ether groups are ortho or meta to one another are more amine

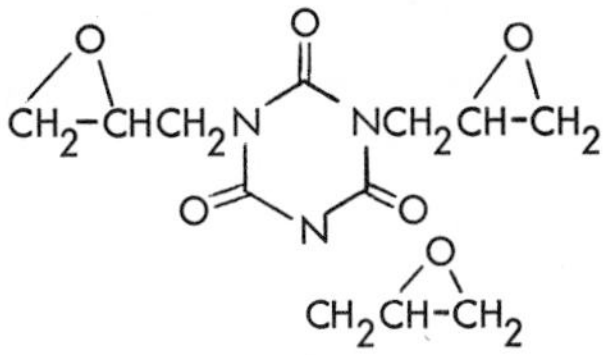

1,3,5-Triglycidyl Isocyanurate

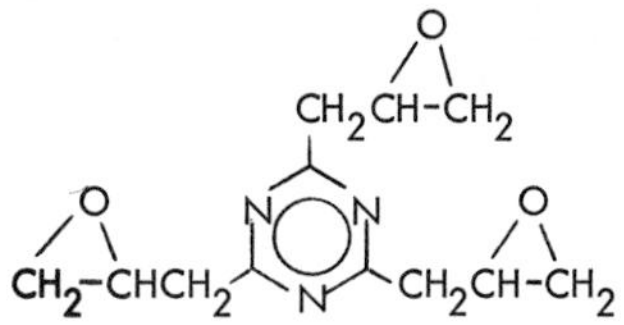

2,4,6-Triglycidyl-s-triazine

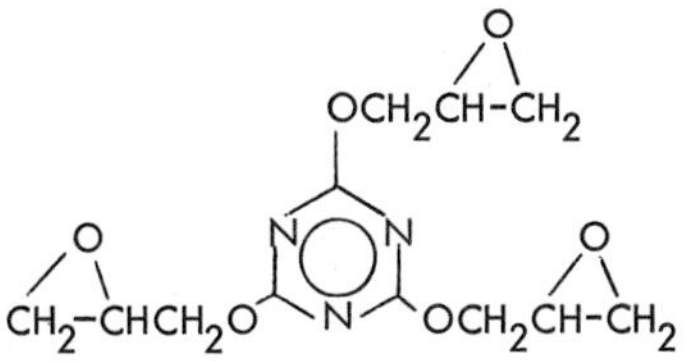

2,4,6-Triglycidoxy-s-triazine

Figure 12. Epoxy resins derived from symmetrical triazines

reactive than resins having para substitutions, the meta substituted resins being the most reactive.

2. Tetrafunctional polynuclear aromatic resins are amine reactive owing to their high functionalities and meta substituted glycidyl ether groups but are too viscous and lack the mobility necessary for fast reactions at room temperature.

3. A methyl group on an aromatic nucleus at a position ortho to a glycidyl ether group does not retard reaction with amine curing agents whereas two methyl groups decrease reactivity primarily because of steric hindrance.

4. The presence of fluorine on or adjacent to the glycidyl ether group of an epoxy resin decreases reactivity toward amine curing agents possibly owing more to steric factors than electronic effects.

5. Fluorine substitutions on aromatic rings attached to glycidyl ether groups tend to result in decreased amine reactivity.

6. Aromatic glycidyl amine epoxy resins are more reactive than aliphatic glycidyl amine epoxy resins and are more reactive than glycidyl ether epoxy resins. This is attributed to the increased electronegativity of N over O.

The methods of synthesis of the resins are described in Appendix 1.

Table I. Relative Order of Reactivities of Resins Studied Toward 1,4-Cyclohexane Bis(methylamine) in Decreasing Order of Reactivity

	Relative Reaction Rates
Triglycidyl ether of phloroglucinol	5
Diglycidyl ether of resorcinol	10
Triglycidyl aminophenol	20
Diglycidyl aniline	25
Triglycidyl ether of trihydroxybiphenyl	25
Tetraglycidyl ether of bisresorcinol	90
Tetraglycidyl ether of bisresorcinol F	90
Diglycidyl ether of bisphenol A	100
Diglycidyl ether of hydrogenated bisphenol A	105
Diglycidyl ether of tetramethyl bisphenol A	125
Diglycidyl ether of bisphenol C	150
Diglycidyl ether of bisphenol hexafluoroacetone	150
1,3-Bis [1-(2,3-epoxypropoxy)-1-trifluoromethyl-2,2,2-trifluoroethyl] benzene	200
1,4-Bis [1-(2,3-epoxypropoxy)-1-trifluoromethyl-2,2,2-trifluoroethyl] benzene	200
Diglycidyl ether of octafluorobiphenyl	400
β-trifluoromethyl resins	∞
2,4,6-Triglycidoxy-*s*-triazine	Immiscible at room temperature
1,3,5-Triglycidyl isocyanurate	Immiscible at room temperature

Appendix 1

Synthesis of Epoxy Resins

The diglycidyl ether of bisphenol A (DGEBA) was used as received from commercial sources.

$$CH_2\overset{O}{—}CHCH_2O-C_6H_4-C(CH_3)_2-C_6H_4-OCH_2CH\overset{O}{—}CH_2$$

Diglycidyl Ether of Bisphenol A (DGEBA)

The diglycidyl ether of resorcinol was molecularly distilled using a two-phase rotary film molecular still.

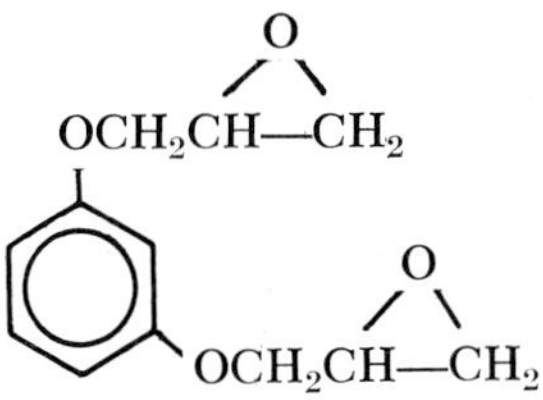

Diglycidyl Ether of Resorcinol

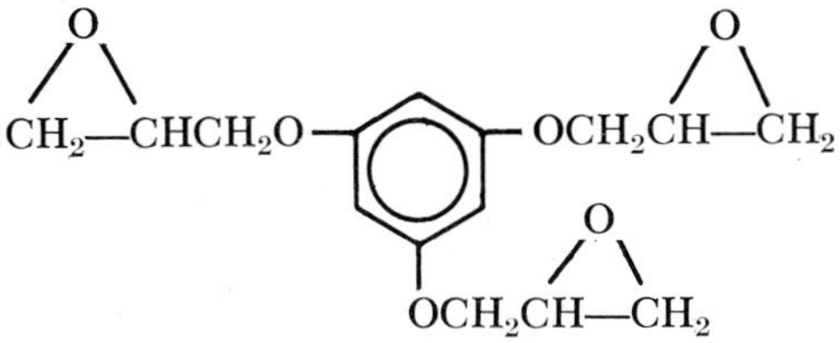

Triglycidyl Ether of Phloroglucinol (TGEP)

A mixture of 620 grams (3.82 moles) of phloroglucinol hydrate and 6950 grams (75 moles) of epichlorohydrin was refluxed with a Dean-Stark trap to remove the water of hydration. The solution was cooled to 40°C., and 107.5 grams (0.58 mole) of benzyltrimethylammonium chloride were added. Stirring with heating at 50°C. was continued overnight. The excess epichlorohydrin was removed under vacuum to 80°C. pot temperature. A sodium methoxide solution was prepared by adding 340 grams (14.8 moles) of sodium to 4000 ml. of methanol. This solution with 3500 ml. of benzene was added to the viscous reaction residue. A mildly exothermic reaction took place, and sodium chloride came out of solution. The reaction mixture was then poured into 8 liters of water, and the oily layer was removed by the use of a separatory funnel. This benzene layer was washed with water and dried over magnesium sulfate. The solvent was then removed on a rotary evaporator.

Extraction of the viscous mass with benzene three times gave 800 grams (71 percent yield) of an amber, benzene soluble cut, WPE 153 and 400 grams (36.5 percent yield) of a dark benzene insoluble cut.

A 360 gram portion of the benzene soluble material was molecularly distilled to 248 grams (69 percent yield) of pale amber resin, WPE = 115 (Theory 98) b.p. at 20 microns, 220°–250°C.

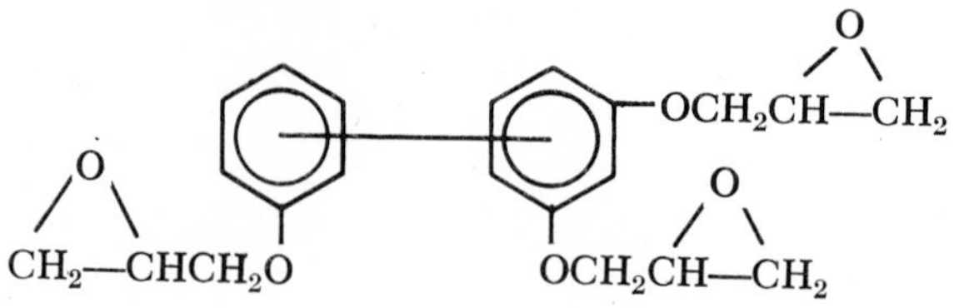

Triglycidyl Ether of Trihydroxybiphenyl

This is an epoxy resin made from resorcinol still-pot residue. The main component is the triglycidyl ether of 2,4,4′-trihydroxybiphenyl. A 200 gram charge of resin was distilled in a two-stage molecular still at 10 microns with the upper stage at 180°C., and the lower at 213°C., to give 132 grams (61 percent yield) of amber (Gardner 8) resin, and index of refraction 1.5835. The resin was then taken up in benzene and treated with decolorizing carbon twice to give a pale amber (Gardner 2) but somewhat cloudy resin. The material was distilled again to give a clear resin with a color of Gardner 1.5.

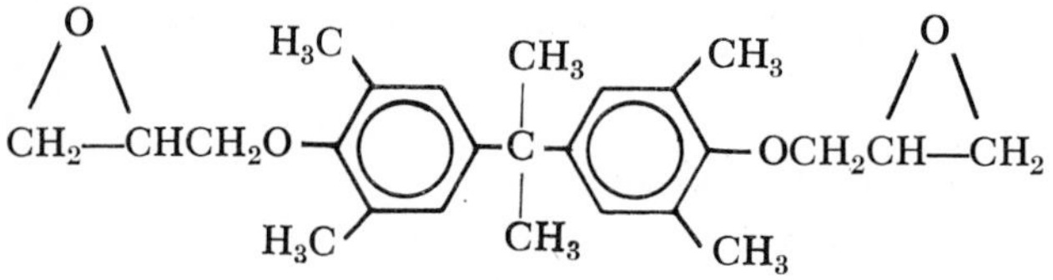

2,2-Bis [3,5-dimethyl-4-(2,3-epoxypropoxy) phenyl] propane

To a refluxing solution of 28.4 grams (0.1 mole) 2,2-bis(3,5-dimethyl-4-hydroxyphenyl)propane in 185 grams (2.0 moles) of epichlorohydrin, 8 grams (0.2 mole) of sodium hydroxide in 12 ml. of water was added. The water was removed by Dean-Stark trap. The excess epichlorohydrin was removed under vacuum up to a pot temperature of 100°C. The residue was taken up in benzene, and the salt was filtered off. The benzene was then removed under vacuum at 125°C. at 2 mm.

pressure to give 40.5 grams (102 percent yield) of pale amber resin, index of refraction 1.5547, WPE 208 Theory 198).

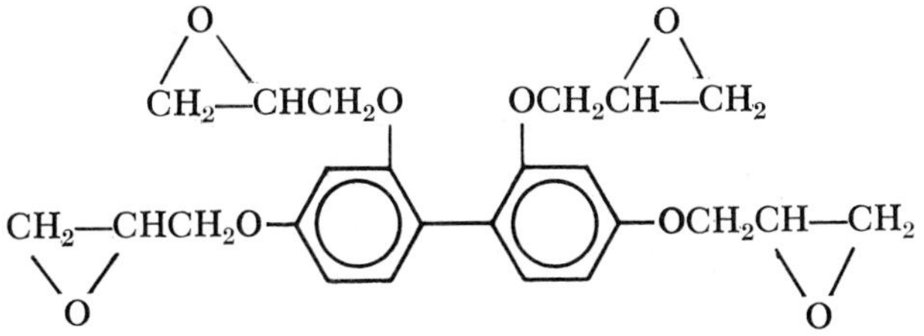

O O
CH_2—$CHCH_2O$ OCH_2CH—CH_2
CH_2—$CHCH_2O$— —OCH_2CH—CH_2
O O

2,2′,4,4′-Tetraglycidoxybiphenyl (TGB)

Using the same procedure as for the triglycidyl ether of trihydroxybiphenyl, 22 grams (0.1 mole) of 2,2′,4,4′-tetrahydroxybiphenyl and 185 grams (2.0 moles) of epichlorohydrin were allowed to react to give 41 grams (95 percent yield) of a very viscous, brown resin, index of refraction 1.5750, WPE 149 (Theory 108).

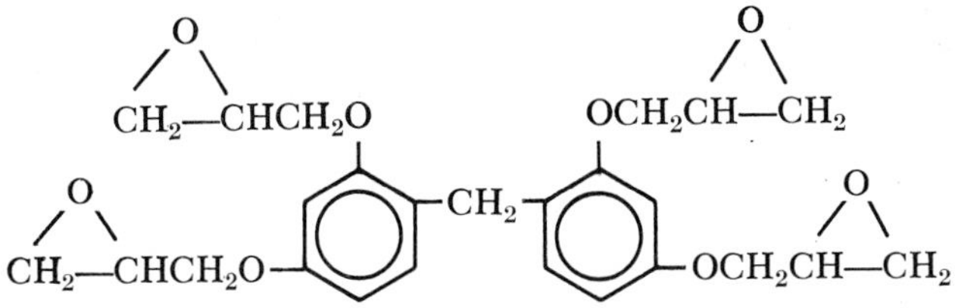

O O
CH_2—$CHCH_2O$ OCH_2CH—CH_2
O CH_2 O
CH_2—$CHCH_2O$— —OCH_2CH—CH_2

Tetraglycidyl Ether of Bisresorcinol F

The tetraglycidyl ether of bisresorcinol F was used as received from commercial sources.

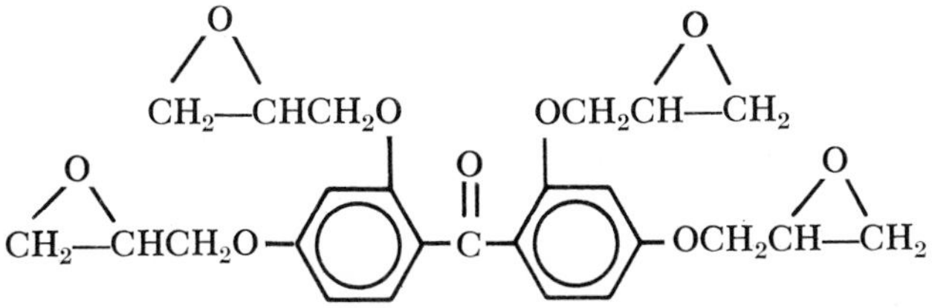

O O
CH_2—$CHCH_2O$ OCH_2CH—CH_2
O O O
CH_2—$CHCH_2O$— —C— —OCH_2CH—CH_2

2,2′,4,4′-Tetraglycidoxybenzophenone

Using the same procedure as for triglycidyl ether of phloroglucinol, 24.6 grams (1.0 mole) of 2,2′,4,4′-tetrahydroxybenzophenone and 1.85 grams (2.0 moles) of epichlorohydrin were allowed to react to give 96 percent yield of a semisolid, yellow resin. The oily phase was soluble in acetone, but the solid was not. By use of acetone, a white solid, WPE 187, and a yellow, viscous resin, WPE 226 (Theory 118) were obtained.

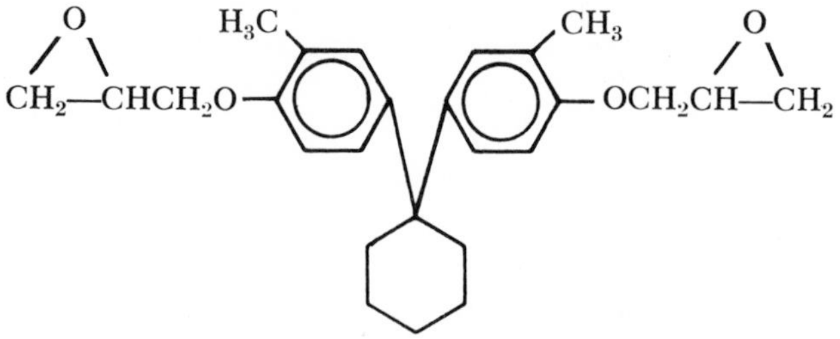

O H$_3$C CH$_3$ O

CH$_2$—CHCH$_2$O— —OCH$_2$CH—CH$_2$

1,1-Bis [4-(2,3-epoxypropoxy)-3-methylphenyl] cyclohexane

Exactly 98 grams of 1,1-bis(hydroxy-3-methylphenyl)cyclohexane reacted with 607 grams of epichlorohydrin by the one-step method described in Table II. The brown colored crude product was refined by molecular distillation (evaporation at 213°C., 0.01 mm. Hg), and the final product was obtained in 56 percent yield. The epoxy equivalent WPE was 215 (theoretical 204). Mechanical losses contributed to the low yield.

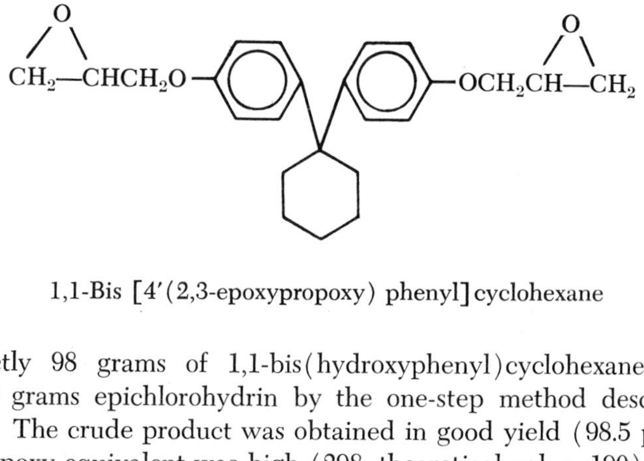

O O

CH$_2$—CHCH$_2$O— —OCH$_2$CH—CH$_2$

1,1-Bis [4′(2,3-epoxypropoxy) phenyl] cyclohexane

Exactly 98 grams of 1,1-bis(hydroxyphenyl)cyclohexane reacted with 680 grams epichlorohydrin by the one-step method described in Table II. The crude product was obtained in good yield (98.5 percent), but the epoxy equivalent was high (298, theoretical value, 190), and the infrared spectrum showed strong absorption by hydroxyl groups. No further purification was attempted.

The presence of free hydroxyl groups, coupled with the high epoxy equivalent and good preparative yield indicated that some of the epoxy groups were subject to secondary reaction. The most likely cause for this was that in the course of preparation, the removal of the water-epichloro-

Table II. Methods Used to Replace Active Hydrogens with Glycidyl Ether Groups

One-step method: An excess of about 10 equivalents of epichlorohydrin are contacted with the compound containing the active hydrogen—e.g., phenols, alcohols. Formation of the chlorohydrin derivative and subsequent dehydrochlorination is carried out by slow addition of aqueous sodium hydroxide and removal of water in the form of its azeotrope with epichlorohydrin removed by vacuum distillation.

Two-step method: Anhydrous benzyltrimethylammonium chloride, 10–15 weight percent, based on the active hydrogen containing reactant, is added to the initial reaction mixture (described in method A) and kept at a 45°–65°C. temperature for a prolonged period of time (usually overnight).

The excess of epichlorohydrin is removed by vacuum distillation, and the residual chlorohydrin is dehydrochlorinated with sodium methoxide in methanol solution. The epoxy compound is extracted with chloroform or other suitable solvents from dilute, aqueous methanol.

hydrin azeotrope was not started immediately parallel with the addition of the sodium hydroxide solution.

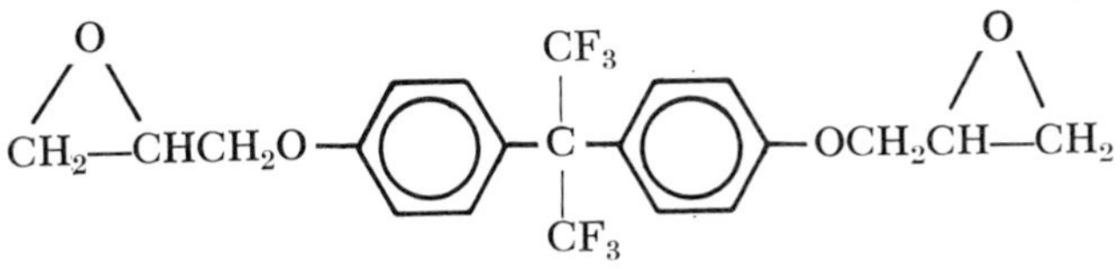

O CF$_3$ O
CH_2—$CHCH_2O$—C$_6$H$_4$—C(CF$_3$)$_2$—C$_6$H$_4$—OCH_2CH—CH_2
CF$_3$

Diglycidyl Ether of Bisphenol-Hexafluoroacetone (DGEB-HFA)

This bisphenol derivative was prepared from 910 grams of bisphenol hexafluoroacetone (from General Chemical Division, Allied Chemical Corporation) and excess epichlorhydrin by the one-step method described in Table II. The crude product was purified by molecular distillation (evaporating surface temperatures 213°C., 0.01–0.02 mm. Hg), yielding 78.5 percent of the theoretical, with an epoxy equivalent of 277 (theoretical WPE-234).

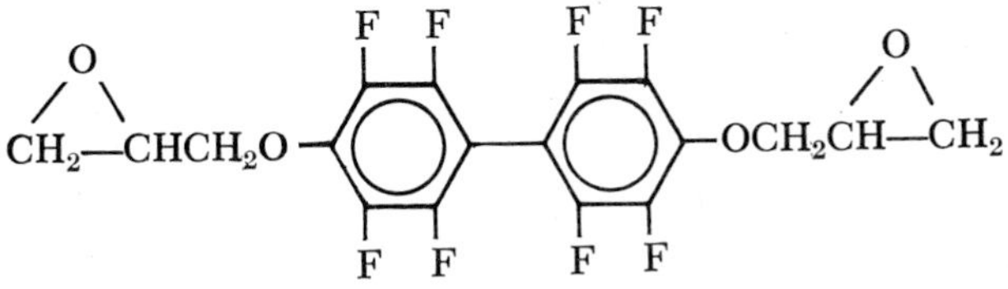

F F F F
O O
CH_2—$CHCH_2O$—C$_6$F$_4$—C$_6$F$_4$—OCH_2CH—CH_2
F F F F

4,4′-Bis (2,3-epoxypropoxy) octafluorobiphenyl

The epichlorohydrin reaction was carried out by the two-step method described in Table II. The crude product was purified by crystallization from benzene-cyclohexane mixture, yielding 75 percent of theory, with epoxy equivalent of 340 (theoretical WPE 221).

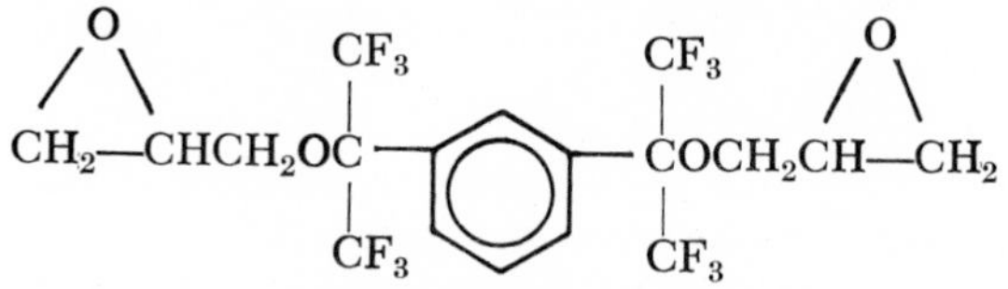

O CF$_3$ CF$_3$ O

CH_2—$CHCH_2OC$—⟨benzene⟩—$COCH_2CH$—CH_2

CF$_3$ CF$_3$

1,3-Bis [1-(2,3-epoxypropoxy)-1-trifluoromethyl-2,2,2-trifluoroethyl] benzene (BETTB)

For the preparation of the 1,3-isomer, 25.0 grams of the corresponding alcohol and 126.0 grams epichlorohydrin were mixed, and the two-step method of Table II was followed. Exactly 29.0 grams of the resin (91 percent yield) were obtained as a solid, melting in the range of 84°–94°C., with an epoxy equivalent of 314. The product was not purified further (Theory 261).

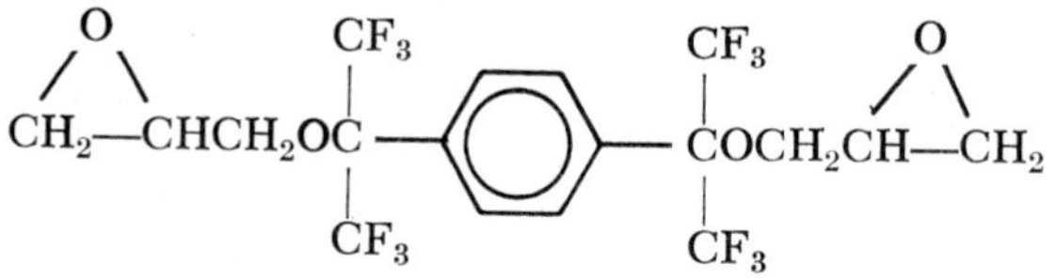

O CF$_3$ CF$_3$ O

CH_2—$CHCH_2OC$—⟨benzene⟩—$COCH_2CH$—CH_2

CF$_3$ CF$_3$

1,4-Bis [1-(2,3-epoxypropoxy)-1-trifluoromethyl-2,2,2-trifluoroethyl] benzene

From 84.1 grams of 1,4-bis(1-trifluoromethylhydroxy-2,2,2-trifluoro-1-ethyl)benzene and 378 grams of epichlorohydrin, 93.3 grams (87.2 percent yield) of the resin was prepared using the two-step method described in Table II. The analysis showed 288 as epoxy equivalent (Theory 261).

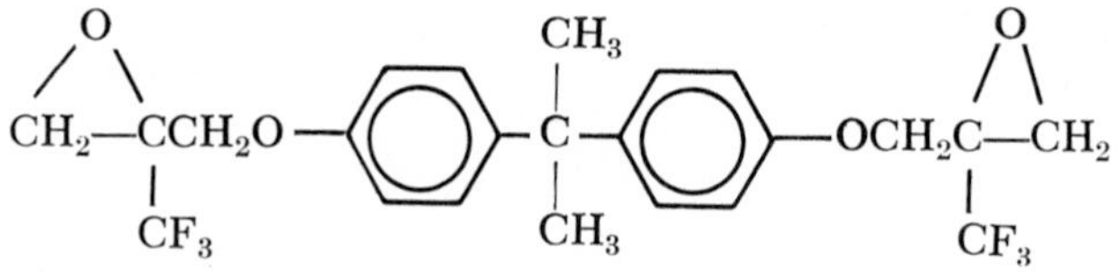

O CH$_3$ O

CH_2—CCH_2O—⟨benzene⟩—C—⟨benzene⟩—OCH_2C—CH_2

CF$_3$ CH$_3$ CF$_3$

Bis beta-trifluoromethyl DGEBA

An ethereal solution of 5.4 grams of diazomethane was added to 15.4 grams of 3-bromo-1,1,1-trifluoro-2-propanone for the preparation of the 3-bromo-2-trifluoromethylpropylene oxide intermediate. After an extended reaction period at room temperature, this compound was obtained from the crude product by distillation (b.p. 114°–117°C., lit. 115°–118°C.) in 63.5 percent yield.

The usual method of epoxy assay did not indicate appreciable amounts of the expected compound, but the infrared absorption spectrum showed the presence of the epoxy group and the parallel disappearance of the carbonyl absorption of the starting material.

The title compound was obtained by the reaction of the above intermediate (2.05 grams) with the disodium salt of bisphenol A (1.36 grams) in ethylene glycol dimethyl ether (crude yield 93.3 percent).

The epoxy assay did not give meaningful results, but the bisphenol residue and the carbon-fluorine bonds were identifiable in the infrared spectrum, and a stoichiometric amount of sodium bromide was separated from the original reaction mixture.

The analytical method is based on the generally fast reaction of the epoxy group with hydrobromic acid at room temperature. The above, β-perfluoro substituted epoxy compound, however, failed to react with hydrobromic acid even after standing at room temperature and warming to 40°C. for about 5 minutes. Although ring-opening reactions of similar epoxy compounds are described in the literature, the methods require prolonged refluxing and/or stirring of the reaction mixtures and are not quantitative.

It was concluded that in spite of the strong electron-withdrawing effect of the fluorine atoms, the size of the substituent group might interfere sterically with the reaction of the epoxy group.

O O O

CH_2—$CHCH_2N$ NCH_2CH—CH_2

O N O

CH_2CH—CH_2

O

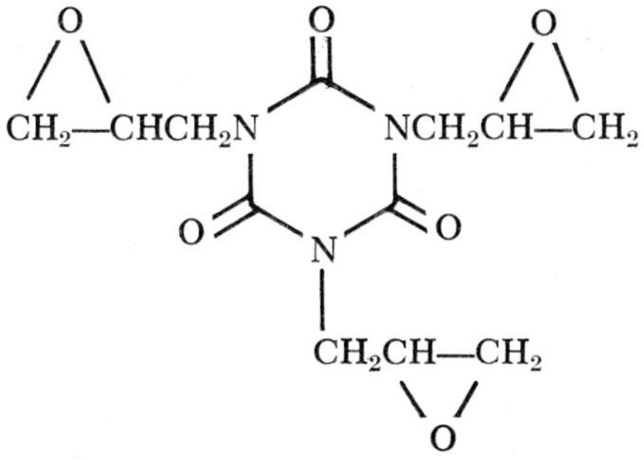

1,3,5-Triglycidyl Isocyanurate

The synthesis of the trifunctional monomer was attempted by several methods. The direct epoxidation of 5.0 grams of 1,4,5-triallyl-2,4,6-triazinetrione (triallyl isocyanurate, from Nitrogen Division, Allied Chemical Corp.) with 25.8 grams of 3-chloroperbenzoic acid in chloroform yielded

62.8 percent of a crude product with an epoxy equivalent of 147 (theoretical 99). Repeated epoxidations, however, produced erratic results.

Formation of the trichlorohydrin of the above starting material was also attempted, using calcium hypochlorite, and trichloroisocyanurate, respectively, as a source of hypochlorous acid. The products, after dehydrochlorination, showed inadequate epoxy equivalents (WPE 296 and higher).

In the presence of basic catalyst, 2,4,6-trihydroxy-1,3,5-triazine (cyanuric acid) reacts in the form of isocyanuric acid.

Reportedly, with large excess of epichlorohydrin, the intermediately formed trichlorohydrin yields the title compound, and an equivalent epichlorohydrin is converted to 1,3-dichloro-2-propanol. Based on this reaction sequence, *N,N*-dimethylaniline and a tertiary amine-type ion exchange resin (Amberlyst A21, from Rohm & Haas) were employed as catalysts, respectively in several experiments. The best results showed the presence of two epoxy groups for a triazine molecule (WPE = 153), and the infrared spectrum proved strong hydrogen bonding in the 2.8–3.0 micron range.

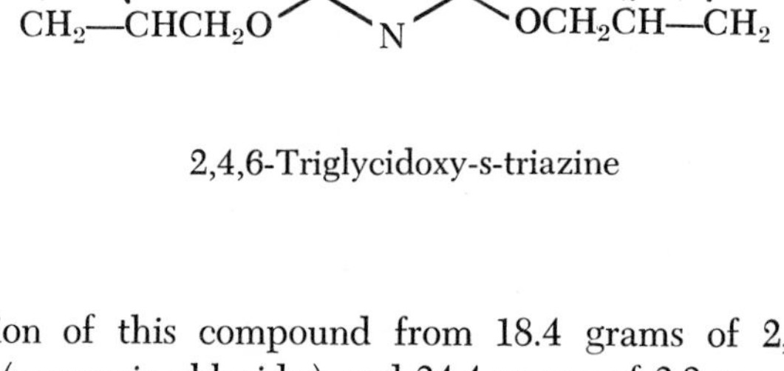

$OCH_2CH{-}CH_2$ (O)

N N

$CH_2{-}CHCH_2O$ (O) N $OCH_2CH{-}CH_2$ (O)

2,4,6-Triglycidoxy-s-triazine

Preparation of this compound from 18.4 grams of 2,4,6-trichloro-1,3,5-triazine (cyanuric chloride) and 24.4 grams of 2,3-epoxy-1-propanol (glycidol) proceeded in chloroform solution with aqueous sodium hydroxide, at below 10°C. Epoxy equivalent of 133 (theoretical 99) indicates more than 2 epoxy groups per triazine molecule. Such material was obtained in 76 percent yield, while one experiment (using metallic sodium instead of sodium hydroxide) yielded 44.5 percent with epoxy equivalent of 124.

2,4,6-Triglycidyl-s-triazine

No synthesis was attempted.

Acknowledgment

The work described in this paper was performed under contract to the National Institutes of Health, National Institute of Dental Research, under Contract 43-64-548.

Literature Cited

(1) Burdon, J., McLoughlin, V. C. R., Tatlow, J. C., *J. Chem. Soc.* **1960,** 3184.
(2) Bruins, "Epoxy Resin Technology," Interscience, New York, 1968.
(3) Lee, Henry L., Neville, Kris, "Epoxy Resins—Their Applications and Technology," McGraw-Hill Book Co., New York, 1957.
(4) Lee, Henry L., Neville, Kris, "Handbook of Epoxy Resins," McGraw-Hill, New York, 1967.
(5) Lee, Henry L., Cupples, Arthur L., Swartz, Michael L., "Epoxy Resin Dental Materials," Annual Report to the National Institute of Dental Research (May 1967).
(6) Paquin, Alfred Max, "Epoxydverbindugen Und Epoxydharze," Springer-Verlag, Heidelberg, 1958.
(7) Schrade, Jean, "Les Resines Epoxy," Dunod, Paris, 1957.
(8) Skeist, Irving, "Epoxy Resins," Reinhold, New York, 1958.
(9) Society of the Plastics Industry, Inc., "Methods of Test for Gel Time and Peak Exothermic Temperature of Epoxy Compounds," Epoxy Resin Formulators Division, ERF 2-61.
(10) Weigel, Kurt, "Epoxidharzlacke; Wissenschafltiche Verlagsgesellschaft M. B. H.," Stuttgart, 1965.

RECEIVED September 20, 1968.

16

Phosphorus Amide Cured Epoxy Resins II. The Effects of Amide and Resin Structures and Curing Conditions on Reactivity

RICHARD W. HUNTER and ROBERT M. WASHBURN

McDonnell Douglas Astronautics Co.—Western Division,
Santa Monica, Calif. 90406

The mechanism of the reaction of phosphorus amides with epoxy resins has been studied using differential thermal analysis (DTA), thermomechanical analysis (TMA), vibrating reed analysis (VRA), and infrared spectroscopy. Structure reactivity correlations have been made. The thermal data (TMA, DTA) and infrared spectra indicate that the major reaction occurs between the amide hydrogen and the epoxide group. Amide reactivity was observed to be a direct function of amide melting point and an inverse function of precursor amine basicity. VRA, which has been shown to be a good method for cure analysis, indicated that phosphorus amide cured Epon 828 retained a higher proportion of its modulus at elevated temperature than diethylenetriamine cured Epon 828.

Organophosphorus-nitrogen compounds are known to increase the oxidative, thermal, and radiation stability of epoxy resins (*9*). However, the simple addition of organophosphorus compounds to epoxy formulations generally has a deleterious effect on the physical and mechanical properties of the cured resins. In addition, when phosphorus-containing additives are present as a part of a mixture, they can "bleed out" or be leached out of the cured resin and their protective qualities become lost.

It has been demonstrated previously that phosphorus amides can be used as curing agents for epoxy resins and that the phosphorus amide-epoxy systems can be used as the matrix materials for the fabrication of composites (*10*). The phosphorus amides studied previously were solids which exhibited low or negligible solubility in epoxy resins. However, it was found that intermediate reaction products could be prepared from the phosphorus amides and epoxies (B staged) which were soluble in common organic solvents. The solutions of B staged materials were used for the preparation of composites.

Discussion

Based upon the results of the previous studies (*10*), a program was initiated to elucidate further the cure mechanism and to evaluate the effect of phosphorus amide structure and epoxy structure on the reactivity of phosphorus amide-epoxy blends and to determine the effect of the reactants on the physical properties of the cured resins.

The investigation involved the use of (a) differential thermal analysis (DTA) of the neat epoxy resins, the phosphorus amides, and of the phosphorus amide-epoxy blends; (b) thermomechanical analysis (TMA) of selected phosphorus amide cured epoxies; (c) the use of vibrating reed analysis (VRA) to study the cure of phosphorus amide epoxy blends; and (d) infrared analysis to determine the mechanism of the reaction between phosphorus amides and epoxy resins.

Materials

The epoxies used in this investigation were Epon 828 (I) (Shell Chemical Company), a diglycidyl ether of Bisphenol A; DEN 438 (II) (Dow Chemical Company), an epoxy novolac; and ERLA 4221 (III) (Union Carbide Corporation), a dicycloaliphatic diepoxide.

$$\overset{O}{\overbrace{H_2C\text{—}CH}}CH_2\text{—}\left[O\text{—}C_6H_4\text{—}C(CH_3)_2\text{—}C_6H_4\text{—}OCH_2\overset{OH}{CH}CH_2\right]_{n\,\approx\,0.14}\text{—}O\text{—}C_6H_4\text{—}C(CH_3)_2\text{—}C_6H_4\text{—}OCH_2\overset{O}{\overbrace{CH\text{—}CH_2}}$$

$$C_6H_4(OCH_2\overset{O}{\overbrace{CH\text{—}CH_2}})\text{—}CH_2\text{—}\left[C_6H_3(OCH_2\overset{O}{\overbrace{CH\text{—}CH_2}})\text{—}CH_2\right]_{n\,\approx\,1.5}\text{—}C_6H_4(OCH_2\overset{O}{\overbrace{CH\text{—}CH_2}})$$

II

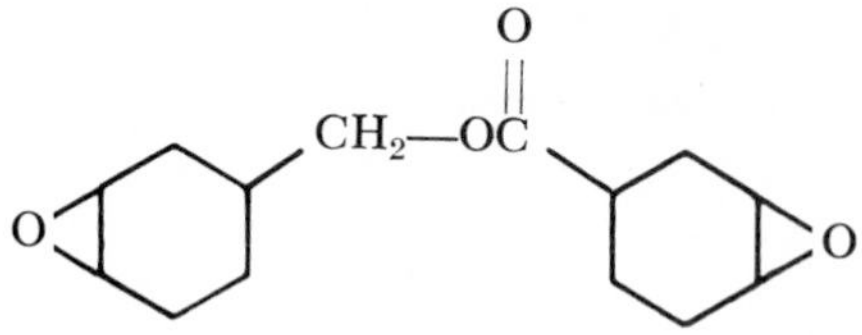

O
||
CH_2—OC

O O

III

Nine phosphorus amides have been investigated which exhibit a wide range of chemical and electronic structural variations around a single phosphorus atom: trisanilinophosphine oxide (IV); trismethylaminophosphine oxide (V); trisaminophosphine oxide (VI); tris-*p*-methoxyanilinophosphine oxide (VII); tris-*p*-chloroanilinophosphine oxide (VII); bisanilinophenylphosphine oxide (IX); trisanilinophosphine sulfide (X); bisanilinophenylphosphine sulfide (XI); and trisaminophosphine sulfide (XII). One phosphorus amide based on an arylenediphosphorus compound, *p*-phenylenebis(anilinophenylphosphine oxide) (XIII), was investigated. The nomenclature chosen for the phosphorus amides was based on that used previously by Washburn and Karle (*11*).

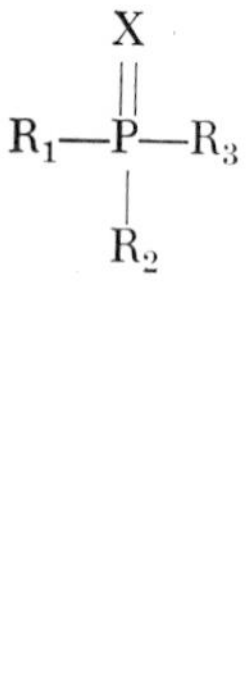

R_1—P(=X)—R_3, with R_2 on P

	R_1	R_2	R_3	X
IV	C_6H_5NH	C_6H_5NH	C_6H_5NH	O
V	CH_3NH	CH_3NH	CH_3NH	O
VI	NH_2	NH_2	NH_2	O
VII	*p*-$CH_3OC_6H_4NH$	*p*-$CH_3OC_6H_4NH$	*p*-$CH_3OC_6H_4NH$	O
VIII	*p*-ClC_6H_4NH	*p*-ClC_6H_4NH	*p*-ClC_6H_4NH	O
IX	C_6H_5NH	C_6H_5NH	C_6H_5	O
X	C_6H_5NH	C_6H_5NH	C_6H_5NH	S
XI	C_6H_5NH	C_6H_5NH	C_6H_5	S
XII	NH_2	NH_2	NH_2	S

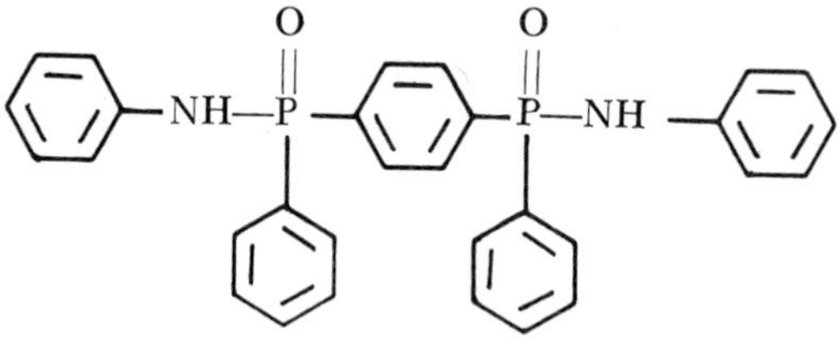

O O
|| ||
—NH—P— —P—NH—

XIII

The phosphorus amides used were prepared by standard techniques and were completely characterized by elemental analyses, physical constants, and infrared and ultraviolet absorption spectroscopy (*12*).

Cure Mechanism

Reactions in phosphorus amide-epoxy resin systems can occur in three principal ways:

Reaction between the phosphorus amide and the epoxy resin [Equation 1] (*10*),

$$\underset{\text{(epoxide)}}{H_2C\!\overset{O}{\frown}\!CH}-R-\underset{\text{(epoxide)}}{CH\!\overset{O}{\frown}\!CH_2} + R'NH-\overset{\overset{O}{\|}}{\underset{\underset{NHR'''}{|}}{P}}-NHR'' \rightarrow H_2C\!\overset{O}{\frown}\!CH-R-\overset{\overset{OH}{|}}{CH}-CH_2\underset{\underset{R'}{|}}{N}-\overset{\overset{O}{\|}}{\underset{\underset{NHR'''}{|}}{P}}NHR'' \quad (1)$$

The phosphorus amides can also react to form diazadiphosphetidines [Equation 2] (*2, 3, 6, 7*),

$$2(RNH)_3PO \rightarrow \begin{array}{c} RNH-\overset{\overset{O}{\|}}{P}-NR \\ |\qquad | \\ RN-\underset{\underset{O}{\|}}{P}-NHR \end{array} + 2RNH_2 \quad (2)$$

The epoxy resin can homopolymerize (*5*).

The conversion of ethylene oxide to acetaldehyde at elevated temperatures is a known reaction, and Anderson (*1*) ascribed an observed exothermic reaction in the DTA thermogram as caused mainly by the formation of aldehydes in the case of primary epoxides and ketones for secondary epoxides. We have also observed exotherms in the same general temperature range for the neat epoxides, but the products have not been characterized.

Reaction 1 is characterized by the consumption of the epoxide group, the consumption of the amide group, and the formation of a hydroxyl group. Reaction 2 is characterized by the consumption of the amide group and the formation of a diazadiphosphetidine ring. A homopolymerization would be characterized by the consumption of the epoxide group and the formation of an ether group.

The reaction mechanism was determined as follows: Stoichiometric ratios of Epon 828 and trisanilinophosphine oxide were allowed to react at approximately 200°C. for 3.0 minutes, 4.0 minutes, etc. The reactions were stopped by chilling rapidly the reaction mixture, and the reaction mixture was then dissolved in acetone. The solutions, analyzed by infrared spectroscopy, showed a decrease in the epoxide group (shoulder at 930 cm.$^{-1}$), a decrease in the amide group (band at 3320 cm.$^{-1}$), and an increase in the hydroxyl group (band at 3460 cm.$^{-1}$). The portions of the infrared spectra of interest for the reaction of Epon 828 and trisanilinophosphine oxide are shown in Table I. The alkyl ether group has a sharp absorption peak at 1070 cm.$^{-1}$. Hydroxyl groups also show peaks in this region. Since the ether peak is stronger than the hydroxyl peak, the formation of significant amounts of alkyl ether linkage because of homopolymerization of the epoxy resin should show in the infrared spectra in spite of the masking effects of the formation of the hydroxyl groups. No absorptions which could be attributed to ether formation were observed, and therefore it was concluded that the homopolymerization reaction was not an important factor in the reaction.

Table I. Infrared Studies: Reaction of Epon 828 with Trisanilinophosphine Oxide

		% Transmittance After Cure Time at 201°C.		
Group	*Frequency, cm.$^{-1}$*	*5 min.*	*8 min.*	*15 min.*
NH	3320	61.8	62.6	66.0
C—C (epoxide, O bridging)	930	58.0	61.2	65.4
OH	3460	85.2	82.4	78.6

Differential Thermal Analysis (DTA)

The epoxy resins were examined as received. The phosphorus amides were screened (−100, +200 mesh) prior to testing. The blends were ground, using a mortar and pestle, until the phosphorus amide formed a smooth suspension in the epoxy resin. The neat resins, phosphorus amides and blends were analyzed using a DuPont model 900 differential thermal analyzer. A heating rate of 10°C./minute was satisfactory for the investigation of the epoxy resins and phosphorus amides, but the blends exhibited excessive foaming at this heating rate, and therefore a heating rate of 5°C./minute was used.

Two temperatures have been used to study the thermally induced reactions which occur during the DTA analysis of the test materials. One temperature is the onset temperature, the other is the peak temperature. The onset temperature is defined as the intersection of the extrapolated base line and the extrapolated initial slope of the reaction exotherm or endotherm. The peak temperature is the temperature at the maximum (or minimum) point observed during reaction (Figure 1).

The results of the DTA studies of the neat epoxy resins are given in Table II; the results of the DTA studies of the phosphorus amides are given in Table III; and the results of the DTA studies of the phosphorus amide-epoxy blends are given in Table IV. The results of the DTA studies indicate that the reactions of amide cyclization and epoxy homopolymerization occur at temperatures much higher than the reaction temperatures of the phosphorus amide-epoxy reaction [Equation 1].

These DTA data substantiate the conclusions drawn from the infrared data (Table I) and suggest that the side reactions of amide cyclization and epoxy homopolymerization are not of major importance at the cure times and temperatures used.

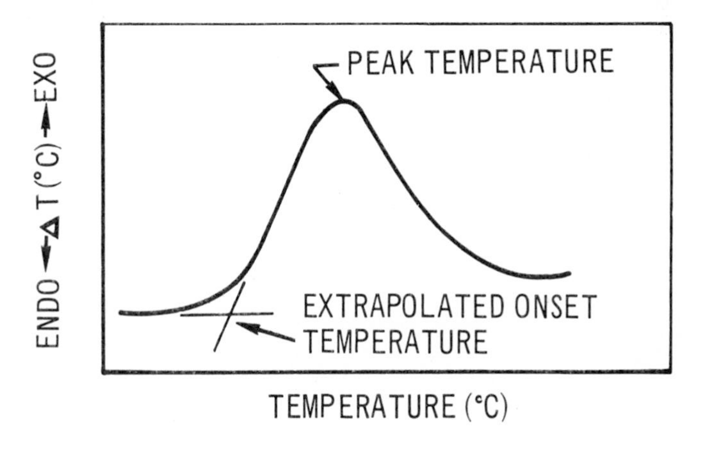

Figure 1. Methods of calculating extrapolated onset temperature and peak temperature for DTA thermograms

Table II. DTA Data of Epoxy Resin Exotherm Temperatures

	Exotherm Temperatures (°C.)			
Resin	*Onset*	*Peak*	*Onset*	*Peak*
I	285[a]	320[a]	360	397
II	—	—	336	373
III	—	—	319	348, 376

[a] Heating rate 2.5°C./minute (*1*).

Table III. Differential Thermal Analysis for Phosphorus Amides

Amide	Capillary m.p. Range °C.	Endotherm °C.		Exotherm °C.	
		Onset	Peak	Onset	Peak
IV	210–213	215	218	—	—
V	102.6–103.4	59	100	326	327
VI	—	125	156	—[a]	170
VII	185.5–187	189	191	419	432
VIII	247.5–250	200	203	327	331
		253	255	—	—
IX	217–220	224	225	—	—
X	154–156	156	158	—	—
XI	178–178.5	177	178	—	—
		253	315	—	—
XII	118–119	107	120		
		148	164		
XIII	314–320	283	287, 299	—	288[b]

[a] Onset temperature obscured by endotherm peak.
[b] Possible nematic mesoform.

Table IV. DTA Data for Phosphorus Amide Epoxy Blends

Blend	Exotherm °C.	
	Onset	Peak
Epon 828 + IV	175	236
+ V	87	190
+ VI	83	148
+ VII	169	229
+ VIII	200	234
+ IX	200	229
+ X	180	219
+ XI—run 1	115	156
—run 2	120	158
+ XII	119	159
+ XIII	259	274
DEN 438 + IV	193	235
+ VI—run 1	79	154
—run 2	104	134
+ X	187	229
+ XI	106	156
ERLA 4221 + IV	204	244, 254, 260[a]
+ X	129	159[b]
	209	228[b]

[a] Multiple exotherm with maximum at 260°C.
[b] Multiple exotherms and onset temperatures.

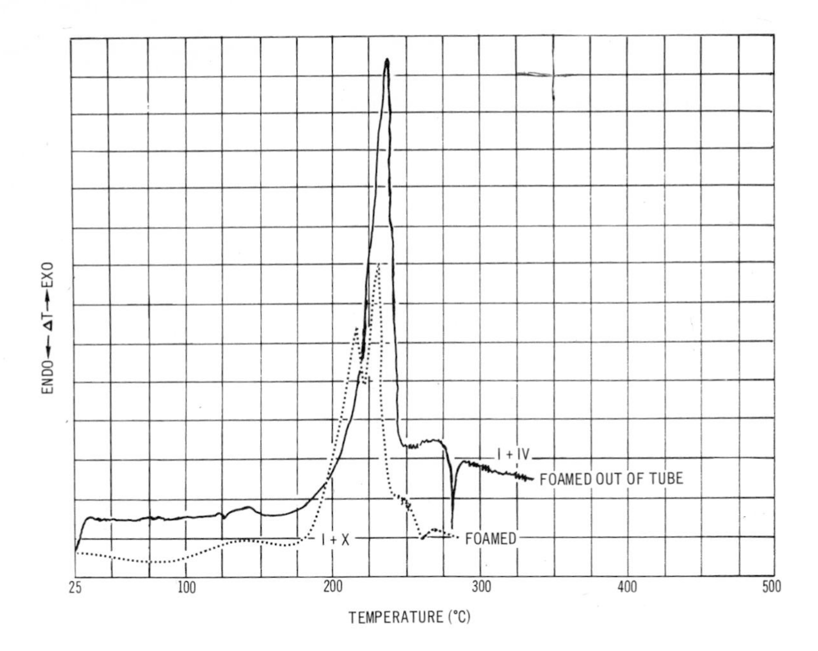

Figure 2. Differential thermal analysis: comparison of phosphine sulfide and phosphine oxide reactions with Epon 828

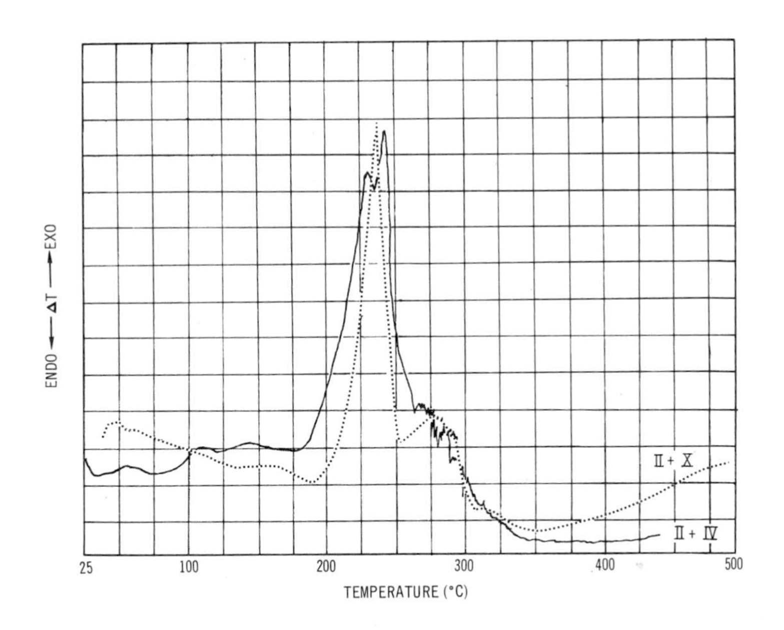

Figure 3. Differential thermal analysis: comparison of phosphine oxide and phosphine sulfide reactions with D.E.N. 438

The order of the onset temperatures for the reactions of trisanilinophosphine oxide (IV) with the epoxy resins was Epon 828 (I) < DEN 438 (II) < ERLA 4221 (III). The order of the peak exothermic temperatures was I $\approx$ II < III. The thermograms for the reactions of trisanilinophosphine sulfide (X) with I and II were similar to the phosphine oxide (IV) reaction thermograms (Figures 2 and 3). However, the thermogram for the reaction of trisanilinophosphine sulfide (X) with ERLA 4221 (III) was markedly different from the thermogram for the reaction of trisanilinophosphine oxide (IV) with ERLA 4221 (III) (Figure 4). The trisanilinophosphine oxide (IV) exhibited a single onset temperature followed by three exothermic peaks indicating a very complex reaction.

The trisanilinophosphine sulfide (X) showed a small peak indicating an initial reaction at a much lower temperature than the initial reaction of the phosphine oxide (129°C. *vs.* 204°C.). This was followed by a larger exotherm starting at approximately the same temperature as that for the phosphine oxide (IV) (209°C. *vs.* 204°C.) but reaching its peak at a much lower temperature (228°C. *vs.* 244°C.).

The onset temperature data for both the phosphine oxides- and phosphine sulfides-Epon 828 (I) blends are plotted as a function of capillary melting point in Figure 5, and the data for the phosphine oxides-Epon 828 (I) as a function of basicity of the amine from which the phosphine oxide amides are derived (8) are plotted in Figure 6. In general, the onset temperature is directly proportional to the melting

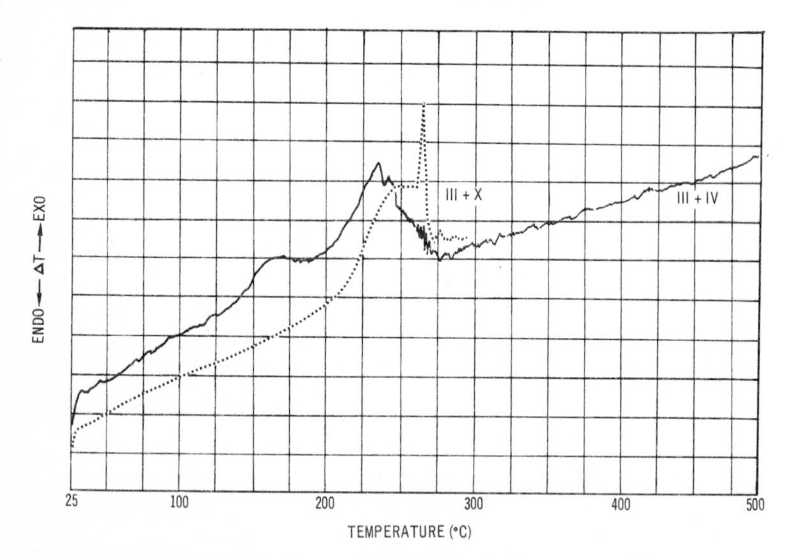

Figure 4. Differential thermal analysis: comparison of phosphine sulfide and phosphine oxide reactions with ERLA 4221

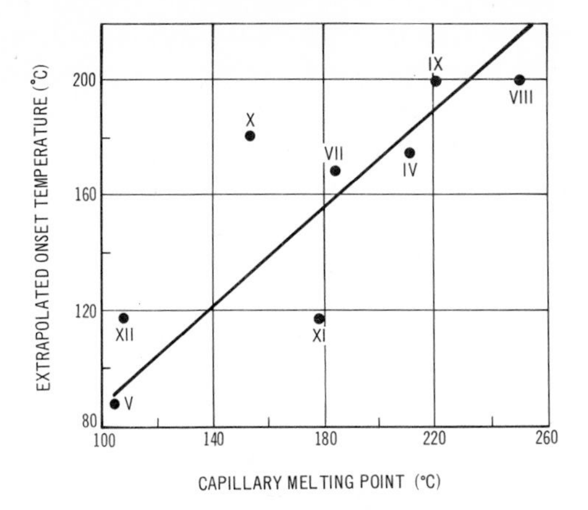

Figure 5. Comparison of phosphorus amide melting points with extrapolated onset temperatures of reactions with Epon 828

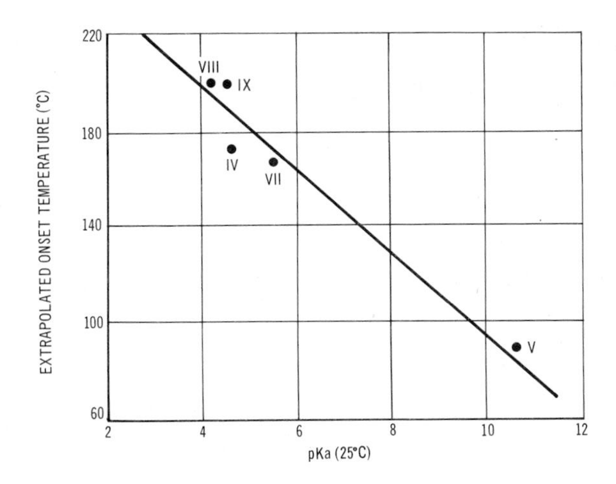

Figure 6. Comparison of amine basicity (pKa) with extrapolated onset temperature for reaction of phosphorus amides with Epon 828

point of the phosphorus amide and inversely proportional to the amine basicity. The order of reactivity of Epon 828 with the various phosphorus amides was (in order of increasing onset temperature), VI $<<$ V $<$ VII $<$ IV $<$ IX $=$ VIII.

Three phosphine sulfide compounds tested (X, XI, and XII) exhibited reactivities that followed a regular pattern like the phosphine oxide compounds (Figure 6). Stoichiometric mixtures of trisanilinophosphine sulfide reacted with Epon 828 at 185°C. Samples were removed at 1.5 and 10 minutes. DTA examination of the unreacted mixture, and the two partial reaction products yielded the curves shown in Figure 7; as can be seen, the initial sharp reaction peaks at 220° and 230°C. decrease in size to almost zero as the reaction time is increased, and the reaction mixture increases in thermal stability. Further investigations of the reactions should be performed with phosphine sulfides more quantitatively to confirm the correlations assumed.

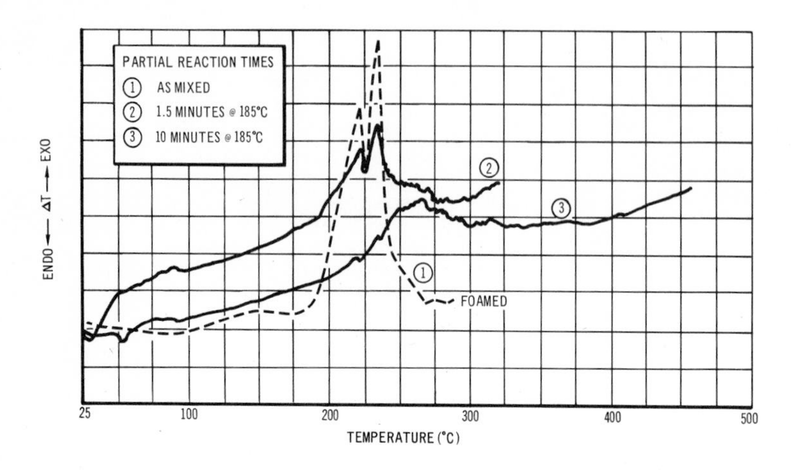

Figure 7. Differential thermal analysis of reaction between I and X

Table V. Cure Conditions for TMA Specimens

Resin	Phosphorus Amide	Bath Temp., °C.	Cure Temp. (°C.)	Cure Time (hrs.)
I	IV	190	180 → 160	12
			+ 190	2
I	V	95	95	12
II	IV	210	180 → 160	11
III	IV	190	180 → 160	10

Thermomechanical Analysis (TMA)

A duPont model 940 thermomechanical analyzer was modified to operate at temperatures up to 650°C. (*4*). The apparatus applies a fixed load (22.5 p.s.i.) to the surface of the specimen and the coefficient of expansion is measured as a function of temperature. Any property or transition which changes with temperature (state of cure, glass transition point, etc.) and which causes a change in coefficient of expansion can be detected and measured.

The phosphorus amides were mixed in stoichiometric ratios with the epoxy resins and cured by heating in an oil bath for 15 minutes at temperature. The partially cured material was then transferred to a circulating air oven and heated for the times and temperatures shown in Table V, and then studied using TMA.

Both D.E.N. 438 (II) and ERLA 4221 (III) resins when cured with trisanilinophosphine oxide expanded under load to approximately 230°C. whereupon softening occurred, suggesting that the cause of failure was the phosphorus amide curing agent. However, changes in the expansion rates at low temperatures (*ca.* 150°C.) indicate that the resins may not have been fully cured. The Epon 828 (I) cured with trisanilinophosphine oxide (IV) softened initially at 97°C. Two hours additional cure at 190°C. raised the softening temperature to 107°C. Heating the sample of cured resin at 190°C. for 14 hours reduced it to the consistency of firm gelatin. The trismethylaminophosphine oxide (V) cured Epon 828 (I) showed an initial contraction (possibly softened) at 230°C. followed by further expansion to 300°C. at which temperature foaming of the resin occurred. The preliminary TMA data indicate that additional work must be done to learn the effects of extended heating.

Vibrating Reed Analysis (VRA)

Vibrating reed analysis can be used to determine the dynamic modulus and the mechanical energy absorption characteristics of materials by subjecting reeds fabricated from these materials to forced transverse vibrations and determining the resonance characteristics of the reeds.

Composites were fabricated using glass tape as the reinforcement and uncured resin-curing agent mixture as the matrix. The initial room temperature resonance characteristics of the reeds were determined. The test chamber was then raised to the cure temperature and the resonance characteristics again determined. The resonance characteristics were periodically determined at cure temperature until cure was complete. In these tests cure completion was defined as the point at which the modulus and the energy absorption characteristics of the reed were constant. The vibrating reed results are given in Table VI.

The DETA-Epon 828 (I) combination cured satisfactorily at 114°C., but became black and softened at 122°C. suggesting thermal decomposition. The trisanilinophosphine oxide (II) cured Epon 828 (I) showed a satisfactory cure at both 195° and 205°C. and a good retention of modulus at both temperatures. This retention was much higher for the trisanilinophosphine oxide (IV) cured Epon 828 (I) than for the DETA cured Epon 828 (I) at 114°C.

Table VI. Modulus and Damping Factor of Glass Tape Composites Derived from Phosphorus Amide Cured Epoxy Resins

Resin	*Curing Agent*	*Cure Temp. (°C.)*	$E^{a,b}$ *dynes/cm.² × 10⁻¹⁰*	*DF*[c]	*Temp. °C.*
I	DETA[d]	114	1.6	0.26	114
			5.6	0.09	20
		122[e]	—	—	—
I	IV	195	3.5	0.17	195
			12.7	0.03	20
		205	3.3	0.21	205
			15.6	0.05	20
II	IV	201	5.3	0.17	201
			10.5	0.04	20

[a] Dynamic modulus.
[b] p.s.i. = (dynes/cm.²) × 1.45 × 10^{-5}.
[c] Half width damping factor.
[d] Diethylenetriamine used as standard.
[e] Material degraded during test.

The D.E.N. 438 (II) cured with trisanilinophosphine oxide showed a much greater retention of its modulus at 200°C. than did the Epon 828. The data is also interesting in that the complex nature of the cure mechanism is also shown (Figure 10).

Cure Cycle Discussion—Nature of Complexities Shown in Cure Cycles

The modulus and energy absorption changes during the standard cure cycle and two phosphorus amide epoxy cure cycles are shown in Figures 8 through 10. The standard cure cycle [Epon 828 (I) cured with DETA] (Figure 8) is typical of the simpler cure mechanisms. The dynamic modulus increases smoothly and then levels off to a constant value as the cure reaction becomes complete. The absorption coefficients (damping factor and loss modulus) increase to a maximum and then drop to a minimum at approximately 2400 seconds as the cure becomes complete. At this point, the modulus remains constant, but the damping factor starts to increase. At normal temperatures the energy absorption would remain constant when the cure became complete. In the control cure at normal cure temperature, the temperature is close to the upper service limit of the DETA cured epoxy resins and the final increase is therefore attributed to degradation of the resin.

The trisanilinophosphine oxide molecule is larger and more complex than the DETA molecule. Thus, steric hindrance could become a major factor in the reaction between the trisanilinophosphine oxide and the Epon 828. It can be seen in Figure 9 that the modulus after an initial change owing to the melting of the curing agent rises to a maximum in

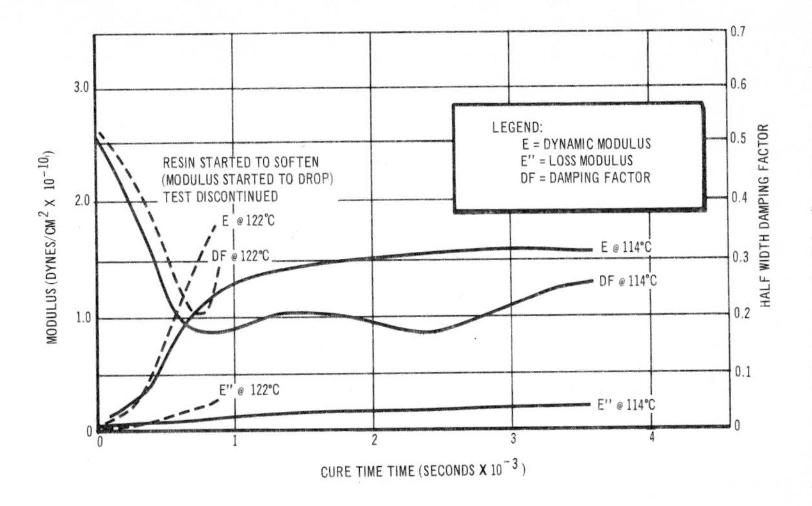

Figure 8. Epon 828 cured with diethylenetriamine

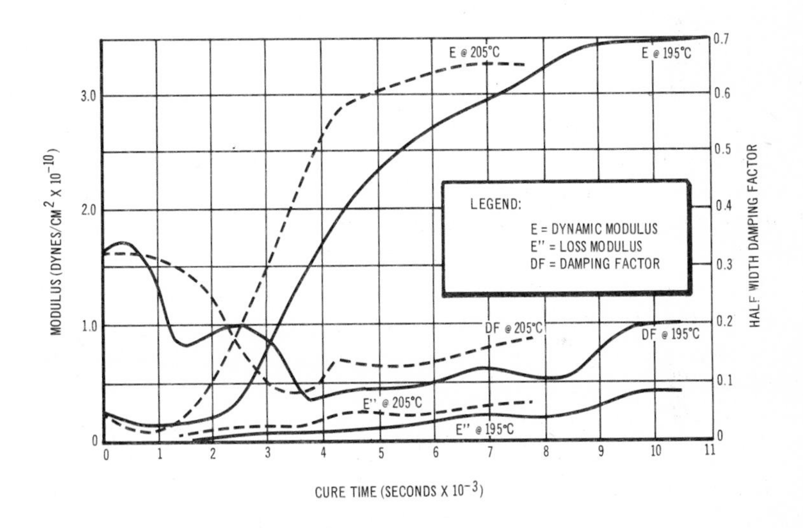

Figure 9. Epon 828 cured with trisanilinophosphine oxide

two stages. The rate of increase in modulus is more rapid during the first stage than in the second. This is to be expected since the effects of steric hindrance would be expected to be more severe as the reaction proceeds. The postulation of a two-stage reaction is supported by the fact that two energy absorption peaks occur; one peak occurring in each stage of the reaction.

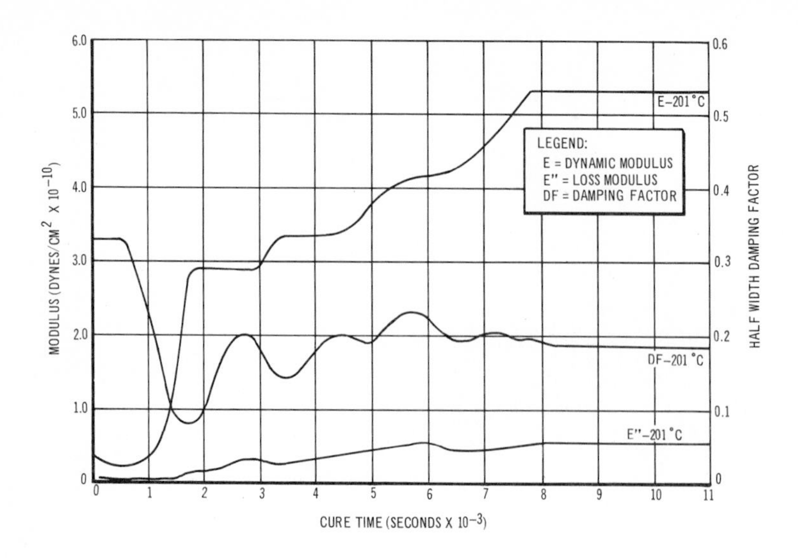

Figure 10. DEN 438 cured with trisanilinophosphine oxide

The D.E.N. 438 molecule is more complex than the Epon 828 and has a higher degree of functionality. Examination of the data in Figure 10 shows that the dynamic modulus undergoes a four step increase with an apparent incubation period after each increase. It is interesting to note that the time for the first increase is approximately the same as the gel time of the resin at that temperature (*10*). Each increase in dynamic modulus is accompanied by an inflection in the absorption properties that (except for the last inflection) occurs near the end of the apparent incubation period (the last inflection occurs near the end of the last increase in modulus).

A simple cure mechanism consists of (1) an increase in modulus to a maximum value and (2) an inflection in the energy absorption caused by the changes in internal friction as the resin passes from a fluid state where the internal friction is low, through a condition of partially immobile and partially fluid molecules where the internal friction is high, to a final condition where the friction is low within the limits of motion.

A cure mechanism can be postulated for the D.E.N. 438-trisanilinophosphine oxide, using the simple cure mechanism just outlined and the structures of the resin and phosphine oxide as follows: the first stage is the reaction between the monomeric resin and phosphine oxide. This is followed by the incubation period while the molecules realign so that the second stage reaction occurs. This reaction-incubation period is then repeated until all available reactions occur.

Acknowledgment

The authors express their appreciation to W. T. Thompson for the infrared spectra, S. E. Gordon for the differential thermal analyses and thermomechanical analyses, and especially to D. W. Karle for helpful discussions.

Literature Cited

(1) Anderson, H. C., *Anal. Chem.* **32,** 1592 (1966).
(2) Arcenaux, R. L., Frick, J. G., Leonard, E. K., Reed, J. D., *J. Org. Chem.* **24,** 1419 (1959).
(3) Buck, A. C., Lankelma, H. P., *J. Am. Chem. Soc.* **70,** 2398 (1948).
(4) Gordon, S. E., *ACS Polymer Preprints* **8** [**2**], 955 (Sept. 1967).
(5) Lee, H., Neville, K., "Handbook of Epoxy Resins," p. 5, McGraw-Hill Book Co., New York, New York, 1967.
(6) Michaelis, A., Silberstein, E., *Ber.* **29,** 716 (1896).
(7) Michaelis, A., *Ann.* **407,** 209 (1915).
(8) Perrin, D. D., "Dissociation Constants of Organic Bases in Aqueous Solution," Butterworths, London, England, 1965.
(9) Wagner, R. I., Washburn, R. M., Eilar, K. R., "Research on Borophane, Borozine, and Phosphorus Polymer and Fluid Research," **ASD-TDR-62-372,** p. 524 (May 1962).
(10) Washburn, R. M., Hunter, R. W., *Proc. 23rd Ann. Conf., Western Section SPI,* p. 35 (March 1966).
(11) Washburn, R. M., Karle, D. W., *Proc. 23rd Ann. Conf., Western Section SPI,* p. 28 (March 1966).
(12) Washburn, R. M., Marsi, K. L., Karle, D. W. (to be published).

RECEIVED May 9, 1969.

INDEX

INDEX

M

N

O

P

R

S

T

U

V

W